COMMUNICATION TRAINING

IN

CHILDHOOD BRAIN DAMAGE

Publication Number 660
AMERICAN LECTURE SERIES®

A Monograph in
The BANNERSTONE DIVISION *of*
AMERICAN LECTURES IN SPEECH AND HEARING

Edited by
ROBERT W. WEST, Ph.D.
Professor Emeritus, Brooklyn College
Brooklyn, New York
and
Visiting Professor of Speech, University of California
Los Angeles, California

COMMUNICATION TRAINING
IN
CHILDHOOD BRAIN DAMAGE

Compiled and Edited by

MERLIN J. MECHAM, Ph.D.
Director, Speech Pathology and Audiology
Professor of Speech
University of Utah
Salt Lake City, Utah

MARTIN J. BERKO, Ph.D.
Research Associate
Department of Psychology
Cornell University
Ithaca, New York

FRANCES GIDEN BERKO, LL.B., M.A.
Executive Director
Special Children's Center, Incorporated
Ithaca, New York

MARTIN F. PALMER, Sc.D.
Founder and Director, Institute of Logopedics, Inc.
Founder, Professor, and Head, Department of Logopedics
Wichita State University
Wichita, Kansas

CHARLES C THOMAS · PUBLISHER
Springfield · Illinois · U.S.A.

Published and Distributed Throughout the World by

CHARLES C THOMAS • PUBLISHER

BANNERSTONE HOUSE

301-327 East Lawrence Avenue, Springfield, Illinois, U.S.A.

NATCHEZ PLANTATION HOUSE

735 North Atlantic Boulevard, Fort Lauderdale, Florida, U.S.A.

© *1966, by* CHARLES C THOMAS • PUBLISHER

Library of Congress Catalog Card Number: 66-18934

With THOMAS BOOKS *careful attention is given to all details of manufacturing and design. It is the Publisher's desire to present books that are satisfactory as to their physical qualities and artistic possibilities and appropriate for their particular use.* THOMAS BOOKS *will be true to those laws of quality that assure a good name and good will.*

Printed in the United States of America

N-1

PREFACE

A SINCERE EFFORT has been made in the compilation of the book to condense the enormous amount of information taken from the works of the best scholars in various professional journals and convention reports and to integrate this information into a common frame of reference for practical use in therapy and education.

In the foreground of the authors' thinking have been students who will be taking classes on cerebral palsy in speech pathology, psychology or special education. To them, the book may serve as a text containing what the authors believe to be the latest information and techniques in these areas. To nurses, therapists and other persons in related disciplines, it should serve as a practical reference or source book.

Although the authors have deliberated closely in the compilation of the entire contents of the book, the major author contributions are Chapters I through VI, Merlin J. Mecham; Chapter VII, Martin J. Berko, and Chapter VIII, Frances G. Berko. Dr. Martin F. Palmer served as special author consultant and made general contributions which are invaluable throughout the book. The many practical suggestions contained herein are presented as merely illustrative rather than model suggestions.

ACKNOWLEDGMENTS

W E WISH TO THANK generously the many persons who have taken of their time to give advice and criticisms. The number is too great for us to name each one individually.

We must also thank those professional persons in the field from whom we have borrowed freely but with, we hope, proper acknowledgment. To graduate students in seminars, who have given helpful comments and to our colleagues with whom we work who have given friendly criticisms we extend our appreciation. Especially do we wish to say how much we appreciate our families and friends who have tolerated us and encouraged us in our efforts. Special thanks to Neva Mecham, wife of the first author, as well as Bruce Ensign, Harriet L. Holloway, Darien L. Lydecker and John Willis, who helped to correct and proofread the manuscript.

M. J. M.
M. J. B.
F. G. B.

CONTENTS

COMMUNICATION TRAINING
IN
CHILDHOOD BRAIN DAMAGE

Chapter I

INTRODUCTION—NATURE AND SCOPE OF THE PROBLEM

MERLIN J. MECHAM

Ostensibly, this is a book dealing with cerebral palsy. However, at this relatively late date in clinical history, we feel that there is little need to dwell upon the fact that "cerebral palsy" is but one of many forms of brain damage which is faced daily by clinicians in speech centers, special education classrooms, and in the vast variety of therapeutic and educational centers which are currently serving the needs of our "special children." This book, therefore, is predicated upon the supposition that, while for clinical and administrative purposes the various diagnostic entities such as "cerebral palsy," "childhood asphasia," "minimal brain damage," "organically-based mental retardation" and a host of other possible classifications and subclassifications must be recognized and catalogued, there is, nevertheless, an underlying commonality of psychological problems associated to a greater or lesser extent with all of these diagnostic groups. Therefore, the clinician's awareness of, and sensitivity to these problems is essential to good habilitative practice regardless of whether the discipline be clinical psychology, education, speech therapy or any other therapeutic modality. In the following pages, therefore, it is to be understood that unless otherwise specified, we are speaking about "brain-damaged children in general"; also unless specified, the term *specialist* is being used in a broad generic sense and refers to any practitioner rendering a specialized service to brain-damaged children.

ETIOLOGY

Factors causing cerebral palsy are generally divided into three categories: (1) prenatal; (2) paranatal, and (3) postnatal. This temporal division was suggested by Hayman in 1938 and has been popular since.[9] Although the causes of cerebral palsy are myriad, only the more important ones can be mentioned here.

Some years ago, the general consensus was that, in most cases, cerebral palsy was due to mechanical injury occurring during the birth process. More recent literature indicates that mechanical birth injuries are not quite as common causally as was originally thought, and more significance is being attached to hazards occurring in early stages of fetal development and to problems of oxygen deficiency which may occur at any time before, during, or after birth.[29,46] Many authorities feel that the most common cause of cerebral palsy is anoxia.[29]

Deaver[13] has classified the generally accepted etiological factors in cerebral palsy as follows:

Prenatal (time of conception to time of birth).
  1. Hereditary (Tay-Sachs disease and tuberous sclerosis).
  2. Congenital (anoxia, maternal infection, metabolic disease and Rh factor).

Natal (from onset of labor to birth).
  1. Anoxia (due to obstruction of cord).
  2. Asphyxia (result of mechanical respiratory obstruction).
  3. Analgesics (affecting respiratory center).
  4. Trauma (injuring brain during labor or by forceps delivery).
  5. Sudden changes in pressure (caesarean section).
  6. Prematurity.
  7. Low vitamin K level.

Postnatal (after time of birth of child).
  1. Trauma (skull fractures or wounds).
  2. Infections (meningitis and encephalitis).
  3. Vascular (hemorrhage, thrombosis, and embolus).
  4. Anoxia (carbon dioxide poisoning).
  5. Neoplasms.

CLASSIFICATIONS

Diagnosis of cerebral palsy has been mainly the responsibility and ability of the orthopedic specialist. Dr. Little, an English orthopedist, first described the condition according to what he saw.[32,31] *Orthopedic classifications* in cerebral palsy were thus derived from outward symptomatology from a neuromuscular point of view. During the orthopedic examination, diagnosis is made of the *location* of neuromuscular involvement (indicated by the terms *monoplegia, paraplegia, hemiplegia, triplegia* or *quadriplegia*), the *type* of neuromuscular involvement (indicated by the terms *spastic, athetoid, ataxic, tremor* or *rigidity*), and the *severity* of neuromuscular involvement (indicated as mild, moderate, or severe).

Example:

place	type	severity
left hemiplegia	spasticity	moderate

A monoplegic involvement would be limited to one extremity, either an arm or leg or perhaps just the hand or foot; a hemiplegic involvement includes one side of the body with usually the arm and leg on that side being impaired; paraplegia is an involvement in both legs; triplegia includes legs and an upper extremity or vice versa, and quadriplegia indicates involvement of both sides and probably all four extremities. The central musculature of speech may be involved in any of the above classifications, but it is least likely to accompany the monoplegic or paraplegic involvements.

Neurological classifications are based more on neuropathological syndromes than on clinical manifestations and are not as dichotomous as the orthopedic classifications. They have been labeled variously by different investigators, but in general they tend to include anomalies in the pyramidal or extrapyramidal motor systems arising from congenital defects, subdural hematoma, traumatic scars, cerebral-vascular defects, cerebral atrophy, central-degenerative disorders and a miscellaneous group of causative lesions.[9]

Correlation of orthopedic and neurological classifications results in a system of classification which has often been used because it gives a more general and combined understanding of the complex cerebral palsy conditions. There is some, but not universal agreement, on the following descriptions.[29]

Spasticity is thought to be usually the result of a combined lesion in the pyramidal (excitatory) and extrapyramidal (inhibitory) system either cortically or somewhere along the descending fibers. Symptoms resulting from the lesions in the extrapyramidal system (exaggerated reflexes and hypertonic or spastic state) usually predominate, but those resulting from the lesions in the pyramidal system (flaccid paresis or weakness) may also be detected. The heightened muscle tone and increased stretch prevent normally performed motion and often the muscles become short and atrophied or may result in flexion deformities called contractures.

Athetosis is characterized by involuntary muscular activity and is felt to be the result of a lesion or anomaly in the extrapyramidal system (specifically the globus pallidus in the basal ganglia). It appears as a twisting, writhing series of movements progressing from proximal to distal areas in waves. In more extreme cases, the movements may resemble "a non-swimmer thrashing about in the water." A mixture of spasticity and athetosis is often found in the same individual. Tension, nontension, dystonic and tremor athetoses have been described as unique types and Phelps has gone so far as to describe twelve different types of athetosis.[42]

Ataxia is characterized as a stumbling gate accompanied by poor kinesthetic awareness of amount or direction of body movement in space; the lesion prevents normal kinesthetic monitoring and is thought to be connected with the cerebellum. The body musculature is often hypotonic and frequently there is an accompanying deficit in normal stereognosis and depth perception.

Rigidity is a lead-pipe-like movement thought to be the result of inadequate phase relationship between excitation and inhibition of antagonist muscles. It is similar in some respects to spasticity, but the stretch reflex is absent and the muscle stiffness is continuous. The exact nature of the causitive lesion is unknown.

Tremor is marked by involuntary, rhythmic, reciprocal movements, often referred to as a "trembling" or "shaking" motion. "Intentional" tremor is that which occurs primarily when one initiates volitional movement but is absent when the muscles are at rest; it is thought to result from lesion in the cerebellum.

"Nonintentional" tremor is that which occurs when one is at rest but ceases when one makes a volitional movement; it is thought to result from a lesion in the globus pallidus.

DEVELOPMENTAL PROBLEMS

The cerebral palsied child may be plagued with a complexity of difficulties in many areas of development. Some of the important areas which may have an influence upon the communicative potentialities are discussed briefly below.

Motor Development: An attempt was made by Denhoff and Holden to illustrate differences between cerebral palsied children and normal children in *motor* development.[14] Their chart shows the normal infant motor development compared with average development of one hundred cerebral palsied cases in the Meeting Street School for Cerebral Palsy. The skills of head balance, reaching, sitting, crawling, standing, and walking are very much delayed in the average cerebral palsied child, and speech is necessarily delayed as a consequence of the delay in general motor development.

In a study of motor performance of cerebral palsied children as a function of their success or failure in achieving material rewards, Garmezy and Harris[22] found that variations in incentive conditions play an important part in the achievement of motor skills. The results of their study indicated that frequent variation in incentive conditions should be used during training to provide the increments of motivation needed to aid these children in the learning of complex motor tasks.

Statistics are not available on the actual number of cerebral palsied children who have neuromuscular involvements in the speech mechanism or hand-arm involvements which might interfere with writing.

A survey by Hopkins, Bice and Colton[28] with a sample of 1293 cerebral palsied children revealed that 64.9 per cent had quadriplegia involvement, 13.6 per cent had right hemiplegia, 10.8 per cent had left hemiplegia and 3.5 per cent had triplegia. Clinical evidence suggests that most quadriplegics have involvement of the speech musculature and that at least half the children in the other categories have a central-muscular involvement which interferes with speech. About 92.8 per cent of cerebral palsied children have some type of arm involvement, and 78.5 per cent have an arm and/or hand involvement on the right side. These figures suggest that a majority of the cerebral palsied persons suffer from some degree of neuromuscular involvement in their endeavors to speak and write.

At least one-third of the cerebral palsy population have a history of convulsive seizures. Many different types of seizures found in cerebral palsy have been described and the most common of these include grand mal, petit mal, psychomotor, Jacksonian and minor convulsions. Although the condition of cerebral palsy is generally considered to be nonprogressive, there is always the danger of progressive organic damage and increasing motor disability as a result of the complicating presence of epilepsy.[46]

Sensory Development: DiCarlo aptly states that the motor aspects of communication do not grow, divorced from the sensory components: "Visual, auditory, tactile and kinesthetic components are inextricably interwoven with the motor act."[17]

The survey by Hopkins, Bice and Colten showed that a high incidence of impairment in the primary senses of hearing and vision coexist with cerebral palsy. The cerebral palsied (CP) who had impaired or questionable hearing comprised 13.3 per cent of the sample; those who had defective or questionable vision comprised 27.6 per cent. In addition to visual and auditory difficulties, current interest has also been directed toward the probability that disturbances of tactile and kinesthetic sensory functions are present in a large portion of the cerebral palsy population.[28,29]

Perceptual Disturbances: Perceptual disturbances which may affect language integration have been observed and described by various investigators. Strauss and Lehtinen[45] found poor function in the visual-perceptual field of brain-injured children. Although Strauss has had difficulty copying the experiments on visual perception in the area of auditory perception, he believes that audio-perceptual difficulties similar to those of visuo-perception exist in the brain-injured.[44]

The studies by Strauss and Lehtinen led Cruickshank and Dolphin to investigate the visual and tactile perceptual disturbances which might have a direct bearing on the educational problems in cerebral palsy.[12] They found abnormal functions in visuo-motor performance and figure-background organization, and an unusual amount of perseveration in the children under their observation.

The educational implications of the perceptual disturbances of the cerebral palsied child have been elaborated by Cruickshank and Dolphin;[12] many methods, materials and techniques are used in the education of normal children which may operate to hinder the learning process in a large portion of the cerebral palsied children. Some important danger cues are (1) forced response to stimuli or hyperactiveness (the child is unable to refrain from reacting to stimuli in the environment) ; (2) perseveration, external or internal; (3) dissociation (inability to synthesize aspects of a situation into a meaningful Gestalt) ; (4) disinhibition (exaggerated attention, hyperactivity, restlessness, inability to avoid manipulation of objects which serve as stimuli for motor activity as well as motor disinhibition in which the child attends to more objects at once than the normal child) , and (5) pathology of the figure-background relationship, the impact of which was great on visuo-motor and tactile-motor tasks, as well as on more abstract tasks.

Additional perceptual implications have been enumerated by Cruickshank and Bice,[11] but these are too numerous to be discussed here. It is not difficult to conclude from the above findings that perceptual difficulties in the visual, auditory and kinesthetic fields may be barriers in the development of communication.

Emotional Adjustment: Glick[23] surveyed 200 cerebral palsied adults selected from case loads of two social agencies in New York City. These cerebral palsied adults were ambulatory and between the ages of eighteen and forty-five. By means of a questionnaire, information was obtained regarding the emotional problems of this group. In almost three-fourths of the cases, indications of emotional maladjustment were reported. The emotional instability of 20 per cent was serious enough to preclude the possibilities of job placement. The various factors of instability were as follows:

1. Unrealistic attitudes.
2. Intense feelings of insecurity.

3. Extreme immaturity.
4. Excessive fears, almost completely out of line with reality.
5. Strong feelings of inferiority.
6. Low frustration tolerance.
7. Problems in interpersonal relationships, such as inability to get along with family, friends, and contemporaries.
8. Lack of motivation.

Instability was reported more frequently in the cases having mild physical handicaps. Of those who were mildly disabled 80 per cent had difficulty in adjusting to their handicaps, accepting their limitations, and planning realistically for their future. Some of the background factors which apparently had a significant influence on psychological adjustments of these adults were overprotection, parental rejection and unrealistic or compensatory attitude of parents.

Lack of motivation seemed to be the most frequent problem presented by the group, being present in 70 per cent of the cases. Forty-two per cent showed an inability to face reality and 51 per cent had excessive fears and anxieties. The need for psychiatric help in the early habilitative process was stressed.

Little's observations of the emotional complications in families of cerebral palsied children made at the Children's Hospital in Buffalo, New York, revealed that of twenty-one families studied, only one did not show marked evidence of emotional disturbance secondary to having cerebral palsy in the family.[33] The types of emotional reactions ranged through depression, guilt feelings, overprotection, rejection and even denial of the existence of the cerebral palsy condition. Boles[7] found mothers of cerebral palsied children to be significantly more overprotective and maritally less well adjusted than mothers of noncerebral palsied children.

These studies indicate that in addition to his physical "noticeability," the cerebral palsied person may also have an emotional crippling which enhances his noticeability and reduces his ability to make a social adjustment. The emotional difficulties of the cerebral palsied child may have a decided influence upon his responsiveness to therapy and education.

Intellectual Development: During the past few years, much discussion and study has been directed toward two problems having to do with the intelligence of the cerebral palsied child: (1) How do IQ scores of the cerebral palsied persons compare to those of the normal population? (2) How valid and reliable are testing methods used in evaluating the intelligence of the cerebral palsied individual?

Varying reports are found on the first problem. Little reported that cerebral palsy was usually caused by cerebral hemorrhage at birth and described the children as having cross-legged gait, drooling, speech defects and mental deficiency.[31] Phelps reported later that 25 per cent of the cerebral palsied were mentally retarded.[40]

More recent studies by Asher and Schonell, Miller and Rosenfeld and Hohman have thrown new shadings on the problem of intelligence of the cerebral palsied. The general conclusions of these three studies were approximately the same in "that at least seventy-five per cent of all cerebral palsied children are below average in contrast to twenty-five per cent of the normal population, and that at least fifty per cent are seriously retarded and mentally defective."[26] In a later study, based upon 1003 cases, Hohman reported that 16.1 per cent were found to have IQ's above 90, 3.1 per cent were rated above 110, 58.8 per cent were below 70, and 25.1 per cent were in the 70 to 89 range.[27] Figure 1 is a graphic representation of the results of this study.

With regard to the problem of validity and reliability of the testing methods, differences in opinion exist. Two basic assumptions regarding any psychometric device must be accepted: (1) the child must have had the same opportunity to learn and gain experience as the average child, and (2) the child must do his best on the test.

Crowell and Crowell[10] found in testing and retesting sixty-one cerebral palsied patients that mental ages obtained on standard tests were reliable for ordinary diagnostic purposes provided that the tester had had adequate training and experience. Kogan[30] later reported similar findings.

Doll[18] reports that the administration of standard testing procedures is valid only when it can be assumed that there are no barriers to expressive and receptive experience. He describes instances where standard testing of individual brain-damaged cases was very much in error. Bice[6] also discusses the complex problems involved in testing cerebral palsied children and warns of the danger of using the IQ in an evaluation. He suggests that a careful analysis of test responses aids in the finding of answers to such questions as What causative factors can be discovered? What ability does the child have to adjust? What are his assets? What are his liabilities? In what manner can the assets be best put to use? In what ways may his liabilities be overcome? How can the results be best interpreted to the parents or professional per-

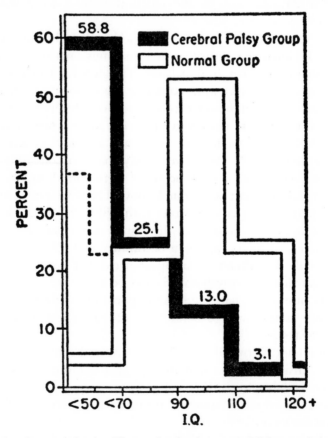

Figure 1.   Comparative intelligence levels of normal children and those with cerebral palsy.

sonnel who will assist in carrying out recommendations? He emphasizes that since examinations are scheduled because there are problems to be solved, a clear statement of all known factors about the child is taken as a starting point.

Adaptive Development: Since the ultimate needs of the preschool and school-age cerebral palsied children are those of social and vocational adjustment, and since communication plays a vital role in both of these, it may be wise to discuss briefly some of the facts regarding environmental, educational, and vocational adaptations which the teacher, the parent and the cerebral palsied child must ultimately face.

Cruickshank and Bice[11] describe some major conditions which have an effect on *environmental* or *social* adjustments of the cerebral palsied child. Part of the dilemma presented to the cerebral palsied child stems from the effects of his *environmental relationships* with himself, his parents, and his peers. Included in this category are overprotection, rejection, experiential immaturity and an unrealistic self-concept.

The child may be overprotected by his parents and develop a lack of self sufficiency and self-confidence which may later lead to rejection. He may expect to gain acceptance and rewards without earning them. The development of social skills and shadings of interpersonal etiquette may be lacking. Consequently, the peers of the cerebral palsied child may reject him for this faster than they will for his "unsightly" physical appearance.

Early in life, the cerebral palsied child may find that he cannot keep up with other children and is not wanted as a playmate. Because of his lack of ambulation and/or presence of sensory handicap, he cannot gain units of successful experience as rapidly as normal children and thus he is more immature than they are in many areas of social competence. Because he may be unable to communicate freely, he cannot readily effect changes in barriers to his adjustment. His behavior may reflect frustrations and bizarre compensatory actions.

An important factor (suggested by Cruickshank and Bice) influencing the child's behavior, is his *self-concept.* His own image of himself may be revealed in his actions or expressed desires. His concept may be morbid or unrealistic and thus elicit reactions that can develop into personality maladjustments which are deep seated and dynamic.

According to Cruickshank and Bice, another point of view from which adjustment of the cerebral palsied child must be viewed is the recognition of the extent to which the brain damage affects behavior. In a previous section of this chapter, perceptual and psychomotor difficulties of the cerebral palsied children were mentioned. A further treatment of these problems can be found in Chapter II.

Denhoff's study of factors in successful *educational* adjustment of cerebral palsied children indicated that the key to "good" adjustment is family understanding and acceptance. He states that "even though good medical treatment and evaluation is necessary, nevertheless, the *family* must be the first consideration in the treatment of cerebral palsy."[15]

It was rather definite that the most advantageous triad for successful adjustment in regular school was mild physical handicap, average intelligence and a "good" family. "Similarly, success in a *special class* seems to be associated with moderate handicap, borderline intelligence, and a fair family. The children with a severe handicap but with average to borderline intelligence and a 'good' or 'fair' family were able to make good adjustments with home teachers."[15] This information is valuable in the consideration of proper placement of the child in the educational setting.

Glick[24] found, in her study of the vocational adjustment of 200 cerebral palsied adults in New York City, that only 21 per cent of the group were employed. Of the 158 not employed, a large number needed counseling or therapy plus intensive training before they could become employable.

The main problem sources in employment were (1) limitations resulting from physical, mental, and emotional problems; (2) inadequate vocational guidance and preparation for job placement, and (3) resistance of employers to hiring the cerebral palsied because of a lack of knowledge of the cerebral palsy condition, prejudice or fear. In contrast to natural expectations, 6.9 per cent of those mildly handicapped physically were employed, whereas 21.6 per cent and 5.1 per cent of the moderately and severely disabled respectively were employed. It was found that the mildly disabled had more difficulty in adjusting to their handicaps, accepting their limitations, and planning realistically for their future. A large portion of this latter group were emotionally unstable.

The fact that ninety-one people in the unemployed group answered that they wanted just any kind of job they could do, indicated that adequate vocational guidance was greatly lacking. A series of guiding principles, showing activities which the individual with cerebral palsy should experience in the guidance process, has been presented by Fleishcher.[21]

Benson[5] studied a group of fifty adults with cerebral palsy and found communication ability highly influential on their employability level.

Communication Development: Communication by means of speech, listening, reading, and writing depends upon development or maturation of many related areas. One cannot talk or write, for example, until a certain degree of ability to control and integrate *motor* activities has been reached. There must also be a certain psychological readiness which will depend upon intelligence as well as emotional and adaptive maturation. Before one can learn to communicate adequately, one must also be able to perceive and discriminate with the highly specialized *sensory* processes, particularly those of vision, hearing and kinesthesia.

It is customary to think of communication as composed of three major processes: (1) sensory input, which affects the organism; (2) associational mechanisms, which give meaning to the sensory input in terms of how the organism should react to the sensory stimuli, and (3) the motor output as the final leg in the communication circuit. As can be seen in Figure 2, the brain plays a leading role in each process of the communication act. Damage may have a devastating effect.

In addition to primary motor, sensory and associational mechanisms in communication, there is also an important system called the "monitoring" or "feedback" system which normally guides the individual through correct patterns of performance in the speaking and writing processes.[37] As an example of this, the extremely simplified diagram in Figure 2 is illustrative of the monitoring system which guides an individual in the act of speaking. The source of the ordered speech patterns is the brain, and the transmitter is the speech mechanism. As can be seen, the auditory, proprioceptive and tactile "feedback networks" allow some of the output energy transmitted by the speech mechanism to be fed back to the brain. This feedback system provides for the necessary monitoring by enabling a comparison of ordered input and actual output and permitting an altering of the input if a discrepancy exists between the forms of the two so that the discrepancy may be corrected.

The feedback networks in the human communication system assure correct output by analyzing and facilitating correction of the discrepancy between "command" and the output. In writing, these networks are composed mainly of proprioceptive, tactile and visual feedback channels.

The feedback channels in communication have circuits on lower levels of the central nervous system, and speech and writing may become routinized, stereotyped and automatic. Breakdown of these circuits may occur on any of the neurological levels: the level of primitive reflexes, primary projection or associational areas of the brain. Vegetative action will take priority over some of these circuits since they were originally intended for vegetation: the sneeze, for example, will interrupt speech. Emotional expression may also take priority: it is difficult for one to communicate verbally while crying or laughing. It is for the above reasons that communication is susceptible to all sorts of interruption and is first to break down when traumatic injury occurs.

Although the exact nature of feedback distortion in the communication of the cerebral palsied person is not known, it may reasonably be postulated that feedback is primarily disrupted through damage or anomaly in the central nervous system and secondarily obscured by hyper-or hypo-tonicity and excessive involuntary movements.

Development of the motor and sensory processes and utilization of feed-back for monitoring in communication contribute to the highest type of integration that a human being can achieve. Lack of such development is one of the most crippling factors in the achievement of life adjustments in the human race.

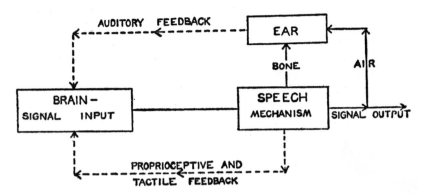

Figure 2. Simplified diagram of the speaker system in speech communication including some self-monitoring networks.

It is small wonder that even the saying of "Hi"—one little word—is the beginning of a whole new vista of life for the cerebral palsied child.

REFERENCES

1. ABBOTT, M.: *Basic Organization and Management of Cerebral Palsy Facilities.* New York, Coordinating Council for Cerebral Palsy in New York City, Inc., 1953.
2. ABBOTT, M.: *Cerebral Palsy — Its Scope and Management.* New York, Public Affairs Pamphlets (22 E. 38th Street) , 1956.
3. ALBERMAN, E.: Birth weight and length of gestation in cerebral palsy. *Develop. Med. Child Neurol., 5:*388-394, 1963.
4. ANDERSON, B.: Cerebral palsy. *J. Oslo City Hospital, 4:*65-87, 1954.
5. BENSEN, J. F.: An analysis of the speech of cerebral palsied individuals in an effort to determine employability levels. *Cereb. Palsy Rev., 23:*3,9-13, 1962.
6. BICE, H. V.: Psychological services for the cerebral palsied. *Nerv. Child, 8:*183-192, 1949.
7. BOLES, G.: Personal factors in mothers of cerebral palsied children. *Genet. Psychol. Monogr., 59:*159-218, 1959.
8. CARDWELL, V. E.: *Cerebral Palsy — Advances in Understanding and Care.* New York, Assoc. for the Aid of Crippled Children, 1956.
9. COURVILLE, C. B.: *Cerebral Palsy.* Los Angeles, San Lucas Press, 1954.

10. CROWELL, D. H., and CROWELL, D. C.: Intelligence test reliability for cerebral palsied children. *J. Consult. Psychol., 18:*276, 1954.
11. CRUICKSHANK, W. M., and BICE, H. V.: Personality characteristics. In *Cerebral Palsy,* ed. by W. M. Cruickshank and G. M. Raus. New York, Syracuse Univ. Press, pp. 115-165, 1955.
12. CRUICKSHANK, W. M., and DOLPHIN, J. E.: The educational implications of psychological studies of cerebral palsied children. *J. Except. Child., 18:*1-8, 1951.
13. DEAVER, G. G.: *Cerebral Palsy, Methods of Evaluation and Treatment.* New York, The Institute of Physical Medicine and Rehabilitation (400 East 34th Street) , 1955.
14. DENHOFF, E., and HOLDEN, R. H.: Significance of delayed development in diagnosis of cerebral palsy. *J. Pediat., 38:*452-456, 1951.
15. DENHOFF, E., and HOLDEN, R. H.: Family influences on successful adjustment of cerebral palsied children. *J. Except. Child., 21:* 5-7, 1954.
16. DENHOFF, E.: Emotional and psychological background of the neurologically handicapped child. *J. Except. Child., 27:*347-349, 1960.
17. DiCARLO, L. M., and AMSTER, W. W.: Hearing and speech behavior among children with cerebral palsy. In *Cerebral Palsy,* ed. by W. M. Cruickshank and G. M. Raus. New York, Syracuse University Press, 1955.
18. DOLL, E. A.: Intelligence in cerebral palsy. *Cereb. Palsy Rev., 15:* 8-9, 19, 27, 1954.
19. DOLPHIN, J. E., and CRUICKSHANK, W. M.: Visuo-motor perception in children with cerebral palsy. *Quart. J. Child Behav., 3:*198-209, 1951.
20. DOLPHIN, J. E., and CRUICKSHANK, W. M.: The figure-background relationship in children with cerebral palsy. *J. Clin. Psychol., 7:*228-231, 1951.
21. FLEISCHER, E.: Higher education for the cerebral palsied. *Amer. J. Occup. Ther., 7:*254, 267, 1953.
22. GARMEZY, N., and HARRIS, J. G., JR.: Motor performance of cerebral palsied children as a function of their success or failure in achieving material rewards. *Child. Devel., 24:*287-300, 1953.
23. GLICK, S. J.: Emotional problems of 200 cerebral palsied adults. *Cereb. Palsy Rev., 14:*3-5, 1953.
24. GLICK, S. J.: Facing an unsolved problem: employment of cerebral palsied. *J. Rehab., 19:*7-9, 1953.

25. HANSEN, E.: Cerebral palsy in Denmark. *Acta Psychiat. Neurol. Scand., Suppl., 146:*35, 7-148, 1960.
26. HOHMAN, L. B.: Intelligence levels in cerebral palsied children. *Amer. J. Phys. Med., 32:*7-9, 1953.
27. HOHMAN, L. B., and FREEDHEIM, D. K.: Further studies on intelligence levels in cerebral palsied children. *Amer. J. Phys. Med., 37:*90-97, 1958.
28. HOPKINS, T. W., BICE, H. V., and COLTON, K. G.: *Evaluation and Education of the Cerebral Palsied Child.* Washington, D. C., International Council for Except. Child., 1954.
29. KEATS, S.: *Cerebral Palsy.* Springfield, Illinois, Thomas, 1965.
30. KOGAN, K. L.: Repeated psychometric evaluations of pre-school children with cerebral palsy. *Pediatrics, 19:*619-622, 1957.
31. LITTLE, W. J.: On the influence of abnormal parturition, difficult labors, immature birth, and asphyxia neonatorum, on the mental and physical condition of the child, especially in relation to deformities. *Trans. Obst. Soc. London, 3:*293-294, 1862.
32. LITTLE, W. J.: Lectures on the deformities of the human brain. *Lancet, 1:*5, 38, 78, 141, 174, 238, 285, 318, 350, 382, 534, 564, 598, 679, 705, 745, 777, 808, 1843.
33. LITTLE, S.: A note on an investigation of the emotional complications of cerebral palsy. *Nerv. Child., 8:*181-182, 1949.
34. LORD, E. E.: *Children Handicapped by Cerebral Palsy.* New York, The Commonwealth Fund, 1937.
35. MARTIN, J. K.: Cerebral Palsy in Manitoba. *Canad. Med. Ass. J., 82:*411-417, 1960.
36. McDONALD, E. T., and CHANCE, B.: *Cerebral Palsy.* Englewood Cliffs, N. Y., Prentice-Hall, Inc., 1964.
37. MECHAM, M. J.: Complexities in communication of the cerebral palsied. *Cereb. Palsy Rev., 15:*9-11, 14, 1954.
38. MITCHELL, R. G.: Medical aspects of a comprehensive survey of cerebral palsy. *Cereb. Palsy Rev., 7:*32-41, 1959.
39. PERLSTEIN, M. A.: Medical aspects of cerebral palsy. *Nerv. Child, 8:*128-151, 1949.
40. PHELPS, W. M. and TURNER, A.: *The Farthest Corner.* Chicago, National Soc. for Crippled Children and Adults, Inc., 1945.
41. PHELPS, W. M.: *Let's Talk about Cerebral Palsy.* New York, United Cerebral Palsy Assns., Inc., 1946.
42. PHELPS, W. M.: Description and differentiation of types of cerebral palsy. *Nerv. Child, 8:*107-127, 1949.

43. Russell, E. M.: Cerebral palsied twins. *Arch. Dis. Child., 36:* 187, 329-336, 1961.
44. Strauss, A. A.: Aphasia in children. *Amer. J. Phys. Med., 33:*93-99, 1954.
45. Strauss, A. A., and Lehtinen, L. E.: *Psychopathology and Education of the Brain-injured Child.* New York, Grune and Stratton, 1947.
46. Towbin, A.: *The Pathology of Cerebral Palsy.* Springfield, Illinois, Thomas, 1960.
47. Wallace, H. M., *et al.*: Cerebral palsy in Minnesota: method of study, prevalence, and distribution, Part. I. *Amer. J. Public Health, 51:*417-426, 1961.

Chapter II

DISORDERS OF SPEECH AND HEARING

MERLIN J. MECHAM

SINCE THE NEUROMOTOR and neurosensory involvements of the cerebral palsied person are usually such that they reduce the chances of accurate transmission of information (i.e., introduce distortion), the verbal response of the listener may cue the speaker to such a condition. The listener gives the verbal request, "Huh?" or "What did you say?" or possibly an intentional sympathetic, if misleading, affirmative nod. An awareness of this "trick" arouses resentment on the part of the cerebral palsied person and may cause the listener much embarrassment.

A large number of cerebral palsied individuals have speech which is defective in one way or another and frequently in many ways. Several studies on incidence of speech disorders have been reported. These differ considerably in their results, but, on the average it appears that 70 to 80 per cent of the cerebral palsied group have some involvement of speech and/or hearing.

The incidence of speech and hearing disorders according to types of cerebral palsy has been reported, but reports vary somewhat, possibly as a result of differences in sampling. Achilles[1] reported that 89 per cent of the athetoids, 76 per cent of the spastics, 100 per cent of the ataxics and 94 per cent of the rigidity cases had communicative performance which was rated as fair, poor or none. Hopkins, Bice and Colton[41] reported that 51.9 per cent of the spastics, 88.7 per cent of the athetoids, 72.1 per cent of the rigidity cases and 85.3 per cent of the ataxics were found to have defective speech. The figures in this study are probably fairly representative of the total CP population since they are based upon large numbers.

In addition to incidence, numerous other aspects are to be considered. A question which arises invariably is whether or not such a thing as characteristic "cerebral palsy" speech exists. A second oft-debated question is whether or not the speech characteristics of different cerebral palsied persons vary significantly as a function of the type of cerebral palsy. Third, general aspects of oral communication to be considered are the extent of speech delay which exists in cerebral palsy and the extent to which the existing speech is understandable. Fourth, more specific problems of outstanding importance to be considered are the extent of dysarthria as well as difficulties in articulation, rhythm, breathing, voice and hearing. These problems have been investigated and reported variously in the broad field of literature on cerebral palsy. Each of them will be discussed in some detail in this chapter.

GENERAL SPEECH CHARACTERISTICS OF THE CEREBRAL PALSIED

Is There Characteristic Cerebral Palsy Speech? In comparing the spastic and the athetoid, Blumenthal[10] states that the speech of the athetoid is slow, arrhythmic and inconsistent while the spastic's speech is labored but consistent. Palmer[63] states that spastic paralysis produces losses in reciprocal inhibition of the sucking movements, laryngeal valving, articulation and breathing while in the athetoids are found unusual involvements of position and movement. Choreiform movements of the tongue and athetoses of the intrinsic and extrinsic muscles of the larynx are found in athetoids. Cerebellar lesions manifest distortions of synergic patterns, and rigidities are usually accompanied by complete loss of speech.

West[79] describes visible characteristics by which spasticity can be recognized but makes no allusion to acoustical differences between the spastic and the athetoid. Berry and Eisenson give the following description of the speech of the three major types of cerebral palsy — spastic, athetoid, and ataxic:

> Spastic speech is recognized by its slow, labored rate, lack of vocal inflection, gutteral or breathy quality of voice, uncontrolled volume, and, most important, grave articulatory problems which reflect the inability to secure graded, synchronous movements of the tongue, lips, and jaw. Often the disfunction in the laryngeal muscles produces sudden explosive increases in

volume or abrupt changes in pitch, all without reference to the
content of expression.

. . . The speech of the athetoid presents varying gradations
of a pattern of irregular, shallow, and noisy breathing; whispered, hoarse, or ventricular phonation; and articulatory problems varying from the extremes of complete mutism or extreme
dysarthria to a slight awkwardness in lingual movement.

The speech of the ataxic may be characterized by a slurring
of articulation which lapses into unintelligibility if speech
is continued beyond phrases or short sentences. Rhythm is disturbed and vocal pitch, loudness, and quality tend either to be
monotonal or to vary spasmodically and without respect to
meaning.[7]

They add, however, that the problems in any one type of
cerebral palsy are so diverse that it is practically impossible to
draw a simple or composite picture of cerebral palsied children.

Hyman[42] measured and compared the sound pressure and
duration of speech responses of children in their repetition of
heard speech. He found that both athetoids and noncerebral
palsied children respond to variations in sound pressure and
duration of the stimulus materials. The spastics, however, were
not responsive to variations in sound pressure level. The athetoids
had slower rates of speech than the normals or spastics.

Later, Leith[48] found in a comparative evaluation of sixty
spastics with forty athetoids, that differences in rate, pitch, loudness and articulation were not significant. Hedges[38] also found no
differences between spastics and athetoids in respect to diadochokinetic rate, length of phonation or their ability to make themselves understood. His panel of professionally trained judges
could identify spastic versus athetoid's speech by no better than
chance judgment; he used only acoustically-recorded speech
samples.

Lencione[49] found that spastics were more proficient than athetoids in speech sound production in all positions. In the patterns
of communication performance in her group of 100, the level of
development of the spastics resembled that of the seven-year-old
child, while that of the athetoids more closely resembled the

speech of children below six years of age. In respect to intelligibility, 71 per cent of the spastics as compared to 31 per cent of the athetoids had intelligible speech.

Achilles found similar results to those of Lencione in a study comparing the speech disorders of ninety athetoids with sixty-one patients with other types of cerebral palsy. He found that the athetoids present a greater number of distinct communicative anomalies than any other type of cerebral palsy. Sixty-five per cent of the total anomalies tabulated for 151 cases of cerebral palsy were displayed by the athetoid group, whereas 36 per cent were found in the "other types." His conclusion was that anatomical and physiological deviations which hamper communication tend to be more wide spread in the athetoid group.[2]

In general, we may conclude that differences in the speech of the cerebral palsied children and noncerebral palsied children are more apparent in degree than in quality. The speech characteristics of the cerebral palsy group as a whole tends to be slow, jerky and irregular, labored or effortful and rather unintelligible. Such characteristics may be referred to as "cerebral palsy speech." Because of the extreme variability of the speech of the cerebral palsied children, generalizations regarding differences according to type of CP are not reliable. As much acoustical difference may exist between two athetoids, for example, as between an athetoid and a spastic.

Delayed Speech: Speech output of the cerebral palsied individual may be analyzed in terms of a "continuum," all the way from a complete lack of speech to a very slight or no delay from normal range. Various reports have been given in respect to speech delay in cerebral palsy.

Achilles[1] found that of the 151 children examined by Palmer at CRI (between 1946 and 1952), 66 per cent had *severe* communication problems in the form of no speech or not more than one year of oral language development. Twenty per cent were considered to have a *fair* amount of communication, i.e., could make their primitive wants known but showed a general level of eighteen to twenty-four months of communication development. Fourteen per cent were rated as having *good* communication ability, i.e., were not delayed and were able to express themselves fairly well, in spite of having articulatory, voice and rhythm problems.

Irwin[43] found that the profile of consonant-vowel maturation of the cerebral palsied children is retarded, three years on the average, by the time they reach five and a half years of age.

Denhoff,[19] in a study of children in a school for cerebral palsy, found that 74 per cent of them were delayed beyond twelve months in saying single words. The average age for onset of the first words was 27.1 months. Only 23 per cent were talking in sentences of two or three words by the age of thirty-one months. The average for onset of two or three word sentences was 37.4 months. Byrne's study[15] of verbal development reported a lag somewhat similar to that of Denhoff.

Dunsdon[24] reported on the oral language development of 200 cerebral palsied children in England and indicated that there was an average retardation of from three to four years in vocabulary, verbal recall and reasoning.

In a survey of twenty-six cerebral palsied children selected arbitrarily at the Institute of Logopedics, Mecham[55] found that language development ranged from 1.17 years to 8.50 years as compared to the childrens' chronological age (CA) range of 2.5 to fourteen years. Mean language age was 3.28 years as compared to a mean CA of 7.2 years for the group. Although the sample is not necessarily representative of the CP population, it illustrates discrepancies which one may find within a group of cerebral palsied children.

Love[50] found no difference between twenty-seven older cerebral palsied children with near normal intelligence and their physically handicapped controls in receptive vocabulary, ability to define words, ability to explain their own performance in an objective matching test and color sorting test or quality of language output (in terms of being confused, perseveration, bizarre, stereotyped or characterized by fantasy).

Meyers,[58] however, found that both young athetoids and spastics are inferior to normals on various subtests of the ITPA. The athetoids were inferior to normals and spastics in automatic-sequential language tasks but superior to spastics in representation-level language tasks.

Some speculations have been offered as to the *causes* of delayed development in oral language and articulate speech. Mention will be made of the more important of these.

Many have looked to *aphasia* as a major cause. In the brain-injured adult, one who has acquired an oral language loss, a high correlation has been found between side of involvement and extent to which language function is impaired.[81] The most severe involvements occur when there has been injury to the left side. This is not so, however, in the case of infants with unilateral lesions. Hood and Perlstein[32] studied 334 cerebral palsied children with spastic hemiplegia (injury on one side only). They found the amount of delay to be much less than that reported by the studies that have been done on multiplegic cerebral palsied children. Average delay for the onset of words, as compared to that for normal children was nine months. Average delay for onset of sentences was six months. Contrary to the assumption of the existence of a more severe language involvement (particularly speech) in right hemiplegics based on findings in adults, no significant difference was found between left and right hemiplegics in oral language involvement. Other studies have reported similar findings.[39,86]

Emotional complications and *anxiety* have been known to deter speech and communication in the cerebral palsied.[22] That emotional trauma is an influential factor in many cases of delayed and defective speech, is a fact rather commonly accepted. Glick,[29] in his study of 200 cerebral palsied adults, found a much higher incidence of emotional tension and anxiety in this group than exists in the normal population. Carlson[16] has described many instances of spontaneous improvement in the speech of the cerebral palsied, resulting from release of emotional tensions through means of anesthesia, distraction, relaxation or satisfactory job placement. Mecham[56] found that administration of the drug Tolserol, a relaxing agent which works directly on the muscle, effected speech improvement in cerebral palsied and stuttering individuals in a mental institution. Palmer has described the effects of the emotional dilemma of the cerebral palsied child on his efforts to communicate. His failure to succeed in providing and receiving information may bring increased failure through the disruptive effects of "self-reflexiveness." He states that,

> . . . The self-reflexiveness problem is particularly acute in the field of communication since prior to any communicative effort the former responses under similar situations must be integrated with the new initiation. As these concepts flow across the central nervous system and are recalled and put into feed-back systems, the negative reactions tend to take precedence over the positive reactions. Thus a child with cerebral palsy may respond in ways which are less satisfactory than either his physical condition or his mental limitations should prescribe.[64]

Duncan described what happened to a normal child emotionally when he was unduly restricted during the first six years of his life and was partially ignored and rejected by his parents:

> When he was filled with excitement and had no relief from adults outside, when he could not get out to move around and test his reality and thus develop normally, he sought escape from adults by rejection or sought relief in temper tantrums, a primitive discharge. He even went through a period of shutting out the human voice.[23]

What about the cerebral palsied child confined to a wheel chair? Unger describes sympathetically how some mothers may involuntarily reject the child whose condition demands so much and leaves her no freedom. The child may increase his demands when he sees her rejection or may withdraw to himself. Unger states that,

> So difficult is the physical act of speech for many of these children that they may give up the struggle of trying to communicate with this seemingly unfriendly world and express their difficulties only in tantrums, tears, or silence.[79]

(Techniques for differential diagnosis of emotional complications in the etiology of delayed or defective speech in cerebral palsy are discussed in some detail in Chapter III.)

Many cases of delayed speech are thought to be the result of *perceptual* and/or *motor* disabilities in the child. It would be interesting to know more about the exact relationship of amount of verbal output and severity of perceptual and motor disabilities. Berko and Berko[6] found that perceptual difficulties contributed to the complexities of communication of cerebral palsied adults. Dolphin and Cruickshank studied the perceptual abilities of cerebral palsied children and found gross deficiencies in their visual-motor perception, figure-background relationship, concept formation and tactual-motor perception, when compared to abilities of a group of normal children in these areas. (See Chapter I.)

The close existing relationship of *hearing impairment* to the delayed development of language would lead us to explore the possibilities of a hearing disability in any child who does not talk or is delayed in speaking. Evaluation of hearing in a young and severely involved cerebral palsied child may prove extremely difficult but is essential in the process of locating causal factors.

Lack of proper *stimulation* is felt to be an important factor in the speech delay of the cerebral palsied child. These children are often infantilized and treated on a level comparable to their expressive ability, and thus they are not challenged to improve this ability. A cerebral palsied child's hearing and ability to understand may be on a level with his chronological age while his expressive ability may be on an infantile level. According to Westlake, "When a child can do little more than smile, people are inclined to say only those things that elicit the smile, so that the language used with him is on the 'cuddle' or 'mascot' level rather than being really stimulating."[84] Parents often find it easier to say things for the child with labored speech and save him and the listener some embarrassment. Thus, the challenge for him to struggle and achieve in speech expression may be reduced or absent.

General or specific *intellectual impairment* may be a cause of speech delay in a large number of cerebral palsied children. In general, the speech and language development is expected to be comparable to the child's mental age if development is not marred by other complicating factors. Thus, a child with a general intellectual impairment will always have delayed speech in comparison to his chronological age but not necessarily in comparison to his mental age. If there is specific involvement of the language centers of the brain (aphasia), on the other hand, the speech and oral language delay may be much greater than the child's delay in general mental maturation.

Understandability: Not being verbally understood is more than merely having defective articulation and lack of intelligibility, although articulation and intelligibility are very vital aspects of understandability. Whether or not the meaning of the spoken passage is understood is what is referred to in this text as understandability. This encompasses not only articulation and intelligibility, but also adequacy in the use of language to express meanings.

A very common experience in the life of the cerebral palsied child is not being orally understood. In Wolfe's study of cerebral palsied children, 45 per cent had speech which was only partly understandable or was not understood at all.[85] The athetoids had the greatest amount of trouble in this respect; 40 per cent of this group were rated as being "not understood." The spastic group was much less involved. Only 30 per cent of this group had speech that was partially or totally lacking in understandability. In Lencione's study[46] involving 129 cerebral palsied children in the public schools, the athetoids again were found to be much less understandable than the others. Seventy-one per cent of the athetoids had "unintelligible" speech as compared to 31 per cent of the spastics so rated.

Children with cerebral palsy are often difficult to understand because they are limited in flexibility of extent and variety of oral language function. They seem to be more restricted in extent and variety of choice of oral expression because of the time element in their slow labored movements. People are loath to wait and listen for a very long period of time in this "fast-talking" world. In his attempts to get information across, the cerebral palsied person does not seem to use words and word combinations which will function to get the message through in the shortest time and with the least amount of effort. It is a common experience to hear the child with cerebral palsy repeat over and over again the same word or the same phrase in an effort to be understood.

SPECIFIC SPEECH AND HEARING PROBLEMS

Neuromuscular Involvements of the Speech Mechanism:
Dysarthria is a speech defect which is due to a lesion in portions
of the central nervous system for which, or by which, the organs
of articulation are controlled. This problem is found in all of
those cases of cerebral palsy who have some kind of neuromuscular
involvement of the speech mechanism. Wolfe found that from 31
to 59 per cent of the cases studied by him had some degree of
dysarthria.[85] Hixon and Hardy[35] demonstrated that the degree
of motility of the articulators in the production of /CV/ syllables
involving respiration, phonation and articulation is highly correlated with defectiveness of speech in cerebral palsy.

In the spastic child, there are several possible types of muscular
involvement. The speech musculature may be *hypertonic;* thus,
movement is slow and labored because of the difficulty in getting
adequate and smooth reciprocal innervation. Extreme cases of
hypertonic spasticity are the decerebrate rigidities. Sherrington
described the symptoms of one so involved as having rigid extension of the limbs and tight adduction of the jaw. Fothergill and
Harrington quote several sources which demonstrate that the
muscles of the lower jaw are especially susceptible to the *stretch
reflex.*[25] In reference to some spastics, Phelps has described the
presence of a type of *flaccidity,* or lack of muscular tone, which he
terms "zero cerebral," or "aspastic spasticity." In these cases,
some of the tongue or jaw muscles may be too weak for adequate
movement. There may be overtonicity in some opposing muscles,
making synergistic movement difficult.

Frequently, these abnormal conditions exist in many muscle
groups in the spastic child, and if the tongue and jaw muscles are
so involved, the speech of the individual will be greatly impaired.
If the extensors of the jaw, for example, are activated to open the
jaw, an impulse to the extensor muscles will initiate a strong
contraction, perhaps a maximal one; the joint will begin movement, and the flexor muscles will be stretched. If the flexor
muscles are spastic, they will contract violently as a result of the
stretch reflex. Thus, reciprocal action of the jaw is reduced or
destroyed.[63] If the child attempts further opening of the jaw,

the external pterygoid muscle may contract more strongly and actually pull the condyle forward from its joint (mandibular facet slip).

In the athetoid, the nature of the neuromuscular involvement is different. In this condition, involved muscles suffer from an involuntary movement or series of involuntary movements. If any of the muscles of breathing, voice or articulation are involved with *athetotic* movement, the voice and articulate speech may be jerky, or arrhythmic and may be accompanied by extra clicks and noises resulting from involuntary movements superimposed on the efforts toward regular movements required in the speaking process. Dysarthria seems to be present to a much greater degree in the athetoid group than in the other groups of cerebral palsy. The mandibular facet slip, athetosis of the tongue, etc., have been frequently observed in the athetoid group.

In the ataxic child, the major neuromuscular disability stems from the *disordered feedback* mechanisms. Positional and directional orientations are difficult for the ataxic child and he has difficulty approximating the structures of the speech mechanism for proper pattern formulation. Distorted feedback may be present in the spastic and athetoid children also, but it is the *primary* disorder in the ataxic child.

Severe defects of articulation, voice and breathing are frequently associated with abnormal *reflexogenic release* phenomena as a result of loss of inhibitory control over primitive cranio-oropharyngeal reflexes.[59,60] Stimulation of the face area may trigger off these primitive reflexes and may disrupt attempts at selective voluntary control of the musculature for speech. Detection of the presence of reflexogenic problems in control of the speech mechanism is discussed in Chapter IV.

Articulation Problems and Reduced Intelligibility: Research points to the fact that when part of the mechanism is faulty in function, the whole system may be thrown out of kilter. Articulation is not the entity of a single process but is the result of correlated activity of many structures whose primary functions are of a vegetative nature; any forces which affect the vegetative functions of the structures used in articulation have a devastating effect on one's ability to articulate properly.

From 70 to 80 per cent of all cerebral palsied persons have some type of defect in articulation which may be either functional or organic in origin. In some, the articulation is so affected that the speech is practically unintelligible. On a continuum of articulation ability, the cerebral palsied persons may be roughly divided into three categories: (1) little or no ability; (2) moderately impaired; and (3) slightly impaired or adequate. Achilles[1] found that 43 per cent of the cases in his study had "poor" articulation, 45 per cent had "fair" articulation and 12 per cent had adequate articulation. According to some studies, the greatest number of articulatory errors are found in quadriplegia involving combined athetosis and spasticity, and the fewest errors are found in spastic diplegia.[80]

It is interesting to compare various descriptions of articulation of the different types of cerebral palsy that are found in the literature. Van Riper[80] states that both spastics and athetoids have difficulty with sounds requiring fine coordination and that they find tongue-tip sounds especially difficult. In those cases of mixed spasticity and athetosis, he has observed increased difficulty in articulation. Lencione[49] found that the tongue tip sounds were most difficult for the cerebral palsied child to produce and that voiced sounds were generally easier than voiceless ones.

In approximate agreement with other investigators,[5,42] the spastics were more proficient than athetoids in almost all aspects of sound articulation. The production of sounds in the initial position was easier for the entire group than production of sounds in the medial and final positions. According to Rutherford,[73] the athetoid generally is able to make many of the necessary movements of the tongue, lips, jaw, throat, palate or lungs for speech, but few of these movements will be under constant control. The spastic, however, may be limited in the direction and extent of movement, but his control is consistent. The ataxic who has mainly defective feedback mechanisms will not know whether he has made appropriate movements and is not always certain that movement has taken place.

Irwin[44] studied the status of phonetic speech production of 147 cerebral palsied children in schools, centers and hospitals in seven different states. The chronological ages of the children ranged from three to sixteen years and their IQ's ranged from below 40 to above 111. The majority of the children had IQ's above 70. Contrary to what is known about normal children,[43] chronological age was not significantly related to articulation ability in this group. Mental ages and IQ's of the children did not appear to have a significant influence upon articulation ability. Position of consonant sounds in words had significant influence upon articulation of these sounds, the final position generally having the most devastating effect; initial and medial consonants were significantly less frequently omitted than final consonants. Medial vowels were less freqently omitted than initial vowels. Spastics made higher scores on the integrated articulation tests than athetoids. No significant differences were found between hemiplegics, quadriplegics and paraplegics, although the latter group tended to make higher scores than the other two. No differences were found between right and left hemiplegics. Degree of involvement did not seem to have a significant influence on the total group, but categories of mild, moderate and severe involvements had a significant influence upon the articulation of the subgroups, i.e., hemiplegics, quadriplegics and paraplegics.

Available reports on articulation are based on clinical observations as well as experimental study. More or less general agreement exists among these reports on the following characteristics of articulation of the cerebral palsied child: (1) tongue-tip sounds and those requiring fine coordination are the most difficult; (2) there are significantly more omissions than substitutions or distortions; (3) movements of the tongue are usually the most difficult of all speech movements; (4) rate of diadochokinesis is generally slow; (5) functional defects are often present instead of, or in addition to, dysarthria; (6) the difficulty of movement patterns in producing a speech sound is influenced by the patterns of sounds which have come immediately before and those that are to come immediately after; (7) articulation is inefficient, i.e., a sound may be produced in the easiest possible manner, and if it has any value of sufficiency in serving its purpose, its use is continued even though it might not be the best the person can do, and (8) the final sound positions are more difficult than initial or medial ones.

There are several things which tend to render the speech of cerebral palsied children unintelligible. They may use words which have a low intrinsic value of intelligibility, i.e., monosyllabic words or nonfamiliar words. Familiar words are intrinsically more intelligible than nonfamiliar words. Use of one-syllable words in the main or words with stress on the first syllable reduces intelligibility, but such usage is common in cerebral palsy. Words with more than one syllable and particularly those with the accent on the second syllable, are more intelligible than monosyllables.[54] Cerebral palsied children are also prone to use words containing sounds which are the easiest to produce, and such sounds often obscure the intelligibility of the word; the sounds which most destroy the intelligibility of words are (f), (ɔ), (h), (i), (a), (p) and (o). Intelligibility is also a function of context. Syntactical rules bind connected discourse; verbs, adjectives, nouns, etc., appear in certain patterns. Key words in certain combinations carry most of the information in context. If key words are distorted or omitted, the information is usually lost or gets through only fragmentarily. The effects of distortion on intelligibility have been measured quantitatively. The cerebral palsied person who has a disordered communication system will have distortion, in greater or lesser degrees, which will affect intelligibility accordingly.

Rhythm Problems: Stuttering, or symptoms similar to stuttering, have frequently been reported among the cerebral palsied persons. Van Riper claims that extreme tension often produces contacts so hard as to engender stuttering symptoms.[80] In her studies, Rutherford found twice as many stutterers in children with cerebral palsy as among the defective speech classes of Minneapolis public schools.[73] She reported that 54 per cent of the athetoid children had jerky, arrhythmic speech, while 13.15 per cent of the spastics and 7 per cent of the normals exhibited the same kind of speech. Her findings substantiate the contentions of Pusitz[71] and Zentay[88] that the extrapyramidal tract lesions are highly disruptive to the rhythmic functions of speech.

Many investigators have noted striking similarities in the speech experiences of spastics and stutterers. Palmer has stated that "it is possible to draw close parallels between stuttering and the speech of cerebral palsy at every point of description."[63] Observations at the Institute of Logopedics indicate that psychological introspection, apperception measures, parental attitudes and clinical techniques in cerebral palsy and stuttering correspond very closely. Palmer has also called attention to the spastic's functional muscle disintegration which occurs in situations which evoke fear, anxiety or feelings of inadequacy on the part of the individual. Such disintegration of function was characterized in one spastic as "the jumping of the nerves and contracting of the muscles."[53] This spastic person described the effects of fear upon her own speech. "Fear contracts muscles even in the tongue . . . one just cannot talk on account of contracted tongue muscles." About the spastic situation, she goes on to ask,

> . . . Is it any wonder that intense fear—stage fright—is the fundamental reason why the spastic cannot speak plainly, if at all? Could the normal man, even though he be a well-poised public speaker, and used to appearing in full dress, speak before a house like this one (meaning the situations which the spastics face) —might he not for the moment be struck dumb with stage fright? Is not such a house enough to upset anyone's nerves, and contract the muscles of his tongue beyond the power to speak for the moment?[53]

The present writer suggests that we compare this subjective report with that which we get from the stutterer.

Notation was made by Zentay that many points of similarity exist between disorders resulting from lesions in the striopalidum or in the mesencephalon and the problems of stuttering. "In this sense we may classify stuttering together with tics as 'striate body neurosis.'"[88] Peacher[65] points out that many conditions, including respiratory cycle auditory perception, ontogenetic factors, higher level functions of the nervous system, and coordination between the central and peripheral nervous systems can influence the rhythm function. Rutherford[70] says that a lesion in the dominant side of the brain may be a causative factor in disintegration of paired musculature functions. It is known that children who are delayed or defective in speech tend to be lacking in cerebral dominance.[5] Doll[21] reports having achieved success with a number of cases with retarded and defective speech by strengthening lateral dominance. Other studies, on the contrary, have reported that laterality of involvement does not affect development in oral language abilities.[39,40,86]

The need for more scientific research seems indicated for organic cases with rhythm disorders in speech as well as those cases which are bordering on what would appear to be an organic pathological condition and have definite rhythm disorders.

Breathing and Voice Problems: Normal speech requires the production of phrases and sentences of varying lengths and the ability to sustain exhalation long enough to utter them. The respiration cycle in speech is necessarily modified so that it consists of quick inhalations (about one-sixth of the respiratory cycle) and prolonged exhalations. Vital capacity must be great enough to allow for such modification of the breathing cycle.[67]

According to Westlake:

> The breathing rates of all young babies are very rapid and very irregular. A recent study of a group of newborn infants indicated an average breathing rate of 28 breaths per minute for the group, while the slowest rate was 18 per minute and the most rapid rate was 80 per minute. During the first year the breathing rates become more regular and slow up so that most of the children are breathing from 20 to 25 times in one minute. The cerebral palsied child frequently retains his infantile rate and irregularity of breathing for many years.[84]

Westlake goes on to say that neuromuscular imbalance in speech can cause deformities which limit the performance of the speech mechanism. Very frequently, abnormalities of the thoracic cage can be observed in a child who appears to have excessive activity of the diaphragm and reduced function in the muscles of the anterior chest wall and neck. It appears, in these cases, that the chest and neck muscles are not capable of maintaining the position of the cage during the time that the diaphragm is active so that the chest actually sinks during the time of inhalation rather than rising and expanding as it should; the sternum is also sucked inward. This phenomenon is frequently called "reversed breathing."

> Flattened thoracic cages, indented sternums and exaggerated Harrison's grooves may be deformities which result from ab-

normal function due to muscle imbalance. The persistence of these conditions limits the vital capacity and places permanent hazards to adequate breathing for speech.[84]

The hypothalamus (which lies near the basal ganglia) affects medullary respiration centers through its pneumotaxic center and is significant in regulating the rate and rhythm of respiration.[8] In athetoids, the central respiratory regulating mechanism is affected as a consequence of damage to the basal ganglia and the contiguous hypothalamus. This is usually due to cerebral anoxia at birth.[46]

In Achilles' report, the following breathing anomalies were most outstanding in a group of fifty-one cerebral palsied cases.

Irregular cycling—Gross deviations from normally predictable time and amplitude of the inspiratory-expiratory movements.

Rib flaring—Thoracic expansion in the region of the ninth and twelfth ribs with little anterior abdominal expansion. Probably produced by inadequate standing and sitting posture and by prolonged use of tight chest or belly bands to hold the child in the chair, particularly in cases of opisthotonus.

Thoracic-abdominal opposition—This occurs when the thorax or abdomen makes either inspiratory or expiratory excursions while the other is doing the reverse, called by Phelps "reversed breathing."

Shallow breathing—Rapid series of low amplitude excursions, coupled with low vital capacity when measured on a spirometer.

Breathing interferred with by athetosis—Involuntary motion in the respiratory musculature, usually irregular and arrythmical.

Respiratory-laryngeal incoordination—Asynchronous timing of expiratory movements and valving of the larynx.

Stertorous breathing—Result of the halting or impeding of either inspiratory or expiratory movements by spasmodic or tonic occlusions of the airway. This is brought about most frequently by the retraction of the radix of the tongue to contact the posterior wall of the oropharynx, or the movement of the pharyngeal wall forward to contact the tongue.

Thoracic breathing—Respiration which is performed primarily by the intercostal and other thoracic muscles.

> Abdominal breathing—Respiration which is chiefly carried
> on by abdominal muscles and the diaphragm.
> Mouth breathing—Habitual respiration through the oral
> cavity.
> Deformed thoracic cage—Gross anomalies of the bony forma-
> tion of the chest.
> Non-volitional breathing—Survival oxygen exchange patterns
> which cannot be altered voluntarily.

Kymographic recordings have revealed gross deviations from
normal in both silent breathing and breathing during speech in
cerebral palsied children.[20] The recordings of Cypreanson[18] show
that both the silent and speech breathing in cerebral palsied
children who have only mild speech problems or normal speech,
approach that of the normal child. The recordings of the poorer
cerebral palsied speakers showed gross deviations from the normal
in silent and speech breathing.

Hardy[32] found that breathing of cerebral palsied children
during speech production is much less efficient than that of
normal children. He observed that athetoids have faster breathing
rates and reduced inspiratory capacities. Both spastics and athetoids seemed to have reduced expiratory reserves and were generally less flexible in their breathing patterns than the control
children.

Voice production is highly dependent upon the operations of
the breathing mechanisms and the larynx. In addition to the
many breathing anomalies listed above, Palmer found a number
of laryngeal anomalies which also interferred with normal voice
production.[1]

> Spasmodic anomalies of constriction of the glottis—Constrict-
> ors of the vocal folds tend to hold the folds in a closed position
> by opposing the action of the dialators during attempts to
> phonate.
> Dilator spasm—Slow valving. The roles of opposing muscles
> of the vocal folds are the reverse of that noted above, during
> attempts to phonate.
> Monotones—This included the problems of pitch, inflection
> patterns, volume, etc.

Spasmodic anomalies of extrinsic muscles—Abnormal pulls of the extrinsic musculature of the larynx.

Ventricular fold spasm—Palmer states that "occasionally the ventricular folds are drawn downward to the true folds, or actually serve a sphincter function."

Breathy valving—Asynchronous timing of the expiratory muscles and the valving of the larynx.

Obtuse thyroid angle—Blunt or broad thyroid cartilage in contrast to the normal "V" shape. The condition is a gross deformity as the result of abnormal muscle pulls.

Athetosis of the vocal folds—Occurs when the muscles of the larynx function in an irregular and arrhythmical pattern.

Cerebral palsied children vary in their ability to phonate and prolong sounds and sound combinations in speech; their difficulty may be in any or all of the attributes of voice, i.e., pitch, intensity, quality and variation. Some children are unable to phonate a tone in exciting situations; others have difficulty sustaining a tone for any length of time. The voice of the athetoid tends to be weak in volume and may have irregular spurts of intense volume in conjunction with involuntary spasms of the diaphragm. The final sounds of words and final words of phrases are often whispered. Monotones are common, and in the extreme tension athetoid, the habitual pitch is often near the upper limit of the voice range.

A common voice quality in cerebral palsy, also, is hoarseness, especially in the males. This is usually the result of tension in the vocal cords. If spastic paralysis has affected muscles of the larynx, the cords will be held in varying states of abnormal tautness and will participate sluggishly in those movements of the vocal apparatus which occur in speech. The muscles which tighten the vocal folds, as well as those which loosen them, may be hypertonic, hence the level of pitch will be changed with some difficulty.

If flaccid paralysis is the case, however, speech may be aspirate or breathy and phonation may not be easily possible under stress situations. Athetotic tremor or arrhythmic fluctuations in pitch and intensity may occur from overflow in the athetoid. Tremor in the voice, which is more rhythmic than variations found in the athetoid, may be present in persons having voluntary or involuntary tremor.

Monrad-Krohn,[57] in his description of a thirty-year-old woman who suffered a lesion in the left frontal area of the brain caused by a fragment of bomb shell, tells of a slightly impaired peripheral musculature and of greatly altered pitch, stress and rhythm in her speech. The melody was not absent, as occurs in paralysis agitans or other extrapyramidal lesions, but was merely altered so that she spoke with what sounded like a German accent. There was substantial evidence that the change was due to the brain injury rather than environmental influences. Monrad-Krohn called this speech condition "dysprosody" (or altered melody), but no attempt was made to localize the prosodic faculty in the brain. He stated that aprosody (loss of melody) is found in paralysis agitans and allied disorders and is probably very closely tied up with the lenticular nucleus in the basal ganglia.

The incidence of both breathing and voice anomalies is much higher in the athetoid group than in any of the other types of cerebral palsy. Achilles reports that 97 per cent had anomalies of the larynx.[1] The rate of speech is also much slower in the athetoid group as a whole. Wolfe attributes the greater incidence of speech problems of all types in athetoids to the fact that almost 100 per cent of them have some type of involvement in their speech mechanism.[85]

Problems of Hearing: The differences in the statistics in hearing studies (from 5 per cent to 41 per cent) may be the result of variation in reference points for hearing loss, population sampling, methods of testing, etc. In spite of these differences, the studies suggest that the hearing problem is great enough among cerebral palsied persons to warrant special evaluational and remedial attention.

The close relationship found between defectiveness in articulation of sounds and the ability to discriminate differences among them auditorily has increased concern about discrimination ability in speech development.[78] Wepman[82] reports that on the Templin test of speech sound discrimination, the cerebral palsy group falls far below normal children in auditory discrimination ability.

This difference may or may not be real in the cerebral palsied group as a whole; further investigation is needed.

Lassman[47] conducted a clinical investigation of hearing deficiencies and their possible causes in cerebral palsy. His subjects consisted of one hundred and one hospitalized children, thirty-eight of whom were spastics, forty-one athetoids, nine rigidities, two tremors and eleven of multi-classification. The majority of subjects were quadriplegics around ten years of age, and two-thirds of them were male. The following are the main findings of his study.

1. Athetoids had larger mean hearing loss and greater variability for all tone and speech stimuli at both ears than all other groups.

2. Mean thresholds for pure tones of the spastic, rigidity, and combined groups did not deviate significantly from the reference.

3. More than one-fourth of the athetoids had losses of 20 db or more at 512, 1024 and 2048, while one spastic ear and one combined subject had such losses.

4. Athetoids did not differ from spastics in number of unilateral losses, but athetoids had four times as many bilateral impairments.

5. Subjects with marked bilateral losses for air conduction stimuli tended to have similarly deviant thresholds for bone conducted sounds.

6. Most unilateral losses were judged resultant of middle ear pathology, while two-thirds of the bilateral impairment group were judged to have some impairment of the perceptual-neural system.

7. All spastic losses were classified as conducive, whereas only one bilaterally impaired athetoid was so judged.

8. Erythroblastosis etiology had high positive and significant correlations with hearing loss.

9. All erythroblastosis subjects were athetoids and had a bilateral hearing impairment judged to be perceptive or mixed.

10. The hypothesis was developed that erythroblastosis may

be an etiological factor both for athetosis and for the associated bilateral perceptive hearing loss.[47]

The higher incidence of hearing losses in athetoids and the possibility of the Rh negative factor as a cause of certain types of hearing loss has received considerable attention.[28,37,69,73,76]

The exact location of the lesion in the so called "Rh deaf" child is not exactly known. One study suggested that the level of the lesion was in the basal ganglia rather than in the acoustic nerve or ear itself.[76] Later evidence suggests that the defect may be peripheral or may lie in the auditory nuclei of the brain-stem or in the midbrain.[19,28,30,51]

Hardy[37] reported that in a study of forty-eight kernicterus children, only nine (eighteen per cent) demonstrated normal hearing. Twenty-six (52 per cent) were felt to have pure nerve deficit while eleven (28 per cent) were considered to have higher level imperception. Perlstein[67] reported that 43 per cent of 499 kernicterus children investigated had hearing loss or hearing imperception. Hearing deficits in the kernicterus group are frequently associated with defective upward movements of the eyes.[87]

There has been a question as to whether the Rh child with a hearing loss is hard of hearing or "aphasic." This problem was discussed in a symposium at the 1955 convention of the American Speech and Hearing Association in Los Angeles, and the discussions of the various participants were reported in the *Journal of Speech and Hearing Disorders* in December, 1956.[17,31,36,72]

In conclusion, it may be generally said that the incidence of hearing problems in the cerebral palsy population is much higher and more complex than in the normal population. Experimental and clinical evidence suggests that these children may have peripheral losses or may have auditory involvement of the acoustic nerve, acoustic nuclei or of higher portions of this cephalo-acoustic analyzing system.

SUMMARY

In this chapter, an attempt has been made to show that the speech and hearing problems of cerebral palsied persons are not simple but are numerous and complex. Although definite peculiarities of rate, rhythm and movement control may be found in their speech, the problems are so variable that a description of speech which could be called strictly "cerebral palsy speech" is not possible. The speech of cerebral palsied children is usually delayed from two to four years, and that speech which develops is normally difficult to understand. The underlying brain damage in cerebral palsy plus the psychosocial problems which result give rise to many specific speech and hearing problems including neuromuscular involvements of the speech mechanism; reduced articulatory ability and intelligibility; voice and breathing irregularities; disorders of rhythm, rate and symbolic functions; and problems in listening discrimination, hearing acuity and auditory-linguistic functions.

REFERENCES

1. ACHILLES, R. F.: Communicative anomalies of individuals with cerebral palsy: I. *Cereb. Palsy Rev., 16:*15-24,27, 1955.
2. ACHILLES, R. F.: Communicative anomalies of individuals with cerebral palsy: II. *Cereb. Palsy Rev., 17:*19-26, 1956.
3. ASHER, P.: A study of 63 cases of athetosis with special reference to hearing defects. *Arch. Dis. Child., 27:*475-477, 1952.
4. BARR, B. and KLOCKHOFF, I.: Förekomst av hörselnedsättning i ett material av barn med cerebral pares. *Nord. Tidskr. Dov., 2:* 101-106, 1961.
5. BECKEY, R. E.: A study of certain factors related to retardation of speech. *J. Speech Hearing Dis., 7:*223-249, 1942.
6. BERKO, M. J., and BERKO, F. G.: Implications of language difficulties in the cerebral palsied adult. *Cereb. Palsy Rev., 14:*11, 14, 1953.
7. BERRY, M. F., and EISENSON, J.: *Speech Disorders.* New York, Appleton-Century-Crofts, Inc., 1956.
8. BLUMBERG, M. L.: Respiration and speech in the cerebral palsied child. *J. Dis. Child., 89:*48-53, 1955.
9. BLUMBERG, M. L.: Vital capacity and related therapies in cerebral palsy. *Cereb. Palsy Rev., 16:*24-25, 1955.
10. BLUMENTHAL, E. M.: Speech correction for cerebral palsy. *Physiother. Rev., 21:*71-72, 1941.
11. BOHME, G.: Stimm-, Sprach- und Hörstörungen als Folge fruhkindlicher Hirnschädigungen. *Folia Phoniat., 15:*189-200, 1963.

12. BOSLEY, E.: Normal language development in its application to the cerebral palsied child. *Cereb. Palsy Rev., 15*:17-18, 1954.
13. BROWN, S. F.: Cerebral palsy. In *Speech Handicapped School Children,* ed. by W. Johnson. New York, Harper and Bros., 1956, pp. 345-365.
14. BYERS, R. K., PAINE, R. S., and CROTHERS, B.: Extrapyramidal cerebral palsy with hearing loss following erythroblastosis. *Pediatrics, 15*:248-254, 1955.
15. BYRNE, M. C.: Speech and language development of athetoid and spastic children. *J. Speech Hearing Dis., 24*:3:231-240, 1959.
16. CARLSON, E.: The problem of cerebral palsy. *Proc. Amer. Acad. Cereb. Palsy,* 1950, 20-21.
17. COHEN, P.: Rh child: deaf or "aphasic?" 2. "Aphasia" in kernicterus. *J. Speech Hearing Dis., 21*:411-412, 1956.
18. CYPREANSON, L. E.: An investigation of the breathing and speech coordinations and speech intelligibility of normal speaking children and of cerebral palsied children with speech defects. Ph.D. Dissertation, Syracuse Univ., 1953.
19. DENHOFF, E.: Cerebral palsy, medical aspects. In *Cerebral Palsy,* ed. by W. M. Cruickshank and G. M. Raus. New York, Syracuse Univ. Press, 1955, pp. 21-86.
20. DiCARLO, L. M., and AMSTER, W. W.: Hearing and speech behavior among children with cerebral palsy. In *Cerebral Palsy,* ed. by W. M. Cruickshank and G. M. Raus. New York, Syracuse Univ. Press, 1955, pp. 166-255.
21. DOLL, E. E., and WALKER, M. S.: Handedness in cerebral palsied children. *J. Consult. Psychol., 15*:9-17, 1951.
22. DUNCAN, M. R.: Anxiety as a speech deterrent among cerebral palsied children. *West. Speech, 17*:155-162, 1953.
23. DUNCAN, M. R.: Emotional aspects of the communication problem in cerebral palsy. *Cereb. Palsy Rev., 16*:19-23, 27, 1955.
24. DUNSDON, M. I.: *The Educability of Cerebral Palsied Children.* London, Newnes Educational Publishing Co., Ltd., 1952.
25. FOTHERGILL, P., and HARRINGTON, R.: The clinical significance of the stretch reflex in speech reeducation for the spastic. *J. Speech Hearing Dis., 14*:353-355, 1949.
26. FROESCHELS, E.: Pure word deafness in a child. *Quart. J. Child Behavior, 1*:228-240, 1949.
27. FROESCHELS, E.: *Dysarthric Speech.* Magnolia, Mass., Expression Co., 1952.
28. GERRARD, J.: Kernicterus. *Brain, 75*:526-570, 1952.

29. GLICK, S. J.: Emotional problems of 200 cerebral palsied adults. *Cereb. Palsy Rev., 14:*3-5, 1953.

30. GOODHILL, V.: Nuclear deafness and the nerve deaf child: the importance of the Rh factor. *Tr. Amer. Acad. Ophth., 54:* 671-687, 1950.

31. GOODHILL, V.: Rh child: deaf or 'aphasic'? 1. Clinical pathological aspects of kernicteric nuclear 'deafness'. *J. Speech Hearing Dis., 21:*407-419, 1956.

32. HARDY, J. C.: Intraoral breath pressure in cerebral palsy. *J. Speech Hearing Dis., 26:*4:309-319, 1961.

33. HARDY, J. C., REMBOLT, R. R., SPRIESTERSBACH, D. C., and JAYAPATHY, B.: Surgical management of palatal paresis associated with speech problems in cerebral palsy. *J. Speech Hearing Dis., 26:*4:320-325, 1961.

34. HATCHUEL, W.: The importance of performing adequate hearing tests in children with cerebral palsy. *S. Afr. Med. J., 36:*237-238, 1962.

35. HIXON, T. J., and HARDY, J. C.: Restricted motility of the speech articulators in cerebral palsy. *J. Speech Hearing Dis., 29:*3:293-306, 1964.

36. HANNIGAN, H.: Rh child: deaf or "aphasic?" 3. Language and behavior problems of the Rh "aphasic" child. *J. Speech Hearing Dis., 21:*413-417, 1956.

37. HARDY, W. G.: Auditory deficits of the kernicterus child. In *Kernicterus in Cerebral Palsy,* ed. by C. A. Swinyard. Springfield, Illinois, Thomas, 1961, 255-266.

38. HEDGES, T. A.: The relationship between speech understandability and the diadochokinetic rates of certain speech musculatures among individuals with cerebral palsy. *Speech Monogr., 23:*144-145, 1956.

39. HOOD, P. N.: A study of the speech development and related factors in spastic hemiplegia. *Speech Monogr., 21:*209-210, 1954.

40. HOOD, P. N., and PERLSTEIN, M. A.: Infantile spastic hemiplegia: V. Oral language and motor development. *Pediatrics, 17:*58-63, 1956.

41. HOPKINS, T. W., BICE, H. V., and COLTON, K. C.: *Evaluation and Education of the Cerebral Palsied Child.* Washington, D. C., International Council for Exceptional Children, 1954.

42. HYMAN, M.: An experimental study of sound pressure level and

duration in speech of cerebral palsied children. *J. Speech Hearing Dis., 17:*295-300, 1952.

43. IRWIN, O. C.: Speech development in the young child: 2. Some factors related to the speech development of the infant child. *J. Speech Hearing Dis., 17:*269-279, 1952.
44. IRWIN, O. C.: Correct status of vowels and consonants in the speech of children with cerebral palsy as measured by an integrated test. *Cereb. Palsy Rev., 22:3:*21-24, 1961.
45. IRWIN, O. C.: Short test for use with cerebral palsy children. *J. Speech Hearing Dis., 21:*446-449, 1956.
46. KOVEN, L. J., and LAMM, S. S.: The athetoid syndrome in cerebral palsy: Part II. Clinical aspects. *Pediatrics, 14:*181-192, 1954.
47. LASSMAN, F. M.: Clinical investigation of some hearing deficiencies and possible etiological factors in a group of cerebral palsied individuals. *Speech Monogr., 18:*130-131, 1951.
48. LEITH, W.: Comparison of judged characteristics of athetoids and spastics. *Speech Monogr., 20:*195, 1953.
49. LENCIONE, R. M.: A study of the speech sound ability and intelligibility status of a group of educable cerebral palsied children. *Speech. Monogr., 21:*213-214, 1954.
50. LOVE, R. J.: Oral language behavior of older cerebral palsied children. *J.S.H.R., 7:*349-359, 1964.
51. MARKLE, D. M., and MILLER, M. H.: Nature of deafness in cerebral palsy. *Arch. Otolaryng., 78:*794-796, 1963.
52. McCANDLESS, G.: A study of the relative effects of different mental age and chronological age levels upon the speech intelligibility of a group of institutionalized mentally deficient children. M. A. thesis, Brigham Young University, 1965.
53. McKIBBEN, S.: The spastic situation. *J. Speech Hearing Dis., 8:*147-153, 1943.
54. MECHAM, M. J.: Complexities in communication of the cerebral palsied. *Cereb. Palsy Rev., 15:*9-11, 14, 1954.
55. MECHAM, M. J.: Measurement of verbal language development in cerebral palsy. *Cereb. Palsy Rev., 21:3:*3-4, 1960.
56. MECHAM, M. J., STROMSTRA, C., and SODERBERG, G.: Effects of Tolserol on the speech errors of mentally defective children. *Amer. J. Phys. Med., 34:*535-536, 1955.
57. MONRAD-KROHN, G.H.: Dysprosody, or altered melody of language. *Brain, 50:*405-415, 1947.
58. MYERS, P.: A study of language disabilities in cerebral palsied children. *J.S.H.R., 8:2:*129-136, 1965.

59. Mysak, E. D.: Dysarthria and oropharyngeal reflexology. *J. Speech Hearing Dis., 28:*252-260, 1963.
60. Mysak, E. D.: *Reflex therapy in the treatment of cerebral palsy.* New York: Bureau of publications, Teachers College, Columbia University, 1963.
61. Palmer, M. F.: Similarities of the effects of environmental pressures on cerebral palsy and stuttering. *J. Speech Hearing Dis., 8:*155-160, 1943.
62. Palmer, M. F.: Speech therapy in cerebral palsy. *Pediatrics, 40:* 514-524, 1952.
63. Palmer, M. F.: Speech disorders in cerebral palsy. *Nerv. Child, 8:* 193-202, 1949.
64. Palmer, M. F.: Recent advances in the scientific study of language disorders in cerebral palsy. *Cereb. Palsy Rev., 15:*3-6, 1954.
65. Peacher, W. G.: The etiology and differential diagnosis of dysarthria. *J. Speech Hearing Dis., 15:*252-265, 1950.
66. Perlstein, M. A.: The clinical syndrome of kernicterus. In *Kernicterus in Cerebral Palsy,* ed. by C. A. Swinyard. Springfield, Illinois, Thomas, 1961, 268-279.
67. Perlstein, M. A., and McDonald, E. T.: Nature, recognition and management of neuro-muscular disabilities in children. *Pediatrics, 11:*166-173, 1953.
68. Phelps, W. M.: Description and differentiation of types of cerebral palsy. *Nerv. Child, 8:*107-127, 1949.
69. Phelps, W. M.: Etiology and diagnostic classification of cerebral palsy. In *Proc. Cerebral Palsy Institute,* ed. by M. Abbott. New York, Assoc. for Aid of Crippled Child., Inc., 1950, 1-19.
70. Phelps, W. M.: Factors influencing the treatment of cerebral palsy. *Phys. Therapy Rev., 21:*50, 1941.
71. Pusitz, M. E.: Speech correction in cerebral palsies. *J. Speech Hearing Dis., 4:*205-218, 1939.
72. Rosen, J.: Rh child: deaf or "aphasic?" 4. Variations in the auditory disorders of the Rh child. *J. Speech Hearing Dis., 21:* 418-422, 1956.
73. Rutherford, B. R.: A comparative study of loudness, pitch, rate, rhythm, and quality of the speech of children handicapped by cerebral palsy, *J. Speech Hearing Dis., 9:*263-271, 1944.
74. Rutherford, R. R.: Extraneous movements in cerebral palsy. *Physiotherapy Rev., 25:*63-67, 1945.
75. Rutherford, B. R.: *Give Them a Chance to Talk.* Minneapolis, Burgess Publishing Co., 1956.

76. SALTZMAN, M.: *Clinical Audiology.* New York, Grune and Stratton, 1948.
77. SCHLANGER, B. B.: Speech examination of a group of institutionalized mentally handicapped children. *J. Speech Hearing Dis., 18:*339-349, 1953.
78. SPRIESTERSBACK, D. C., and CURTIS, J. F.: Misarticulation and discrimination of speech sounds. *Quart. J. Speech, 37:*483-491, 1951.
79. UNGER, D. M.: An understanding basic to cerebral palsy therapy. *J. Except. Child., 20:*193-197, 1954.
80. VAN RIPER, C.: *Speech Correction, Principles and Methods.* New York, Prentice-Hall, Inc., 1954.
81. WEPMAN, J. M.: *Recovery from Aphasia.* New York, The Ronald Press Company, 1951.
82. WEPMAN, J. M.: Speech therapy for cerebral palsy patients. *Physiotherapy Rev., 21:*82-87, 1941.
83. WEST, R., ANSBERRY, M., and CARR, A.: *The Rehabilitation of Speech.* New York, Harper and Brothers, 1957.
84. WESTLAKE, H.: *A System for Developing Speech with Cerebral Palsied Children.* Chicago, National Soc. Crippled Child. and Adults, Inc., 1952.
85. WOLFE, W. G.: A comprehensive evaluation of fifty cases of cerebral palsy. *J. Speech Hearing Dis., 15:*234-251, 1950.
86. WOOD, N. E.: A study of the speech and language development of right spastic hemiplegics as compared with left spastic hemiplegics, with reference to motor, intellectual, and visual perceptual findings. *Speech Monogr., 20:*191-192, 1953.
87. WOODS, G. E.: *Cerebral Palsy in Childhood.* Bristol, John Wright and Sons, Ltd., 1957.
88. ZENTAY, P. J.: Motor disorders of the central nervous system and their significance for speech. Part I. Cerebral and cerebellar dysarthrias. *J. Speech Hearing Dis., 2:*131-138, 1937.

Chapter III

APPRAISAL OF SPEECH AND HEARING PROBLEMS

MERLIN J. MECHAM

THERAPEUTIC PLANNING must be preceded by a thorough case study of the individual child. The first approximations that the teacher or therapist makes of the cerebral palsied child's abilities are usually in terms of how such abilities compare with normal development. As exploration proceeds in greater detail and therapeutic procedures are outlined, the examiner is forced to make an estimate of *efficiency* rather than *normalcy* for any given child. It is in reference to both of these points of view in analysis that the present chapter is written.

Before adequate diagnosis can be made, the communicative problems of the child must be viewed in terms of the total child. Complete evaluation must be performed by a team of experts, sometimes over a rather long period of time. In many cases, a period of trial therapy is needed before prognostications can be made with any degree of confidence.

CASE HISTORY AND PARENT INTERVIEW

The first step in the case study is usually the collection of background data from the parents. Investigation should be made of environmental, physical, emotional, intellectual, educational and developmental factors which may have had or may now have an influence on the speech and hearing maturation of the child. Information relative to the birth of the child, family background on cerebral dominance, relationship of the child to others in the home and community and the attitude of the child and parents toward the cerebral palsy condition may throw considerable light on the real child lying beneath the cloak of cerebral palsy. It is usually during the case-history interview that the diagnostician gets an initial impression of the entire problem picture. He is

49

then ready to request reports of specialists in related areas who have seen the child.

EXPLORATION OF AREAS RELATED TO SPEECH AND HEARING

Complete reports of medical, psychological, educational and social evaluations offer much information to the therapist in the planning of an effective speech and hearing program. If the child in question has had thorough evaluations in these areas by competent specialists, the speech therapist should request summary reports from them for his own guidance. If such evaluations have not been made, the child should be referred.

Medical Report: A medical report on the physical examination in which the nature of the neuromuscular disability is defined is basic in consideration of the whole problem. A detailed report showing type and extent of neuromuscular involvement will be helpful to the speech examiner in appraising muscle involvements in the speech mechanism. It is important to know not only the type and extent of cerebral palsy involvement, but also the general development and health of the child and to have knowledge of any specific physical defects which he might have, such as dental abnormalities, eye or ear impairments, etc.

Information should be available to the speech and language examiner on possible presence of seizures or other neurological involvements, reflexological involvements, long or short term drug therapy, surgery and/or bracing which the child may be undergoing, difficulty in bowel or bladder control, feeding or allergic aversions, oromaxillofacial or respiratory disturbances, hyperkinesia, and metabolic or other associated disorders, etc.

Psychological Report: The importance of psychological information in planning treatment cannot be over emphasized. Psychometric evaluation as an adjunct to communication training was felt to be so important that an entire section on that topic has been included in the present text. (See Chapter VII.) Only a general statement on psychological evaluation will be made here.

Because of the nature of cerebral palsy, a psychological evaluation is extremely difficult. Even a trained psychologist who has had extensive experience in testing the cerebral palsied children will add a warning of caution in his psychological report in regard to the validity and reliability of his testing results. A cerebral palsied child should be referred, whenever possible, to a competent psychologist for evaluation—preferably a psychologist who knows and understands something of the problem of cerebral palsy. Although most speech therapists are quite familiar with procedures in psychological testing, the actual diagnostic evaluations should always be done by a certified psychologist rather than the speech therapist.

Evaluation of Social Maturity: Evaluation of social maturity is related but not identical to psychological evaluation of intellectual abilities. Measurement of social maturity is the measurement of one's overall capability of functioning adequately in society. Since speech and other modes of communication are primarily social tools, they necessarily become part of the areas of consideration in measuring social competence of the individual. Social competence may be measured progressively in terms of performance in self-help, communication, locomotion, occupation, self-direction and socialization by sampling representative activities in these various areas at successive life ages. The Vineland Social Maturity Scale is a test which was devised to do just that.[10]

The estimate of social maturity is of particular importance as an additional criterion to be used in grouping children together for speech training. Children of about the same social maturation will function together in a group even though a difference exists in chronological age levels. This fact is of prime importance in respect to group planning and group dynamics in the speech therapy program.

APPRAISING STRUCTURE AND FUNCTION OF THE SPEECH MECHANISM

The mechanisms underlying breathing, phonation and articulation in speech may be either malstructured or they may function with difficulty. In some cases, both structural and functional anomalies can be found. Muscular imbalance, often occurring in cerebral palsy can cause deformities of the speech mechanism, as in other parts of the body. In a thorough observation of the speech mechanism, one should note any structural or functional anomaly which can be detected. The following are some *structural* anomalies which have been found to occur frequently in cerebral palsy:[3]

1. Flaring rib cage in the region of the ninth to twelfth ribs on either side of the sternum.
2. Abnormally small or otherwise deformed rib cage.
3. Abnormal position, size or shape of the larynx, such as unusually high or low position in the throat, or obtuse thyroid angle created by abnormal muscle pulls on the thyroid cartilage, etc.
4. Lateral deviations in the tongue and/or soft palate.
5. Contractions or atrophy of the tongue or palate.
6. Disjunction of mandible when it is depressed—mandibular facet slip.
7. Overshot or undershot jaw.
8. Lateral deviation of the jaw.
9. Abnormally high palate.
10. Open bite.
11. Severe dental caries or defective tooth enamel.
12. Contracture of the sternocleidomastoideus.

These may be noted according to the severity of the anomaly. Other structural anomalies which are found in the examination should also be noted. The following list of *functional* anomalies frequently found in cerebral palsy may guide the examiner in checking the function of the mechanism:[3]

1. Irregular breathing cycle.
2. Thoracic-abdominal opposition or "reversed breathing."
3. Abnormally shallow breathing.
4. Athetotic movements in breathing.
5. Respiratory-laryngeal incoordination.
6. Stertorous breathing due to clonic or tonic pharyngeal occlusions.
7. Severe tension in the breathing musculature.
8. Spasmodic constriction or dilation of the glottis due to overcontraction of the laryngeal constrictors or dilators.

9. Monotonous voice pitch and intensity patterns.
10. Athetosis in the laryngeal musculature.
11. Inability to elevate tongue tip.
12. Large clumsy tongue.
13. Athetotic involvements of the tongue and/or mandible.
14. Overt lingual apraxia or inaccuracy of voluntary tongue movement.
15. Retracted tongue.
16. Inert or contracted tongue.
17. Slow tongue movement.
18. Lingual stretch reflex.
19. Mandibular stretch reflex.
20. Tremor of the tongue or mandible.
21. Frequent or constant involuntary elevation of mandible.
22. Frequent or constant involuntary depression of mandible.
23. Hyperrhinolalia due to lack of velar closure.
24. Athetosis of the velum.
25. Bizarre opening and closing of the lips.
26. Involuntary facial movements and facial grimaces.
27. Athetosis in the proximal arm muscles and muscles of the neck which overflow into the speech mechanism.
28. Abnormal function of chewing, sucking and swallowing.
29. Drooling.
30. Gross functional defects of the muscles of the eyes.

The presence of abnormal reflexes or "release phenomena" in the cerebral palsied child may impair the degree of motility and coordination of various segments of the speech mechanism. For example, the occurrence of abnormal asymmetric tonic neck reflex may increase extensor tone of the jaw, tongue and breathing muscles. The presence of abnormal symmetrical tonic neck reflexes may increase extensor tone of the speech musculature when the head is ventroflexed and increase the flexor tone when the head is dorsiflexed. Presence of the following positive signs in older cerebral palsied children indicates uncontrolled release of primitive reflexes which may interfere with voluntary and selective control of the speech mechanism:[24]

1. Cephalic reactions (irregular movement of the head upon stimulation of face area).
2. Facial response (pouting protrusion of lips upon tapping around lips).
3. "Rooting" reactions (movement of face toward side of tactile stimulus of lips and mouth).
4. Biting reflex (biting action upon placing stimulus object between teeth or gums).
5. Suckling reflex (forward upward and backward movement of tongue upon touching stimulus to teeth, tongue, gums or hard palate).
6. Chewing reflex (chewing movements resulting from placing stimulation object between teeth).
7. Laughing reflex (uncontrolled laughter on being tickled).

Other positive reflex signs which, when present, may prevent selective voluntary control of the speech musculature are tonic laborynthine reflexes (flexor tone while prone or extensor tone while supine), various "startle" reflexes and the midbrain righting reflexes.

Negative symptoms (paralytic symptoms) are differentiated from the above positive symptoms (release phenomena) by reciprocal types of clues. When reflexes which are normally present in the adult (such as swallowing, palatal valving, yawning and mandibular jaw jerk) are reduced or absent, one must suspect that brain injury has brought about a weakening of the reflexes or an abnormal degree of inhibitory (suppressive) control of these reflexes by higher brain centers. It has been suggested that both release phenomena and paralytic symptoms may be found in the same child. Abnormal drooling, accompanied by difficulty in swallowing and nasality of vocal tone should be noted as symptoms of paresis. The presence of "intradental lisp, rhotacism, lambdacism, dentalization of lingual-velar sounds, labiodental deviations, labiodental production of bilabials and excessive lingual protrusion of linguadentals" suggest that release phenomena may be making a contribution in the etiology of the speech problems.[24]

Westlake[33] has suggested minimum requisites of function of the speech mechanism for normal speech production. The child must be able to (1) prolong a steady tone for a minimum of ten seconds; (2) extend and protrude the lips five times in ten seconds; (3) touch the tip of the tongue to the rugae ten times in ten seconds with the mandible stabilized; (4) open and close the lips ten times in ten seconds with the mandible stabilized; (5) open and close the mouth ten times in ten seconds; and (6) propel foods and fluids from the front to the back of the mouth and swallow them without drooling.

Hixon and Hardy[16] have demonstrated that while production of nonspeech movements of the speech mechanism (such as touching the tongue to the rugae) are not reliable indices of degree of dysarthria in cerebral palsy, speech movements involving coordination of respiration, phonation and articulation (such as production of /CV/syllables /mʌ/ /dʌ/ and /gʌ/) are highly correlated with degree of speech defectiveness in cerebral palsy.

ESTIMATING LEVEL OF ORAL LANGUAGE DEVELOPMENT

There have been several approaches to the study of normal oral language development. Research was centered at first on such aspects as grammatical form, sentence structure and length and frequency of occurrence of various parts of speech. Later investigations related the language growth of the child to his purposes and needs. More recently, studies have been concerned with the relation of the child's personality to oral language development.[4]

Some objective tests in the area of audio-and oral-linguistic assessment have emerged within the past few years and may be used in the appraisal of the linguistic achievement of cerebral palsied children. Usefulness of these may be dependent upon degree and nature of the physical handicaps which the child has. The methods suggested by Allen and Jefferson for selecting tests least likely to be penalized by sensory or motor deficits has a great deal of value in the area of language assessment.

The Verbal Language Development Scale[22] assesses both receptive and expressive language functions, and gives a reliable index of the routine language function in activities of daily living.

There are two versions of the Verbal Language Development Scale. One form (informant-interview version, published in

1959) is given to the parent of the child and is used in a similar manner to the Vineland Social Maturity Scale. The other form (the direct-test version, presently in an experimental stage) is administered to the child directly. Administering both forms of the scale may give a much better overall picture of how the child performs linguistically in both a clinical situation and in functional situations of daily living.

A cerebral palsied child may be considered abnormal when compared to the population of normal children, but not necessarily when using the child himself as the standard. What the cerebral palsied child is doing may be the best that is possible for him, considering the potential output of the equipment with which he is expected to perform. The two most important variables to be considered in determining the child's relative *efficiency* of performance are mental *age* and *extent of neuromuscular involvement*. In cases that do not have extremely severe neuromuscular involvement, oral language development is expected to be comparable to mental age. A child whose mental age and neuromuscular mechanisms are within normal range and whose language development is significantly retarded, for all practical purposes, can be considered abnormal in developmental efficiency. This has very important implications for prognostication, since a child with a low index of efficiency can be expected to be a very profitable candidate for training.

The assessment of language reflects the modes of speaking and listening more or less in their functional totalities. In addition, aspects of oral communication may be analyzed separately in terms of articulation and intelligibility, phonation, respiration, rate and coordination of movement and audition. In the process of "trouble-shooting," exploration must be made in these areas as well as in the overall aspects of language development.

EVALUATING ARTICULATION AND INTELLIGIBILITY

Articulation and intelligibility are highly interdependent but not identical entities. Each will be considered separately in terms of evaluation.

Articulation: Those sounds which require fine coordination and ballistic movement of the tongue and other musculature are the ones with which the cerebral palsied child has the most difficulty; they may be *distorted* because of the slow rate and laborious movement of these muscles, *omitted* because the time element, paralysis, etc., or easy sounds may be *substituted* in their place.

A test of articulation designed specifically for use with cerebral palsied children has been developed by Irwin,[17] using an initial sample of 1,155 cerebral palsied subjects from all parts of the United States. Final standardization of the test was obtained on 147 cerebral palsy children from three to sixteen years of age, selected from the Midwest and central states areas.

The test yields two kinds of information — quantitative and qualitative. Qualitative information provides a basis for articulation-training on the various sounds requiring remediation. Quantitative information allows for comparisons of the child's articulation proficiency with his peer group and also provides a basis for quantitative measures of improvement for research purposes. Validity and reliability studies show that the test satisfies fairly rigorous criteria of test adequacy, i.e., range of item difficulty, discriminating power of items and item uniqueness. The test is subdivided into five short subtests, each of which tests various consonant and vowel sounds. These tests should have practical value in the speech evaluation program both for diagnosis initially and for retesting from time to time to measure progress in therapy. The series of tests help to overcome the short attention span of the cerebral palsied, since they can be given on different days or at different periods on the same day. The sounds are checked in the various positions in which they are normally found by having the child repeat certain words.

If the child cannot, or will not *repeat* words, a picture articulation test may be administered. The examiner may wish to construct his own test in accordance with the suggestions found in Johnson's *Diagnostic Methods*.[18] Picture tests are particularly good for use with very young children or children with extremely delayed speech. Older children are prone to be more interested in repeating words or phrases.

Intelligibility: A study of intelligibility and its various accompaniments gives one a realization of the important part that misarticulation of sounds plays in detering intelligibility. Articulation, however, is not the only factor involved. Intelligibility in either speaking or listening represents the per cent of correct reception of oral linguistic stimuli. The speaking intelligibility of a person is determined by measuring the average percent of correct reception of his speech by a group of normal listeners. His listening intelligibility is determined by measuring his per cent of correct reception of the speech of a group of normal speakers. A simple way to note whether intelligibility is reduced in a child's speech is to observe the frequency of "Huh?" or "What did you say?" or other similar responses which he gets in conversation with others. Reduced speaking intelligibility is much more easily observed and appraised than is reduced listening accuracy in the child.

Many tests have been devised which measure intelligibility objectively. Most available testing procedures were developed for use on adults. A modification of the multiple choice group test technique was recently developed and tentatively standardized for children.[21] It can be used to screen intelligibility or to measure intelligibility improvement.

EVALUATING ADEQUACY OF VOICE AND BREATHING FOR SPEECH

Differential diagnosis of voice difficulties depends not so much on formal testing techniques as it does upon the examiner's ability to recognize normal voice patterns and quality. The examiner must ask such questions as (1) are intensity and intensity-change adequate to meet with the needs of the average speaking situations? (2) Is the pitch flexible and appropriate for the age and sex of the individual? (3) Is the quality clear, resonant and pleasant to listen to? (4) Is the quality unusually nasal or hoarse, etc? (5) Can a steady tone be prolonged at least ten seconds? (6) Are variations in the voice pitch and intensity smooth and controlled or jerky and irregular? (7) Do prosodic aspects of the voice sound normal, or does the child sound like he has a peculiar accent? (8) Can the child coordinate voice with articulation, i.e., produce appropriate voice for voiced sounds and eliminate voice on voiceless sounds? (9) Does the voice sound metallic or raspy? (10) Does voice pitch break into a falsetto occasionally? With these and other questions which may arise, the examiner can come to some conclusion as to adequacy of voice and as to the various problems with which the child may need help in improving voice adequacy. The therapist should be constantly alert to the possibility of an organic voice problem which should receive attention. Suspicion of any laryngeal pathology should cue the examiner to make immediate referral of the child to a laryngologist for a complete medical evaluation. A hoarse, husky, or breathy voice may lead one to suspect organic irregularities in the laryngeal mechanism. Excessive nasality may lead one to suspect palatal paresis. Excessively weak voice may lead one to suspect weakness in the expiratory musculature.

Respiratory function is considered in terms of rate and also amount of air intake and expulsion during speech. It may be observed informally or may be measured in detail upon pneumographic equipment; the method depends upon the need for accuracy in diagnosis of the breathing problem.

In normal, quiet breathing, respiration takes place at the rate of about twenty cycles per minute.[32] Expiration and inspiration times are approximately the same in quiet breathing, but during speech the inspiration is of much shorter duration than expiration (about one-sixth of the respiratory cycle) and the expiration is greatly prolonged.

A very important aspect of breathing for speech is vital capacity. This capacity varies according to age, sex, height, weight, body build, race, etc., of the child. As the child gets older, his capacity increases until, in the average adult, it reaches about 3700 cc.

As a rule, rate of breathing of cerebral palsied children is much faster than for normal children of the same age. Lying in a prone position, the child can be timed on the number of respiratory cycles which occur per minute in quiet breathing. Vital capacity is also reduced in cerebral palsied children in varying degrees. With the aid of the kymograph, recordings can be made of irregularities of breathing which may be present during speech. Particular note should be made of the coordinated activity of the diaphragm and thorax. Normally, the thorax is depressed as the diaphragm relaxes in exhalation. In the cerebral palsied child, this coordinated activity may be reversed (reversed breathing).

Hardy found it possible to measure the subdivisions of lung volume by use of a respirometer.[14] This instrument provides a method of tracing a child's volume of emission of air during speaking activities. Coupled together, the respirometer and the oral manometer can provide measurements of lung volumes as well as increased breath pressures during speech. Assessment of inspiratory capacity and expiratory reserve is of particular importance since both of these functions have been found greatly reduced in cerebral palsied children and may play an important role in the speech problems of the child.

Inefficient expiratory function during speech may be the result of inadequate breathing caused by weak or paretic musculature, opposition of the inspiratory-expiratory musculature, or improper direction of the breath stream due to palatal paresis. Graphic pressure-volume measurements (respirometric-manometric and cinefluorographic studies of palatal functions have been suggested by Hardy[14] as the most helpful methods of evaluating factors involved in adequacy and control of intraoral breath pressures for speech.

TESTING HEARING ABILITY

Testing of hearing in cerebral palsy offers a complexity of problems, and procedures must be modified to allow for various difficulties which are frequently encountered. Methods of testing cerebral palsied children have been described in the literature.

DiCarlo[9] suggests that reflex and startle cues can be utilized with very young children to get a rough idea as to whether or not they have functional hearing. He states that sounds may initiate such reactions as the stretch reflex, rigidity or involuntary behavior. Localization of sounds either with the eyes or mass bodily activity are suggested as good cues that the child is hearing. This type of testing does not reveal auditory acuity threshold but gives only gross evidence of how well the child is hearing.

The Urbantschtitsch whistles have been found useful as instruments for measuring the hearing acuity of cerebral palsied children.[12] Pure-tone and speech audiometrics are preferred over other methods of testing because of their greater accuracy in approximating acuity threshold. The author has found that the brain-damaged child who cannot respond to the regular methods of testing on the pure-tone audiometer, because he does not get the concept of the testing procedures, can frequently be "conditioned" to respond adequately to the audiometer.

The value of the PGSR method in hearing testing is debatable. Its reliability with the cerebral palsied child is especially doubtful because of the possible interference of such variables as involuntary movement, hyper-reflexive activity, the lack of emotional control, etc., which exist in cerebral palsy. The degree of influence which the internal stimuli (arising from abnormal motor activity of the child) has not been established on the PGSR.

Many cerebral palsied children will not respond to formal speech or pure-tone audiometry. Informal observation of the child's auditory reactions may be the only means, in many cases, of estimating their hearing ability; this may take several observations over a prolonged period of time. Even in those cases in which formal audiometric testing is possible, data from additional observations of auditory reaction behavior should be added as supplementary information. A hearing examiner should keep in mind the fact that the hearing of pure tones on an audiometer is not proof that the child is hearing and understanding the complicated sound combinations in speech, or vice versa. The examiner should observe to see whether or not the child seems to interact acoustically with his environment, among other things. Does he respond to sound such as noise makers or bells or his name by turning his head or making some other indicative movement? Are his vocal expressions of laughing, crying, jabbering or speech like those of the normal child? Does he respond to simple commands in such a way that you know he understands them? Can he identify familiar objects or pictures when you name them without having to watch your face or gestures? Can you communicate with him much better with the aid of gestures than just audible speech? These and other questions of a similar nature, which may occur to the examiner will aid him in determining more accurately the functional hearing of the child. One clue which may lead one to suspect hearing loss in the athetoid child is absence of vertical eye movements. Several clinicians have observed that the athetoids frequently have loss of vertical eye movements and this seems to be associated with the presence of hearing loss.

It is preferable in almost all cases to use a multiple testing approach in evaluating hearing. A battery of tests would ideally include (1) a pure-tone audiometric test; (2) a speech reception test, such as the Central Institute's Auditory Test No. W-1 adapted from the Harvard PAL Test No. 9; (3) a psychogalvanic skin resistance test, and (4) informal observational procedures like those suggested above.

A recently developed approach using summating computers with electroencephalographic recordings may open up a new approach to evaluating the responses of cerebral palsied children to sound. Although the equipment necessary for this approach is still beyond clinical practicality expense-wise, successful evaluations are being made on infants a few days old.

In addition to measuring hearing acuity for speech, analysis of other aspects of hearing may be desirable. In the child who has an articulation defect, it is possible that his ability to discriminate heard sounds from each other is poor, even though his hearing acuity is normal. *Speech-sound discrimination* should be sharp enough so that similar phonetic units in speech can be discriminated. *Auditory memory span* must also be long enough to retain two or three consecutive sounds, one second apart, in order to repeat two and three syllable words. Norms for auditory memory span for speech sounds have been suggested by Metraux.[23] Testing the auditory memory span and auditory discrimination of the severely involved cerebral palsied child who cannot speak or even point reliably, as in the case of some severe athetoids, offers somewhat of a problem. Any standard tests usually have to be modified in one way or another in order to get the best responses possible from the cerebral palsied child.

PROGNOSTICATION IN SPEECH AND HEARING EVALUATIONS

Prognostication in speech and hearing evaluation in cerebral palsied children is often a difficult task. There are certain criteria which are felt to be of primary importance in determining the prognosis in speech therapy. These include a consideration of the severity of the cerebral palsy involvement, the removability of causal factors, and amount of improvement resulting from competent trial therapy. Even then, it is probable that one will fall short of making a completely accurate prognosis. Severity of involvement includes severity of impairment of function, motivation, parental and environmental influence, removability of causal factors, etc.

If the child is mentally retarded due to environmental deprivation and if he improves mentally when the environment is changed, the mental retardation will not carry too much negative prognostic weight. If he is inherently mentally retarded, however, and the mental ability remains relatively static regardless of the type of training or assistance that he gets, the mental retardation will be a strong determining factor in the prediction of eventual outcome. The same thing is true of neuromuscular difficulties, visual and hearing losses, perceptual disturbances and aphasia. If the causal factors are removable or compensation for the involvement is possible, there is usually a much better prognostic picture.

Since measurement of severity of involvement and removability of causes is difficult and often unreliable in cerebral palsy, it is usually desirable to supplement these with observations of the child's response to competent treatment over a period of six months to a year. During the trial therapy period, it will be possible to measure improvements which take place periodically and these measurements will add much to the prognosis.

There are actually two reasons for measuring improvement in speech and hearing therapy. One is for referral for, and guidance in, obtaining additional therapy, and the other is for experimental research. For various reasons, a special line of testing has developed for use in clinical speech, i.e., picture cards and loaded word lists. These tests have filled a special need, not particularly different from the need filled by screening tests of hearing. They give a first approximation of where the child should be referred and what type of additional help he should get. Rough measurements of this type are adequate for the need which they were intended to fulfill. Rating scales for measuring speech proficiency and improvement in cerebral palsy have been made available from many sources for clinical use. They are simple and easily administered. There are many safeguards that prevent outlandish results in this type of "referral testing": the time of the therapist, the economics of the employment situation and the fact that the therapist can correct his own mistake when he meets his referral group (referred by himself to himself) for therapy.

This kind of testing, however, is not a safe bet for making diagnoses or for obtaining basic measures for an experimental plan. The individual measures have insufficient reliability. We can improve the reliability of testing by using the following procedures: (1) Substitute group judgment for individual judgment; (2) substitute an unknown vocabulary for a known one for the judges in order to reduce the effects of expectancy; (3) retain the criteria for "referral," and (4) remove any clues that would be prejudicial to the outcome of the test, e.g., knowledge of which signal comes from before-training and which comes from after-training may be prejudicial in a study that involves measurement of improvement.

In an experimental study comparing matched groups or the same subjects in different testing periods, controls should be placed upon such variables as recording-reproducing procedures, presentation of the stimuli, recording responses of the subjects, constancy of the testing environment from one testing period to another including time of day, relationships in space of various things in the testing situation and constancy of all auditory and visual stimuli which are not part of the experimental variable, etc.

In research with the cerebral palsied child that attempts to measure speech efficiency or improvement, careful allowances and modifications must be made for the complex handicaps which the individual may have. It is difficult to generalize findings in a cerebral palsy sample because of the extreme variability of the handicapping conditions among these children.

Measurements of *general* improvement patterns in the individual as a result of habilitation or training are extremely useful. Crothers and Ferdinand[8] have suggested the use of films as a method of keeping permanent records and recording changes which occur over many years in individuals with cerebral palsy. Films can be stored and filed easily. Their usefulness is increased if a detailed medical report is written and filed with the films to aid in definitions and descriptions of the problems which the films may not reveal. Graphing as an aid to therapy problems and as an index to improvements which are taking place in such things as duration of a sustained tone, number of times a child can say p-t-k on one breath, etc., has proved to be a motivational tool.

THE TEAM APPROACH

The final common pathway of all the various evaluations which the cerebral palsied child receives from diagnostic team members should be the joint staffing in a general meeting where all specialists can discuss their tentative findings and come to a more stable agreement on the nature, extent and prognosis of the total problem. Recommendations for programming should be the result of joint thinking of the following nucleus-team members: medical specialist in cerebral palsy, psychologist, speech pathologist, social worker, public health nurse and occupational and physical therapists. Other professional members who might be involved are the neurologist, psychiatrist, ophthalmologist, otologist, audiologist, dentist, brace maker, vocational counselor, preschool nursery consultant, teacher, recreation therapist and the nutritionist.

Securing reports, information and recommendations from various medical and paramedical specialists who have seen the child separately is often looked upon erroneously as achievement of the "team approach."[29]

There are certain assumptions, however, which may be extremely helpful in setting apart the "team approach" in nature and effectiveness.[28] These principles apply directly to the participants: they must (1) have a desire to cooperate; (2) realize that cooperation is work; (3) have needs in common; (4) each have some resources to contribute, and (5) maintain adequate communication.

The practical application of the "team function" requires cooperation and organization. An effective team project should include (1) the active functioning of a coordinator for each specific child (which team member does this is of little consequence) ; (2) recurrent and continued communication between members of the team and the coordinator; (3) establishment of long-term aims for the total adjustment of the child; (4) establishment of more immediate objectives to help achieve long-term aims; (5) collaborative work by all team members toward achieving established aims and objectives, and (6) being as concerned about developing attributes which are *not* seriously impaired as about remedying grossly abnormal functions.

SUMMARY

The present chapter has been devoted to an attempt to present some of the problems and suggestive methods in measurement of speech and hearing difficulties in cerebral palsied children. The need for case history information as well as supplementary information which may be available in the medical, psychological, social and educational areas is stressed.

Evaluative procedures in appraising the level of listening and speaking skills, proficiency in articulation and intelligibility, voice and breathing, neuromotor mechanisms of speech and hearing, etc., have been discussed, and some of the difficulties encountered in testing cerebral palsied children have been presented. Methods of determining a prognosis and improvements in training have been suggested. The treatment of the child by the staff and their final joint analysis of the proposed program have been considered as the final common pathway in the evaluative program.

REFERENCES

1. ABBOTT, M.: *Syllabus of Cerebral Palsy Treatment Techniques.* New York, United Cerebral Palsy Assns., 1954.
2. ALLEN, R. M., and JEFFERSON, T. W.: *Psychological Evaluation of the Cerebral Palsied Person.* Springfield, Illinois, Thomas, 1962.
3. ACHILLES, R. F.: Communicative anomalies of individuals with cerebral palsy. *Cereb. Palsy Rev., 16*:15-24, 27, 1955.
4. BEASLEY, J.: *Slow to Talk.* New York, Bureau of Publications, Teachers College, Columbia University, 1956.
5. BLUMBERG, M. L.: Vital capacity and related therapies in cerebral palsy. *Cereb. Palsy Rev., 16*:23-25, 1955.
6. BRUNYATE, R. W.: Occupational therapy for patients with cerebral palsy. In *Principles of Occupational Therapy,* ed. by H. S. and C. S. Spackman. Philadelphia, J. B. Lippincott Co., 1954, pp. 274-287.
7. CARDWELL, V. E.: *Cerebral Palsy — Advances in Understanding and Care.* New York, Assoc. for the Aid of Crippled Children, 1956.
8. CROTHERS, B., and FERDINAND, R. H.: The value of moving pictures as permanent records. Paper presented before the Fourth Annual Convention of the United Cerebral Palsy Associations, New York City, Nov. 14, 1953. (Mimeographed copy distributed by the United Cerebral Palsy Assns., Inc.)
9. DiCARLO, L. M., and AMSTER, W. W.: Hearing and speech behavior among children with cerebral palsy. In *Cerebral Palsy,* ed. by W. M. Cruickshank and G. M. Raus. New York, Syracuse Univ. Press, 1955, pp. 166-255.
10. DOLL, E. A.: *The Measurement of Social Competence.* Minneapolis, Educational Test Bureau, 1953.
11. EDWARDS, A. L.: *Experimental Design in Psychological Research.* New York, Rinehart and Company, Inc., 1950.
12. FROESCHELS, E., and BEEBE, H.: Testing the hearing of newborn infants. *Arch. Otolaryng., 44*:710-714, 1946.
13. GRAYSON, E. S.: Handedness testing for cerebral palsied children. *Amer. J. Occup. Therapy, 2*:91-94, 1948.
14. HARDY, J. C.: Intraoral breath pressure in cerebral palsy. *J. Speech Hearing Dis., 26*:309-319, 1961.
15. HIRSH, I. J., *et al.*: Development of materials for speech audiometry. *J. Speech Hearing Dis., 17*:321-337, 1952.

16. HIXON, T. J., and HARDY, J. C.: Restricted motility of the speech articulators in cerebral palsy. *J. Speech Hearing Dis., 29*:293-306, 1964.
17. IRWIN, O. C.: An integrated articulation test for use with children with cerebral palsy. *Cerebral Palsy Rev., 22:3*:3-20, 1961.
18. JOHNSON, W., DARLEY, F., and SPRIESTERSBACH, D. C.: *Diagnostic Methods in Speech Pathology.* New York, Harper and Row, 1963.
19. JONES, M. H.: *Newly Developed Methods for Recording the Progress of Cerebral Palsied Children.* Paper distributed by United Cerebral Palsy Assns., Inc., 1952.
20. KEATS, S.: *Cerebral Palsy.* Springfield, Illinois, Thomas, 1965.
21. MECHAM, M. J. and JEX, J. L.: *Speech Discrimination Test For Young Children.* Provo, Utah, Brigham Young University Press, 1964.
22. MECHAM, J. J.: *Verbal Language Development Scale.* Minneapolis, Educational Test Bureau, 1958.
23. METRAUX, R. W.: Auditory memory span for speech sounds: norms for children *J. Speech Hearing Dis., 9*:31038, 1944.
24. MYSAK, E. D.: Dysarthria and oropharyngeal reflexology: a review. *J. Speech Hearing Dis., 28:3*:252-260, 1963.
25. ORTON, S. T.: *Reading, Writing and Speech Problems of Children.* New York, W. W. Norton, 1937.
26. PERLSTEIN, M. A., and McDONALD, E. L.: Nature, recognition and management of neuromuscular disabilities in children. *Pediatrics, 11*:166-173, 1953.
27. POOLE, I.: Genetic development of articulation of consonant sounds in speech. *Elem. Engl. Rev., 11*:159-161, 1934.
28. REMBOLT, R. R.: The 'team' in cerebral palsy. In *Symposium on Cerebral Palsy,* F. L. Darley (Ed.). Washington, D. C., The American Speech and Hearing Assoc., 1962, pp. 49-53.
29. REMBOLT, R. R.: Cerebral palsy—a challenge. *Amer. J. Phys. Med., 40*:47-51, 1961.
30. TEMPLIN, M. C.: *Certain Language Skills in Children.* Minneapolis, Univ. of Minnesota Press, 1957.
31. WALLACE, H. M., SLATER, B. S., and STEINBERG, D.: Checking pupil progress in classes for cerebral palsy. *J. Except. Child., 21*:50-54, 1954.
32. WESTLAKE, H.: *A System for Developing Speech with Cerebral Palsied Children.* Chicago, National Soc. for Crippled Children and Adults, Inc., 1951.

33. WESTLAKE, H.: Muscle training for cerebral palsied speech cases. *J. Speech Hearing Dis., 16:*103-109, 1951.
34. WESTLAKE, H., and RUTHERFORD, D.: *Speech Therapy for Cerebral Palsied.* Chicago, National Soc. for Crippled Children and Adults, Inc., 1961, pp. 1-25.

Chapter IV

ROLE OF THE SPEECH THERAPIST IN SPEECH, HEARING AND LANGUAGE HABILITATION

MERLIN J. MECHAM

As we stated in Chapter III, it is estimated that about 70 per cent of the cerebral palsied children are in need of remedial work in speech and hearing. The problems of this group of handicapped children do not conform to any concrete pattern and generalizing about techniques of therapy for them is difficult. The suggestions offered in the following chapters are meant only to give the therapist a "frame of reference" within which he may develop his own modified "formula" and techniques for each individual child. This fact places a heavy burden of responsibility on the shoulders of the therapist. He must be highly resourceful and able to determine the problems of cerebral palsied children in terms of how they may be approached therapeutically.

The first requisite for a therapist in oral communication of the cerebral palsied is that he know children; he must understand their physical, physiological and psychological needs. He must have an understanding of oral language development in children and of the factors which help or hinder its growth. He must know parents, their emotions and their personalities. He must have a sound basic knowledge about cerebral palsy, about its medical, psychological and educational implications. The minimum professional training requisites for a speech and hearing therapist in cerebral palsy is a certificate of clinical competence in speech with the American Speech and Hearing Association. It is assumed that the speech therapist has had an adequate background before he begins to work with cerebral palsied children, or that he is working closely with someone who does. It is also assumed that he has enough personal resourcefulness to adapt his training to the needs of the child within the general frame of reference which will be set forth in this text.

Difference in Role of Therapist from that of Teacher and Parent: One of the things that a therapist often overlooks is the differentiation of the role of the therapist from that of the teacher and the parent in respect to the child's habilitation program. The responsibilities of the *parents* have been partly defined by legal and moral code and are usually taken for granted. By law, parents are charged with the responsibility of providing food, clothing and shelter for their children. They are expected by moral code to teach them to obey rules of accepted social conduct, to respect their elders and superimpose upon their own self-centered personal hopes, suprapersonal hopes for the general welfare of family, community and/or nation. The controls placed upon the child by the parents arise primarily from the need for security and justice within the unit.

Invariably, the family homeostasis is disrupted by the birth of a cerebral palsied child. Efforts to reestablish a balance may be concentrated upon changing the child, changing the usual family patterns and routine or changing the parents themselves. Some typical efforts to achieve a greater sense of integrity inside of the family unit are seen in parents' becoming aggressive "do gooders," antisocial or critical reactionaries. As a last resort, if a reasonable adjustment is not eventually achieved, the family may reject the child in terms of traditional legal or moral code. On the other hand, parents and members of the family may become exceptionally understanding and tolerant. McDonald has discussed feelings and problems of parents of handicapped children in some detail.[2]

The specialist should try to view the adjustment of the parents not for the purpose of trying to categorize or label them, but rather in terms of whether such adjustments interfere basically with the effectiveness of their major role as parents, i.e., providing a sense of justice, security, freedom and unity in the family.

Therapists should keep in mind the *basic* role of the parents. Suggestions and instructions given to parents in the way of extending therapy or teaching activities for the child into the home should be given with special sensitivity as to whether such "therapy" or "teaching" by the mother is placing in jeopardy the fulfillment of her major responsibility. Parents are often vulnerable because of their feelings of guilt or anxiety and their need to do something "special" to remedy their unusual circumstances.

Therapists working with the cerebral palsied child should also recognize the major role of the *teacher* and how it differs from that of both the clinician and the parent. The separation of the "professional" from the "personal" is sometimes a difficult one to make. Teachers and therapists are usually parents themselves, and it is not difficult for parental instincts to be manifest in the therapeutic or teaching situation. For example, one teacher was unable to make the proper discrimination and so had to forfeit her right to continue as a teacher. It seems that one child was sent to school untidy and hungry most of the time. This teacher felt sorry for the child and so began taking her home during the lunch period to "clean her up" and "feed her a good meal." As a result, the child developed a possessive and jealous attitude toward the teacher and "kicked up a storm" every time the teacher showed an interest in the other children in the classroom. This was disrupting to the discipline in the classroom. The same teacher also periodically helped another child by "trimming" his hair. This child also developed a "special" affection for the teacher which was upsetting to the rest of the class. The teacher was eventually discharged for being unable to manage, discipline or "teach" her class. This is an extreme case but illustrates well what can happen if a teacher permits herself to play the "parent" role to the extent that it interferes with her *primary* responsibility of teaching.

What about the role of the *therapist?* Is not the therapist just a "special teacher" or a special "parent-substitute?" Indeed not. The therapists' professional existence must be justified on the basis of his being able to contribute something to the habilitation program which is required of neither the parent nor the teacher, i.e., a "clinical" atmosphere. Both parent and teacher have fairly well established bounds within which they may adapt. The parent must provide justice and security for the entire family. The teacher must judge and grade the child in terms of his ability to grasp a curriculum which has previously been devised. A clinician has no established legal or moral rules with which he is to "judge" the child as being adequate or inadequate. His charge is to accept the child first for what he is and then attempt to assist the child toward being able to earn a greater acceptance in the home, school or social environment.

Although it is usually the parent, teacher or social milieu which makes the judgment that the child is not adapting acceptably, they cannot always make an accurate judgment as to which clinical specialist or specialist-team is needed to aid the child. One responsibility of the clinician, then, is the help determine for the child the optimal clinical "setting." The proper specialist or specialist-team is then assigned to help the child adjust his attitude, skills and/or anxiety reactions in such a way as to help him achieve a greater feeling of importance and inclusion in his family, social and educational setting.

Importance of a Team Approach: The speech and hearing problems of the cerebral palsied are an intricate part of their total problems; they cannot be isolated from the rest of a child's problems or treated effectively alone. All specialists on the cerebral palsy team must be integrated: It is important that each one understand the fundamental aspects of the others' approaches to the problem in order to present the child with unity.

Close cooperation between the *speech therapist* and the *teacher* can be of great value. For example, if the child has difficulty with reading, the *teacher* can send a list of words to the speech therapist and he can practice on these during therapy; the speech therapist can also orient the teacher as to which words or sounds are difficult or impossible for the child to say. Physical limitations of the speech and breathing mechanisms, as well as the oral language maturation level can be explained to the teacher. The teacher, if she knows what is being done in speech therapy, can often help to carry over some techniques into the social situations which occur in the classroom and in oral reading. If she knows what to expect in the way of oral communication, she can modify her demands to the extent of giving the child greater opportunities for success experiences in speech and oral communication.

Close cooperation between the speech therapist and the *physical* and *occupational therapists* will be of help in integrating the therapeutic activities which the child may be getting. The speech therapist should be so closely associated with these other therapists that avoidance can be made of such errors as regarding a child as completely nonambulatory when the physical therapist has him walking, or as unable to help himself in eating or dressing when the occupational therapist has worked laboriously to get him to the point where he can feed or dress himself to some extent.

The physical therapist may be able to help the speech therapist in such things as selecting the proper seating arrangements so that the child will be in a more comfortable and functional position for therapy. Many physical achievements of the child, such as walking or exercises in reciprocation will stimulate respiration and thus, in turn, may have an effect on the general tonus, energy and alertness of the child, in addition to being directly helpful in speech. The child who is practicing standing for any length of time in physical therapy, either at a standing table or in a stabilizer, may get some speech therapy or occupational therapy while he is standing. This may save considerable time for the child and the therapy program and serves to stimulate a more integrated program among the therapists. Of course, if the physical therapist feels that the addition of speech therapy creates any interference with what the child is trying to accomplish in his standing training, it should be discontinued.

The occupational therapist can be of great help to the speech therapist, in the development of the chewing, sucking and swallowing processes through the feeding training which the child usually gets in occupational therapy. Although the purposes of feeding training may be somewhat different in speech and occupational therapy, the process is the same. Working together, the occupational therapist and the speech therapist can facilitate greater achievement and more successful experiences for the child; if they were working entirely separately, the dissimilarities in the two approaches might confuse the child and even prevent progress from being made.

One of the things that all therapists have in common is their need to communicate constantly with the child. This contact offers a real problem in the case of the child who has little communication ability. If all therapists have a common understanding of what communication abilities the child has and which communicative skills are being taught and need to be strengthened, they can work together to stimulate in the child frequent feelings of achievement and satisfaction in communication.

Palmer has stressed the fact that habilitation should be an integrated approach to the social milieu as well as to the child. *Parents* should be brought into the habilitation circle as part of the team. They should know what is being done for the child in therapy and should be instructed as to what they can do at home. This does not mean that parents must become physical, occupational and speech therapists, for the extra load of constantly caring for the child, the extra financial involvements and the difficult task of playing the role of the objective parents leave them little time to train to become skilled therapists. They can be shown, however, the communicative problems of the child and how to help to overcome them in the activities of daily living. They can be shown how to provide a climate which will stimulate better communication development. They can be given instructions in using certain techniques which will not interfere too much with the time at their disposal for other children in the family. Above all, they should be given literature to read which will help them better understand their cerebral palsied child and how to care for him in the home. Working out such things takes great ingenuity on the part of the therapist, but will add tremendously to the speed of the slow habilitation process and will also "resolve in better outcomes at the end of the clinical program."[3]

Because each therapist must do a certain amount of counseling with the child and the parent, each should ally himself closely with the *counseling psychologist.* Through close association with the psychologist, the speech therapist can become familiar with the things about which the parent and child are being, or should be counseled. The psychologist will be able to appraise the therapists and others who may be working with the child of special psychosocial problems such as impaired perception, low intelligence, personality quirks and social maldevelopment. A psychologist who has had experience with the brain-injured child may be particularly helpful to the speech therapist and teacher in determining any existing asphasic problems and in suggesting ways to cope with such problems.

The vital roles played by *medical specialists* and *nurses* should be recognized in any training or therapeutic program. There should be a continual interchange of information between the medical persons caring for the cerebral palsied child and the speech therapists. The speech therapist and the teacher may need to take extra initiative in correlating their activities with those of the medical persons, since the *educational* setting may be a little more removed from the medical hospital or clinic than the therapeutic activities of the other members of the habilitation team. The speech therapist should always be aware of any special health or medical problems of the child and of any medical treatment that he may be receiving, such as special diet, drugs, braces, surgery, etc., which may be contraindicative of certain therapeutic procedures.

Teamwork among those working with the cerebral palsied child is essentially sharing and mutual respect. There must be a freedom of inquiry and participation. "With the patient always as the central and integrating force, each team member needs to balance an humble attitude of learning and deference for others with a proper respect for his own contributions."[1]

REFERENCES

1. CARDWELL, V. E.: *Cerebral Palsy — Advances in Understanding and Care.* New York, Association for the Aid of Crippled Children, 1956.
2. McDONALD, E. T.: *Understand Those Feelings: A Guide for Parents of Handicapped Children and Everyone Who Counsels Them.* Pittsburgh, Stanwix House, Inc., 1962.
3. PALMER, M. F.: Recent advances in the scientific study of language disorders in cerebral palsy. *Cereb. Palsy Rev., 15*:3-6, 1954.

Chapter V

INDIRECT FACILITATIVE APPROACHES TO SPEECH, HEARING AND LANGUAGE TRAINING

MERLIN J. MECHAM

THE PERSONS ON THE habilitation team who are primarily responsible for speech, hearing and oral language training of the cerebral palsied child are the speech pathologist and the audiologist. Although the profession of speech pathology and the audiology is relatively young and our present knowledge is scanty in terms of research in cerebral palsy, we have accumulated enough clinical experience to enable us to move away from the use of lists of "jingles," "games," or "nonsense" materials, etc., as general formula to be applied to every child; it is now possible to more nearly "custom design" our approach to therapy for each child in terms of the various problems which we have observed during the evaluating process. Differing approaches may be geared to problem areas stemming, for example, from abnormal neurophysiological structure or function, improper developmental sequencing, neuropsychological deficits or emotional imbalance. Since no two children are alike and the complexities of cerebral palsy are variable, it is customary to use various combinations of known approaches and then attempt to adapt techniques to meet the needs of the particular child at any given moment.

Some suggestions which have proved helpful are described for each of a few major problem areas and may serve to help the beginning therapist to formulate a "frame of reference for therapy."

NEUROPHYSIOLOGICAL TRAINING

The act of speaking is made possible by the movement of muscles in patterns prescribed by the input source of the communication system. The parts which are predominantly involved in the transmission of the coded signal in oral communication are those parts whose primary physiological functions are eating,

77

drinking, breathing, etc. The following discussion will consider some of the procedures which are helpful in obtaining better physiological development of those vegetative processes which usually become impaired during their normal maturation in cerebral palsied children.

Relaxation. Evans has stated that there are three ways to treat the speech for the cerebral palsied: "First, relaxation; second, *relaxation;* and third, RELAXATION!" This may be a slight exaggeration, but it is particularly true for athetoids for whom relaxation usually precedes all other forms of treatment. Choiniere[6] found, in a survey of speech therapies for cerebral palsy, a general agreement that relaxation was the most important aspect of therapy.

Jacobson's well known progressive relaxation[21] can be adapted to some cases of cerebral palsy, although theoretically it presupposes normal musculature. The main objective in this method of relaxation is, first, to learn to discriminate between different shadings of tensions by alternately tensing and relaxing and, second, to attain a greater degree of relaxation than usual in different muscle groups. What one does is to become aware of various muscle groups such as the toes, ankles, calves, thighs and so on up and then get each group, separately, to tense and then relax to a greater degree. One continues up the body parts until the muscles of the face and forehead have been tensed and then relaxed. A modification of the Jacobson method is discussed by Egel[12] for use with the cerebral palsied. Some have frowned upon this method of relaxation for the cerebral palsied because of the futility of trying to get them to relax "steel" muscles voluntarily.

Semantic relaxation was developed by Korzybski a few years ago and can be successfully used if one is skilled in its application. This type of relaxation is probably as much an art as it is a science and requires special training by one who knows the system well. Even though the system of semantic relaxation is new, Johnson states that its fundamental features are no doubt as old as the human race.[22] It employs the same principle as that which is used unknowingly by a mother when her baby gets fretful and anxious. What the mother usually does is to hold the baby close and, in doing this, reassures it and gives it a feeling of security. The quieting effect seems to be evaluational rather than purely physiological. It is a semantic reaction to the act of being held secure. The actual procedure in semantic relaxation is somewhat more complicated than just holding, although that is part of it. It also involves a relaxation of the circulatory muscles and the creation of an "all's well" feeling in the entire visceral musculature inside the body.

Another good method of relaxation is a suggestive type which Evans describes as an "adaptation of an East Indian system in which the patient thinks of various muscle groups as the clinician refers to them verbally. As the clinician describes a state of passivity and relaxation and the patient concentrates his thought on creating that condition," the muscles can be taught to duplicate the feeling voluntarily.[13] Another system of suggestive relaxation, similar to this, employs the type of suggestion used in hypnosis. One imagines that what is being suggested by the clinician is actually taking place. One can close his eyes while someone suggests certain states producing tiredness, like that of climbing up a hill very rapidly. Then as one gets to the top of the hill, he imagines that he lies down under a cool tree or on a soft mattress to rest. In this method, a certain state of passivity and relaxation is also suggested, but the patient concentrates on the general feeling of relaxation being suggested.

Other related methods of obtaining relaxation are listening to music, laughing, bathing in warm water, willfully becoming as limp as possible, sun bathing, massaging, etc. Some children respond well to pretending that they are a limp rag doll or a frozen dishrag which has hot water poured on it and other similar relaxing games. Sandbags can sometimes be used to illustrate relaxation. A relaxation chair is often helpful in obtaining a sitting posture more conducive to relaxation.[32]

Drugs have been used for relaxation with varying degrees of success. The use of drugs has been discussed in detail by Denhoff, Keats and others. Although relaxants or behavior-influencing drugs are of limited value for the control of voluntary muscle abnormalities, they may be helpful to the therapist in reducing tensions and in teaching the child how it feels to relax.

Perlstein has suggested that one of the best relaxants is the fact of being successful in an act.[40] Successful achievement of a goal is rewarded and reinforced through the reduction of the psychophysiological anxiety which is motivating the goal directed behavior. Conversely, continued frustration and nonsuccess in the performance of the act may serve to increase an already existing drive-tension and many reduce the ease of successful performance.

Improving General Neuromuscular Control: A vital need of the severely involved cerebral palsied individual is therapy which helps him to learn to control the muscles of his trunk, legs, arms and neck. Since the mechanical difficulties found in speech in cerebral palsy are quite similar to those found in other parts of the body, it might logically be assumed that modalities of neuromuscular training in speech would be identical with those used in the training of arm or leg function. There are some contraindications, however, for isolated and direct treatment of muscles and muscle groups in speech therapy like those employed in physical and occupational therapy. For one thing, the disorders in speech in cerebral palsy are never quite as severe as those of the extremities and body trunk because the speech mechanisms are survival mechanisms.[39] An infant could not survive with severely involved breathing or laryngeal musculatures. Another thing which prevents direct manipulation of the muscles of the speech mechanism to any great degree is that these are (with the exception of the muscles of the tongue) "special visceral" muscles and are less susceptible to voluntary control than are somatic muscles of the body. The muscles for laryngeal control are particularly obscure, and the muscles of the lips and jaw cannot be as readily conditioned as those of an arm or leg.

In spite of the fact that the muscles of speech are less responsive to direct treatment than the somatic muscles, there are some general techniques which can be used to increase the function and control of these muscles.

Stabilization: Stabilization of the muscles of the neck, shoulders, and trunk has been found to reduce the amount of "overflow" into the speech musculature and may also facilitate voluntary relaxation in this area. The use of stabilization is an especially important phase of the speech training program for the athetoid child. Observation of the motor involvements in the athetoid child will show that an attempted movement of one part of the body will set up disturbances in other parts. For example, movements of the hands may trigger involuntary movement in the face, jaw, tongue or other speech musculature. Similarly, when one part of the athetoid's body is restrained, a reduction of movement of the other parts results.

The principle involved in stabilization of the speech mechanism is the same principle involved in stabilization of the extremities of the body through bracing procedures. Westlake[47] has suggested various types of stabilization techniques for speech, including a chin strap, to control the extensor thrust of the lower jaw and sandbags, used with the child lying on his back or sitting in a relaxation chair, to stabilize the shoulder and other gross muscle groups which might cause overflow activity into the speech structures. Sometimes stabilization can be achieved by merely holding steady the involved arm of the athetoid child while he is concentrating on speaking and controlling his speech muscles. Full length braces which stabilize the body for sitting and standing will often reduce the amount of overflow into the speech mechanism and make speech therapy easier, if the child is severely involved.

In some cases, stabilization is a forerunner of relaxation. Through it, the child learns to feel a relative state of stability of the immobile muscle groups. He will then be more able to achieve immobility of muscles voluntarily, through conscious relaxation.

Athetotic tension is somewhat proportional to the amount of emotional stress of a situation. Most older athetoids learn to use certain self-devised methods of stabilization while speaking under emotional stress. One athetoid student in college who enrolled in a fundamental speech course in order to get experience in difficult speaking situations, had to rather strenuously hold one hand in the other to reduce the excessive overflow and involuntary movements into his speech musculature while speaking before the class. This procedure facilitated relaxation and tended to minimize facial grimaces and other unnatural movements which created unsatisfactory cosmetic effects. Another athetoid adult, whose arms continually flailed around his head and shoulders, could talk much more easily while sitting on both hands.

Resistive Therapy: A second general technique to be discussed is resistive therapy. There are two kinds of results which may be achieved through use of resistive therapy. One is confusion motion, and the other is increased muscular contraction.

Confusion motion is that which occurs in one particular part of the body when another part is moved. It is more likely to occur when the movements of the mobile part are resisted or stopped and the desire to move still continues. If a child who cannot flex his ankle dorsally is asked to raise his knee while sitting on the edge of a table, ankle flexion may be prompted by holding the knee down firmly on the table. As he attempts to raise his knee and does not succeed, the ankle may become flexed and an upward movement of the foot will take place in an effort to aid in the fulfillment of the original desire to raise the knee.[46]

Confusion motions have been observed in persons in speech therapy. Some children are more able to close their lips tightly if they bite down hard on a rubber block. Some are more able to close the jaw when this movement is resisted by pulling down on the jaw. A child who could not raise the tip of the tongue voluntarily was able to raise his tongue involuntarily when asked to attempt to push his head back against resistance. Another child's chin was held down as he attempted to close his mouth, and his tongue moved up to the gum ridge.

LeFevre has obtained greater effort on the part of the cerebral palsied child through the use of resistive therapy both for breathing and speech production.[30] According to her, children get better voluntary movement in the process of trying to overcome resistance. This idea evolved from Kabat's method of neuromuscular reeducation through resistance. According to Kabat, resistance increases the facility and summation of excitation in the central motor mechanisms and this enables a maximal response in voluntary motions.[26]

The effectiveness of confusion and facilitation in actual therapy is not well known. These can be used rather effectively in many cases as aids in the appraisal of movement that is possible in various muscles. For example, if the tongue can be made to rise to the rugae as a result of resistance, the therapist knows that the tongue is able to perform this motion; and he may feel that the time spent in helping the child to achieve the activity voluntarily is warranted.

The technique of resistance may wisely be used as a last resort in therapy and avoided if easier and more enjoyable techniques are effective in eliciting the desired result. Children usually are not too happy when strong resistance is used about the face and mouth. The effectiveness of this procedure requires a certain amount of insight on the part of the therapist and cooperation on the part of the child.

Training in Chewing, Sucking and Swallowing: Clinical experience has shown that speech cannot be normally produced unless there is a normal functioning of the chewing, sucking and swallowing movements. The reverse of this, however, is not always true. Sometimes there is impairment of voluntary movement even though reflexive movement is still intact (lingual apraxia).

Palmer has stressed the importance of the chewing, sucking and swallowing processes in the development of speech in cerebral palsy:

> If we assume that the tip of the tongue makes movements in four to six hundredths of a second, and sometimes with even smaller time intervals in this mechanical process of speech, and if we have the tongue unable to manage a bolus of food in five or six minutes, it should be obvious that in order for the speech process to move adequately mechanically, something is going to have to be done about the chewing, sucking and swallowing reflexes.[39]

Techniques which were developed to normalize the chewing, sucking and swallowing reflexes began about 1925 when Muyskens presented a doctoral dissertation entitled "The Smallest Aggregate of Speech Movement Analyzed and Defined. The Hypha."[38] The material from that study was developed further (1932) by Shohara—as being applicable to the development of speech—and by Meader who called attention to the place of the reflexes in the normal developmental picture. Froeschels and others have studied the place of chewing, etc., in speech therapy, and have elaborated on various techniques of training in chewing, sucking and swallowing.[14]

Westlake has used a number of techniques in which he utilized modified feeding activities with the child in a number of different postural positions. Modified nipples are used for very young children as a transition from the bottle to the straw. Even older children may be able to suck a nipple but not a straw and, thus, modifying nipples in gradual degrees may finally develop the child's ability to drink from the straw.[47]

In modified feeding, food is first placed on the back of the tongue, due to greater success in management there and then it is gradually placed more towards the front. At first, palatable semi-liquids are used and then food of thicker consistency, as the child learns to manage it. The postural position varies according to the ability of the child to overcome forces of gravity; from a semire-clining position at first the child is moved to an upright one, then forward-leaning, and finally to a prone position.

"In the prone position the essential tongue activity uses the lingual muscles in much the way they are used in producing consonants. Developing the tongue tip elevation is exceedingly important for speech."[40]

The child is placed on his stomach on a plinth or other solid surface and is encouraged to propel foods to the back of the throat to be swallowed. A mirror is placed in front of the child so that he can see the activity of the masticating structures. If the child is propped up by placing a pillow under his chest, he may rest his elbows on the plinth and be able to watch himself in the mirror without danger of bumping his face. Severely involved children who are beginning this type of activity may have to work gradually from the supine or semisupine position to the sitting and then to the semiprone and prone positions in handling the foods.

Control of Drooling: The mastery of drooling is one of the most troublesome problems which faces the speech and occupational therapists, but there is much that can be done about it. Many children do not know that they drool, for their sensory mechanism has not been trained to distinguish the feeling of saliva running down over their lower lip and chin. The child should be taught to discriminate between the feeling of drooling and that of nondrooling by keeping his lips as dry as possible. Drooling should be brought to his attention and he should learn to recognize the feeling of running saliva. He should be made swallowing-conscious. He should learn to swallow often and should attempt to keep the saliva pushed back to the back part of the mouth, where it can be swallowed. The part played by sensory training in drooling remediation has not been emphasized enough.

In many instances, feeding the child various kinds of tasty fruits which are juicy has been helpful in overcoming drooling (in both speech therapy and occupational therapy [eating]). The child may watch himself in the mirror and should be encouraged to attempt to get the juices "down the back door," rather than let them run back out the "front door."

There is a marked tendency among cerebral palsied children to breathe through the mouth rather than the nose and drooling is often present in children with fairly good chewing, sucking and swallowing ability merely because they are mouth-breathers. One of the first precautions to be taken with mouth-breathers is a thorough medical examination of the ears, nose and throat to determine whether or not medical treatment is needed. Training in nose breathing may be a vital part of the antidrool program.

Since the swallowing reflex is usually active or hyperactive in most cerebral palsied children, it may be used to advantage in therapy against drooling. Dorinson[11] carried out a successful experiment in forcing mouth closure so that enough saliva could be collected in the mouth to stimulate the swallowing reflex. He devised, from pieces of horsehide lined with softer leather, an "anti-drool" mask to fit around the chin and over the mouth and upper lip. The nostrils were left free for breathing. A piece of sponge rubber was placed inside the mask, just in front of the mouth to block the air and secretions from the mouth opening. Strips of old inner tube were used to hold the mask in place. These rubber strips were placed over the crown of the head to give a slight pull on the mask against the mouth. When a quantity of saliva had collected, the child was forced to swallow several times until his mouth was empty of saliva. In time, the child would learn to swallow at regular intervals to avoid the unpleasant collection of saliva at the front of his mouth.

Ten children were trained with this kind of mask. They wore it for intervals of up to thirty minutes, several times a day, while at the same time carrying on their normal activities. When the mask was removed in the early part of the training, the sponge was wet where the saliva had been blocked. As the children improved their swallowing control, there was less and less dampness on the inside of the mask. At the time the child succeeded in keeping the inside of the mask dry, the training was stopped and drooling was found to be mastered by all ten children. The children ranged from three to eight years of age in the experiment, and the length of anti-drool training ranged from one to six months for the different children.

Reflex Inhibition: A method of physiological habilitation has recently evolved in England[2] based upon resistance to primitive reflex patterns that cerebral palsied persons tend to assume, and has gained wide recognition in England, Germany, Holland and other European countries; it has gained no little attention in America. This treatment technique was developed by Berta Bobath, a physical therapist and her husband, Karl Bobath, a neurologist, both of whom are located at the Cerebral Palsy Centre, London.

The approach differs radically from any approach currently being practiced in America and is based on the premise that the fundamental disturbance in the motor behavior of the cerebral palsied person is the lack of inhibitory control over basic postural reflexes. According to the Bobath theory, "Patients suffering from cerebral palsy are unable to contract selectively any one muscle or muscle group of the affected parts. Any attempt to do so will always lead to the simultaneous contraction of all the muscles belonging to the particular type of reflex movement in which the muscle plays a part."[4]

Crickmay has given a succinct description of the underlying Bobath philosophy and its use in speech therapy:

> In the first few weeks of life, a baby's movements are stereotyped and typical, and they involve large portions of his body. This can be seen in the neck righting reflex which is present at

birth. At birth the baby is not able to dissociate the movement of his neck from the movement of his body, and when he turns his head to one side, his whole body turns with it.

With maturation of the central nervous system, new activities and more complex movement patterns appear, and the older and the more primitive patterns are modified, partly discarded, broken up, and resynthetized into new patterns. Gradually movements become more varied and differential and smaller segments of the body are moved independently. In other words, the baby gradually frees himself from his primitive reflex patterns for voluntary activities.

> The Bobaths feel . . . that all cases of cerebral palsy, spastic, athetoid, ataxic and mixed types, show a loss of inhibitory control. As they see it, the injury to the brain has resulted in the release of the lower centers from the inhibitory control of the higher, so that the patient does not possess the capacity for selective and varied movements. He cannot grasp an object as we do by extending arm and wrist and flexing fingers, for if he flexes his fingers his whole arm flexes. He cannot flex his ankle for normal standing and walking, as we do, for he is at the mercy of a few primative reflex patterns which are stereotyped and wide spread involving his whole body in predictable synergies of muscle action.
>
> They also feel that abnormal muscle tone is an important factor in cerebral palsy. When learning to move, a normal child is guided by sensations from muscles and joints, but the sensations a cerebral palsied child receives are abnormal — his muscle tone is either too high, too low, or too fluctuating, with the result that movement can only be abnormal. He cannot perform a normal movement because he cannot feel a normal movement.[7]

The main objective of the Bobath treatment is to teach control of primitive reflex reactions. This control is attained by a special technique of activating passive movements without permitting any reflex contraction. In order to employ the technique, the therapist must have a thorough knowledge of the basic reflex patterns of posture and movement which normally are inhibited and utilized selectively, as needed, by higher centers of the central nervous system. (These reflex patterns and their uninhibited predominance in cerebral palsy are described in some detail by the Bobaths.[3,5])

The therapist places the child in a posture which is the exact opposite of the one desired by the child. This posture is called a "reflex inhibiting posture" or "rip." Each child "has typical postures depending on the site of the lesion, on the position of the body in space, and on the position of the head and neck in relation to the body." The "rip" for any posture which the child wishes to assume involves changing the flexion to extension, pronation to supination, abduction to adduction, etc. These changes are forced by the therapist at the various joints, the proximal joints being the most important.

> At first, the patient will struggle to release himself from a "rip," but he must be held, for it is at the moment when he is prevented from responding to his spasm in his habitual way that inhibition takes place.
>
> After the spasm has subsided a change comes over the patient. It is then that he looks normal. Not only does he look normal, but his muscle tone actually is normal, for it has been found that "rips" have the strange effect of reducing the high muscle tone of the spastic patient, of raising the low muscle tone of the hypotonic patients and of steadying the fluctuating tone of the athetotic or ataxic patient. During this brief period when the patient is completely adjusted to the "rip," his breathing becomes deep and regular; involuntary movement and grimacing stop, and for a time, at least, the whole child becomes completely normal.[7]

The period of "normalcy" is momentary during early treatment. As therapy ensues and as the child is brought into more "rips," the duration of the period of "normalcy" is increased after every spasm, so that the child is able to sense, more and more, normal movement and activity during that period. Gradually the child becomes able to inhibit his own reflex behavior and the active assistance of the therapist is decreased. The child is taken through all the stages of normal "motor" development during the course of treatment. The Bobaths believe that no stage must be skipped, but that development of motor control on one level must be mastered before control on a higher level can emerge;

thus getting into the crawling position precedes getting into the sitting and standing positions, etc.

In the Bobath therapy, physical therapy and speech therapy go hand in hand. Both physical therapist and speech therapist need special training to enable them to predict reflex behavior. Physical therapy must be far enough ahead of speech therapy to insure that the child can tolerate at least one or two "rips" with ease.

The first step in speech therapy is to dissociate breathing and speech from the rest of the body. To do this, it is necessary to assess each patient from the point of view of dissociation. It is necessary to find out whether he can move isolated parts of his speech mechanism, such as the tongue and lips, or parts of his body associated with the speech mechanism, such as neck and shoulders, without moving the whole. Can he move his tongue without moving his head? Can he move his head independently from his shoulders? This information is of great importance to the speech therapist.

In regard to breathing, the therapist needs to find out whether breathing is accompanied by a head movement. Is there an extensor spasm of the neck as the patient breathes in, and a flexor spasm of the neck when he breathes out?

In regard to voice, she needs to find out whether producing voice evokes spasms in other parts of the body. Does the child respond to speech with a spasm? And does producing speech evoke a spasm?[7]

Therapy proceeds by working with the child in "reflex inhibiting postures" in order to dissociate breathing and speech from the posture and movement of the rest of the body. Desensitization of the various parts of the speech mechanism is achieved so that they can be manipulated without producing a spasm. Basic "rips" which permit reflexive and spontaneous speech and voicing depend upon the reflex postures which the child wishes to assume. Typical "rip" patterns are described by Marland:

1. Supine, with flexed abducted knees, shoulders flexed and raised forward on therapist's arm; head falling far back.
2. Knee-sitting with trunk forward on couch, head down between extended arms; dorsal spine extended.

3. Sitting with legs down over side of couch, hips well flexed, spine extended; extended arms raised to therapist's shoulders; head up (and central) but not back.[31]

Many others are suggested by Crickmay and Marland as speech therapy progresses. No claim is made by the Bobaths that their method is the complete answer to the problem of cerebral palsy. They feel, however, that it is a contribution in the field of physiological treatment. "When some small gain is made each time a child comes from treatment, this in itself surely makes the method worth investigating."[7]

Mysak[36] has recently given a very detailed description of the theory and techniques underlying reflex inhibition therapy and reported the results of an initiatory investigation of the application of the method by use of motion picture films.[34,35] His report described changes in oral and arm-hand reflexes and control; differences in thoracic and abdominal breathing records during vegitative and speech activities, and measured changes in speech and articulation duration, rate and quality.[36] His findings revealed that "positive" symptoms (lack of adequate control of overactivity of lower brain centers) seem to prevent the cerebral palsied child "from manifesting his full potential for reflexive evolution," and that through special reflex therapy techniques "these positive symptoms may be weakened and higher reflex centers stimulated and, consequently, a higher level of reflexive evolution with its concomitant higher and more normal motor patterns achieved."[36]

Breath Control: Adequate breathing for speech of the cerebral palsied child requires the minimum goal of an even exhalation of at least ten seconds. The speech therapist should, when possible, share the problem of breathing with the physical therapist who may directly help the child to establish correct breathing patterns.

Westlake and Rutherford[48] suggest that one important reason for establishing proper breathing habits is prevention of deformities of the rib cage. Neuromuscular coordination and synchronization in breathing is especially important in the athetoid, whose breath control may be irregular and jerky and is often asynchronous.

Extreme nasal emission, especially if accompanied by insufficient intraoral pressure for proper production of sounds, may be indicative of extreme spastic or flaccid involvement of the palate.

Directional control is an important aspect in breathing for voice and may be accomplished through blowing the breath and prolongation exercises which have been variously described in the literature. This may be especially necessary for the spastic child who usually has difficulty getting his velum up and his mouth open wide enough to prevent hypernasality in his speech. Holding the child's nose or stroking the throat, tongue and lips gently have been suggested to aid the child in becoming aware of the direction in which the air stream should be projected.[44]

Blowing activities which have been found helpful are blowing a ping-pong ball up an inclined plane, blowing plastic bubbles and blowing toy wind instruments such as the "flutophone," etc. Blowing exercises in group activities will increase motivation through competition for praise and recognition.

Hardy and others[15] have reported successful and beneficial results of pharyngeal flap surgery on cerebral palsied children whose palatal paresis did not seem to respond to nonsurgical treatment. Such surgery may be beneficial in improving intraoral breath pressure in children whose palate is severely disabled but whose tongue and breathing apparatus are not so severely paretic as to make the benefits of such surgery questionable.

Resistance techniques have been found helpful in improving breathing. While the child is in the supine position, a flat sandbag weighing one, two or three pounds, depending upon the size and comfort of the child is placed on his abdomen immediately below the rib cage. Thus, resistance is created on the breathing excursions, but the breathing is not impeded. According to Blumberg,[1] this technique adds to the pulmonary capacity and the efficiency of ventilation and teaches better control of the breathing musculature.

Artificial respiration techniques, with the child in the supine or prone position, have been used to establish correct breathing patterns. With the aid of artificial respiration, the child becomes aware of the location and feel of the breathing movement and of the differences in rate and intensity of breathing. Harrington, at the Orthopedic Hospital in Los Angeles, has experimented with the respirator (iron lung) as a possible training device for the teaching of more adequate speech-breathing movements.[16] He used cerebral palsied subjects ranging from eight to twenty-eight years in age. The length of time in the respirator per period ranged from twenty minutes to one and one-half hours, with an average of approximately thirty minutes. Positive pressure was used at first, but the patients fought it. Negative pressure was used, and, to obtain more normal breathing patterns, the "lung" was operated by hand rather than by motor. This made it possible to produce rapid inhalation and to allow as much time for exhalation during speech as was needed. Although results of the study have been inconclusive, continued research in this type of training was indicated in the study.

Dixon[9] gave respirator training to fifteen children who had breathing and speech problems. He found that his subjects made improvements in both breathing and speech, but, because of his small sample, his conclusions were only tentative.

Research in the use of direct electrical stimulation to muscles of breathing in athetoids has received encouraging results by some investigators. Wilson[49] and Plothin[42] at Northwestern University, were successful in effecting decreased breathing rates and increased vital capacity of fifteen children by superimposing a regulated respiratory pattern over a five week period with a conventional type stimulator. Jones, Hardy and Shipton[25] designed a modified version of the commercial-type stimulator and administered electrical stimulation to two athetoid children over a ten month period. Rates of rest-breathing of the children were reduced and tidal volume was increased. Inspiratory capacities and vital capacities of the children increased while their expiratory reserve decreased. Extent and carryover of improved breathing patterns seemed to be greater as a function of length of the stimulation program.

Increased ability to sustain the voice becomes especially important for cerebral palsied children. As Westlake[46] has indicated, they should be able to sustain the voice steadily for at least ten seconds. Froeschels[14] has suggested the use of a technique he has found helpful with the athetoid and often with other types of cerebral palsy: The child raises his closed hands to the nipples of the thorax and pushes down, at the same time exhaling an "ah" or some other concrete sound, such as "moo" or "baa."

Control of Tongue and Mandible. Basic to the process of articulation is the ability to open and close the mouth. Even more important is the ability to control the tongue, for it is through the activity of the tongue that the intricate characteristics of sounds of speech are produced. In the following paragraphs, the control of mouth and tongue activities for speech and the improvement of their function will be discussed.

The minimum requisite of opening and closing the jaw for speech, as suggested by Westlake, is one per second.[46] In beginning exercises, the therapist often uses passive movement of the mandible (lower jaw). Ordinarily children show some resistance to passive manipulation, and, if they do, other techniques are often preferable. (Like many other specific techniques, the use of passive manipulation depends upon the therapist, the child and the therapeutic situation.) The mechanics of the technique are subject to the creativity of the therapist. The author usually places a finger cot on the index finger. The finger is then placed on the lower teeth while the thumb is placed under the chin. The jaw of a fairly relaxed child can then be moved up and down at will. It is not necessary that the mouth be opened excessively wide—not more than an inch. Passive movements of the mandible are often more effective if done while the child watches in a mirror and at the same time hears a verbal description of what is being done.

Passive manipulation should gradually be reduced as therapy progresses. At the same time, the child be encouraged to increase his voluntary effort to get the desired movement; thus, voluntary movement on the part of the child replaces the passive movement initiated by the therapist. The rate of change from passive to active should not exceed the child's ability to master voluntary control of the desired movement. This rate varies from one child to another and also from one time to another in the same child. Often, a child will regress, or reach a temporary plateau in acquiring skills in voluntary movement and passive movement may have to be introduced again during this interval.

Children may show an inclination in therapy to imitate jaw movements of the therapist, other children or even a mechanical animal, such as a duck or dog. If so, it may be possible to omit passive exercises and begin therapy on an imitative level.

Many cerebral palsied children are prone to hold the mouth in an open position. This may be habitual in some while in others, it is pathological. Westlake describes the "extensor thrust" in which the neuromuscular overflow makes closing the mouth difficult in exciting situations or in any type of voluntary activity. This frequently occurs in the athetoid syndrome and typically involves excessive lowering of the mandible and protrusion of the tongue with the tip extending downward.[47]

Several things may aid the cerebral palsied child who has difficulty in keeping the mouth closed. The child may be periodically reminded to close his mouth if his main trouble is merely remembering to do so. Kinesthetic senses should be sharpened to aid the child in knowing when he has his mouth closed or open. There may be periods in which he practices holding a piece of paper or a tongue blade between the teeth or lips. The length of time may be charted from period to period. Modifications of the above holding technique may include holding a button in the lips or teeth while a tiny animal toy at the end of an attached string swings freely. For strengthening the lips while the mouth is closed, the child may hold a button with a rubber band laced through its holes between the lips and the teeth while the therapist plays a tug of war and applies pressure to the elastic band.[47]

Often, stabilization is necessary for athetoids who have an extensor thrust. Chin slings which allow the mouth to open just enough for speech have been effective in stabilizing the jaw.[47] Other methods of stabilization may be devised by the therapist.

Since elevation of the tongue tip seems to be one of the most difficult problems in articulation for the cerebral palsied child, a discussion of techniques of obtaining this action is considered to be an important item. The development of any of the basic skills needed in the mastication process may aid in the facilitation of the tongue-elevation skill. In fact, the development of general tongue activities of all kinds may make specific tongue-tip skills easier to attain.

Sometimes the child can make the proper movement of the tongue if he imitates the movement as he sees the therapist do it. A mirror will be an aid to him in imitating the therapist. There are two different kinds of exercises which are practiced: (1) those which involve any kind of general tongue activity, and (2) those which involve specific movements required in speech production. For the former, the incentive is usually the lollipop or generous praise. For the latter, the greatest incentive is usually the end product of speech along with the praise and feelings of social achievement which accompanies it. It is difficult to ascertain how helpful exercises are that require general tongue activity not essential for speech. The tongue, for example, is not usually extended outside the mouth in producing speech sounds—as it is for licking a lollipop—even in the *th* sound; but the fact that he can extend the tongue may be an easy step which will spur the child to accomplish the more difficult feats required in speech. It is also probable that certain segments of general muscular activity are utilized in speech production.

Hixon and Hardy suggest that remedial exercises employing speech activities may be much more efficient than those which employ nonspeech movement of these structures. This is based upon their finding that nonspeech movements of the articulators are not closely related to defectiveness of speech.[17]

Tongue tip movements can sometimes be elicited by placing some apple sauce or other palatable food immediately behind the upper teeth with a tongue blade. Peanut butter or a small piece of tape have been effectively used in the roof of the mouth. The child makes vertical movements with his tongue tip in his struggle to remove the substance from the inner gum ridge. Westlake states that when a child is placed in a struggle situation, many movements will be seen that do not ordinarily appear. It is a normal reaction for the child in a struggle situation to make all kinds of random movements in an effort to overcome the particular barriers involved.

Sometimes, when nothing else works, the tongue may be passively manipulated by the therapist using his fingers or a plastic or metal instrument shaped to fit the tongue. Plastic spoons are not only economical but can also be dipped in hot water and molded to fit various portions of the tongue. Metal instruments are easier to sterilize and can be used over and over again.

TRAINING IN PERSONAL-SOCIAL COMMUNICATION

The old saying that you can lead a horse to water but you cannot make him drink is a true analogy in the case of speech and hearing training. You may be able to get the child to learn words and sounds, but merely learning them does not guarantee their effective use in activities of daily living. There must be a definite need for the use of speech as a tool in a child's mastery and manipulation of his world. Increasing the need for speech may involve helping the child to grow up, giving him responsibility, broadening his social environment and giving him successful experiences in speech.

Helping the Child to Grow Up. Hohman states that regardless of a child's "original endowment, we must not forget that the individual is born into a world in which he has the capacity to grow. Growth is a marvelous phenomenon—a process which goes on from birth until middle adult life, perhaps even until old age. It is a process in which there is a continuously unfolding set of patterns."[18] The growth process depends on nurturing and molding which takes place in the environment.

To the newborn child, environment is a gift which acts as the soil for his growth and development; here he is molded through the experiences and training he receives. The adequacy of the growth process, even for the physically handicapped child is greatly dependent upon his ability to advance from one developmental level to another within the framework of his own environment.

One of the major environmental blocks to growth in the child handicapped with cerebral palsy is the problem of infantilization. Infantilization is hard to avoid when one considers the extent to which sympathy may be played upon by the existence of a handicap. Both the child and parent find themselves confronted with many obstacles, and each may be prone to take the easiest course.

There is always the possibility of a child's exploiting his own handicap by using it as an excuse for not trying things which are difficult and unpleasant. Many parents, even parents of normal children are hesitant about letting their children grow up. The tendency to keep children in an infantile stage is especially noticeable among the cerebral palsied group.

Children have to grow up in more important ways than just physically. The latter is usually inevitable, but there must be an accompanying growth in skills of emotional, social and eventually even vocational adjustment. The ever-present goal before parents should not be keeping their babies as long as possible but helping their children to achieve independence—all the physical, social and vocational independence possible.

Westlake has indicated that growing up may be a process of successful rebellion.[47] Speech is a means by which a child gains independence (and the reverse of this may also apply: More independence may stimulate the child to learn to express himself more adequately). The average child becomes independent as he develops the skills of walking and self-help. The cerebral palsied child will more often have to rely on others for a longer period of time for the activation of these fundamental skills of locomotion and self-help. This extreme dependence in the motor areas may prolong the infantilism in other areas of development and have a definitely retarding effect on speech. The author recalls a case of cerebral palsy in which the parents, because of their "devotion" to their child, never allowed him to attempt to crawl, stand or walk because they were afraid he might get hurt. It was not until he left his home and went to college that he got out of his wheel chair and learned to walk. What the parents displayed in this case was not *devotion* but *stupidity*. Although this is an exceptional case of overprotection and infantilization, it emphasizes the importance of proper parental attitude and understanding.

Helping to Increase Emotional Stability: A second problem subservient to psychological readiness is the problem of emotional maturation. Every child, regardless of his physical abilities or talents, desires to be loved, needed, accepted and particularly to achieve a status in which he can be respected as a contributing member of society. The emotional satisfaction resulting from a realization of these basic desires has a direct bearing on the child's ability to communicate. The child who feels loved and accepted will be more outgoing, will feel more like expressing his feelings and ideas and communicating with his peers.[27] On the other hand, a rejected child will be withdrawn and may refuse to communicate with people whose attitude he resents. The retarded or handicapped child has feelings about himself. His feelings need to be understood. The child with cerebral palsy does not want pity; sympathy is not enough. What he needs, first of all, is to be understood and accepted for what he is. From a psychological point of view, a good frame of reference for parents and teachers to follow is to assume that a child is born into the world believing that he is not wanted. It is then our challenge to prove to him that he is not only wanted but needed. Redl and Wineman state that,

> . . . children must get plenty of love and affection whether they deserve it or not; they must be assured the basic quota of happy recreational experiences whether they seem to "have it coming" or not. In short, love and affection, as well as granting of gratifying life situations, cannot be made the bargaining tools of educational or even therapeutic motivation, but must be kept tax-free as minimum parts of the youngster's diet, irrespective of the problems of deservedness.[43]

To gain emotional stability, the cerebral palsied child needs to gain a realistic insight into his potential. He needs to know his limitations; but, even more important, he must know his assets and the extent to which he may achieve a certain status with those assets. Often, cerebral palsied persons are so concerned with their efforts to overcome a physical handicap that their goals become narrowed to mere physical or motor achievement when, actually, they are likely to achieve least in the motor area. They must learn to base their goals on achievement in other areas of development, such as personality improvement, social acceptance and intellectual progress.

Expectations concerning the extent of vocational achievement in a competitive society should be as objective as possible. A college student who had spastic hemiplegia and drooled applied for a job in the library. He wanted to check out books to the students and refused to accept the job when he was told that the only opening for him was replacing books in the stacks. He realized that there was discrimination because of his drooling, and he resented it. Though he was considered for a job which in all probability, he was most suited for, he felt that the offer he received was the result of a personal attitude of rejection toward him, on the part of the librarian.

Johnson states that a therapeutic program should be geared to the understanding of the child, as the "father to the man." Improved attitudes of the cerebral palsied individual are basic to the total improvement program.

Improvement in the attitude toward the cerebral palsy itself consists importantly in the development of greater and greater objectivity. This takes such forms as decreased self-pity, a falling away of feelings of apology and shame, and an increased interest in cerebral palsy as a condition to be studied, observed, experimented with, understood theoretically and practically, and modified advantageously so far as possible, but lived-with gracefully in the meantime.

Second, improvement in the attitude toward self is to be seen particularly in an increase in self-acceptance. By this is meant not apathy or resignation, not acceptance in the sense of giving up hope of improving. What is meant is self-acceptance as contrasted with self-rejection — the acceptance of oneself as a person worth being and worth knowing. . . .

Third, improvement in attitude toward others is . . . observed in the . . . individual's tendency to like others . . . and to spend more time with others.[23]

Allotting the Child Responsibility: The cerebral palsied child is almost always at a disadvantage in his own home. Even when he has brothers and sisters in the home, he is usually sheltered and overprotected. His desires are anticipated quickly and his every need is met for him by someone else. Because of his slow reactions and laborious movement in a busy world, his basic needs are met routinely and he is "taken care of." "Nothing is expected of him and he lives up to his expectations." Competition is possible for these children; and if the cerebral palsied child is placed with other children in sheltered and guided situations with a fair degree of success in competitive activities, he will gain a new feeling of achievement and responsibility.

Normal children usually have routine responsibilities in the home. How can a parent do all the things that must be done for the physically-handicapped child and still do it in such a way that the child feels some degree of independence and "home" responsibility? There is a difference between the process of going ahead routinely with the anticipated needs of the physically-handicapped child in a more or less mechanical way and that of requiring the child to *express* his needs in some fashion—even though you may already know what the needs are—*before he gets things done for him.*

Westlake states that one may create a feeling of responsibility in a child if the child is required to remind one what is to be done and when and how. He states:

> There is a difference between shoving a toothbrush into a child's mouth before he is put into bed and carrying him upstairs and directly to his room unless he struggles, grunts, or by some other gesture indicates that his teeth must be brushed first. If he forgets, he can be held responsible for not brushing his teeth just as any other youngster would. He would be receiving the same service, but he would be exercising control over what was being done, or expressing independence. The same choice can be extended to a large part of daily routine such as watching the clock for bed time, washing hands and face, or making simple purchases. Obviously, the care that develops independence rather than prevents it furnishes the better basis for learning speech.[47]

A child who is ambulatory should be given responsibilities comparable to those of a normal child of the same abilities and level of interest.

Broadening the Scope of Successful Social and Experiential Contact: Language and communication skills represent but one phase of the total maturation of the child. The youngster, regardless of his chronological age, will not be ready to communicate until he has reached a certain level of mental maturation. At the same time, he will not be ready for speech unless he has adequate stimulation and opportunity, regardless of his mental ability.

One of the fundamental steps in achieving psychological readiness for communication is the child's acquisition of an awareness of himself, of others and of things that can have an influence upon others. Westlake says that "one of the first ways by which a child shows his interest in adults is by smiling and making movements, such as turning his head."[47] This is an important step in the social relation. No words are present in the beginning interactions with people. Parents and therapists should be alert to any kind of interpersonal reaction on the part of the child and always make the best effort to reward and encourage it.

The need for speech is proportional to the size of one's social and experimental world. The child with cerebral palsy, because of his physical handicap is deprived of much of the day-to-day experience of other children. If one were to follow both the normal child and the severely involved cerebral palsied child during a day, he would observe the absurdity of experiential comparison. The normal child explores in detail small portions of his surroundings, with his eyes, ears, hands, feet and other modes of sensory intake. In addition, he *learns* through the processes of motor activity: relationships are explored and learned through motor manipulation as well as through perception. The details of the child's experience become part of his communicative background. Because of the cerebral palsied child's limitations in exploring and getting around, much of the environment which is normally encountered must be brought to him and made meaningful for him in terms of language and experience. Huber has made some suggestions for building a world of interests and activity around the child.

> Teach your child to notice more things every day by means of the senses of sight, hearing, touch, smell, and taste. If he must remain seated a great part of the time, place him where there is something worth looking at. Even a tiny baby, if propped up comfortably on pillows where he can see some action going on, will be content for longer periods of time than if left lying on his back or stomach during his waking hours.

If mother is working in the kitchen, wheel him in there so that he can watch her work and she can talk to him about what she is doing, smile at him often, and perhaps sing to him now and then. Take him to the window frequently and point out to him the changes in the sky, the weather, the trees, plants, anything new that has appeared on the landscape. If the weather is good let him sit outdoors for long hours and tell him what to observe; if he is an older child you might get him a pair of binoculars so that he can bring the world of birds, trees, flowers and animals closer.

Teach Jimmy to listen for and to understand the sounds occurring about him; the tick of the clock, the steaming tea kettle, the doorbell, telephone; the sound of wind, rustling of leaves, raindrops on the window pane, bird sounds, little animal sounds, a train whistle in the distance. Talk about all these things while he is experiencing them, imitate these sounds yourself and try to get him to imitate them.

There is also the possibility that Jimmy's hearing is not as acute as it might be. This is not uncommon among cerebral palsied children. It may be that he would hear better with a hearing aid; if this is so every effort should be made to provide him with one, for the learning of speech itself is dependent upon the integrity of the hearing mechanism. Protect his ears against infection, have any suspected ear condition checked by a physician before it can result in permanent loss of hearing.

The sense of touch is another important avenue of experience for the very young child. Various textures have names which should become part of the child's vocabulary. Bring him soft, warm, furry animals to stroke; let him experience the cool hard weight of a stone, the rough dry bark of trees, the silky smoothness of flower petals. Let him run his hands through the green, feathery blades of grass, cool dry sand; and, back in the house, substitute for his blocks once in a while a few, cold, wet, slippery ice cubes; again talk, *talk,* and TALK about it all.

Smells, too, must be brought to his attention to help build up concepts around words; some of these may be associated with the introduction of new foods, but each flower, fruit and even inanimate objects have their distinctive odors or scents. With each change in the weather or season come new olfactory sensations; the peculiar delicious smell of wet pavements and damp cool cellars, dried leaves, burning grass, blossom laden bushes and trees, smoke, food cooking and baking, clean fragrant soap and freshly laundered blankets and linens.[20]

A growing child who goes through actual experience and who gets a few immunizing bumps here and there will readily develop a feeling of independence and self-reliance that no amount of protection can provide. The same is true in the development of speech and language as well as for mental growth and emotional stability. It is often easier for the child to nod or indicate by glancing when he wishes to express something. Gestures are better than no communication; but if allowed to go too far, they may actually weaken the feelings of adequacy in oral speech rather than strengthen them. Transition from gestures to speech attempts may be made easily by providing graduated success experiences in speech. A choice may be given so that a vocalized or verbal reply may be successful, and the only successful behavior. For example, a child may be asked, "Do you want milk or water?" In the multiple choice question, he cannot answer by merely shaking his head, as one can where a plain *yes* or *no* answer is sufficient. He must vocalize if he makes a choice. If the task is easy enough for his success, he will acquire a new feeling of freedom, command, and manipulative power.

There is a positive indication that people make either lighter or heavier demands upon cerebral palsied children than is healthy for the achievement of success experiences. Westlake states that,

> When a child is slow in learning to talk and it is known that there is a reason why he should have difficulty in talking, there is a presumption raised against him, and adults may be reluctant to give him credit for talking. Children probably first utter the sounds which resemble words purely by accident with no meaning attached. The pleasure of the adults encourages the repetition of the sounds and at a much later date the child will learn the meanings from the adults. The first words used frequently do not sound much like the ones the parents think their babies are using and vocabularies which parents accept are often not understandable to friends. Yet within the child's own family circle he is talking. It has been said that most children begin to speak when their parents think they do. The point is that most parents go all out with their children, ac-

cepting as words, sounds which may slightly resemble words and assuming meanings and ideas that are probably not there at all. If adults can extend themselves so far for other children, they should go at least as far with the cerebral palsied child. Every sound or sign which can be associated with an idea should be watched for and used. A smile may mean "yes," puckering the lip or turning the head may mean "no." The most important thing is *not* that there is a good word, but that the child is learning a way to control and affect those about him. Such an atmosphere of encouragement fosters the beginnings of speech, and the lack of it is a serious block.[47]

Rewards of communication may be increased by the presence of an abundance of experiences which are suited to the child's developmental age. His level of ability for language handling may vary in different aspects. For example, his hearing and understanding of speech may be on or near his chronological age, and his expression of speech may be on a low grade, "imbecile" level. A child should be treated in general on a level with his hearing and understanding ability rather than on the level of his expressive ability.

Capitalizing upon Personal Strengths and Potential: Perlstein has stressed the importance of concentration on the assets of the child, perhaps more than on his liabilities.[40]

One good way to gain insight into child's level of readiness for experiences is through the administration of the Vineland Social Maturity Scale, which is given to the parents of the child.[10] This scale is an especially good tool for use with children below six years of age; it is not limited to preschool ages, however.

It behooves us to avoid generalities about the kind of child with which we are dealing. We are never dealing with a cerebral palsied child *per se,* but with a child who is individualistic in every respect and who happens also to have cerebral palsy. The clinical evaluation must attempt to assess the *hopes, aspirations, concepts, fears* and *resentments* which are specific for this particular child. These must be appraised and contrasted to the hope, aspirations, concepts and resentments of the therapist because these will have a decided bearing upon whether the child can be "plugged in," so to speak, by some impedance-matching process to a particular plan of therapy. One cannot join two systems with mismatched impedances and expect them to function efficiently.

Arnold Toynbee stated that "Human hopes are always of two kinds. Normally a human being has hopes for himself—hopes that are individual and personal". . . . At the same time, he may develop "suprapersonal hopes for the human race or for some fraction of it: his tribe, his family, perhaps, or his church."[45] He goes on to state that ". . . self centeredness, which seems to be one of the characteristics of life, is so powerful a force that it (also) involves and sometimes prevents the development of our suprapersonal hopes."[45] Degree of *self-centeredness* is an important attribute (of both child and therapist) to be evaluated. Methods of assessment of autism versus social maturation for speech development have been elaborated by Piaget[41] and others.

In the area of cerebral palsy and generally in our whole culture, our total *aspirations* and *concepts* for the handicapped have been overwhelmingly pathology-centered; we surround the individual with pathological vectors.

Wolberg[50] states that a patient may become so preoccupied with his troubles and pain that he is apt to lose sight of the constructive aspects of his personality; direct assurance or attempts to inflate the ego of the patient in this case are usually futile until his *aspirations* and *self-concepts* undergo some type of change. Pathologically saturated aspirations and concepts are continually generating stimuli which trigger emotional tensions since such stimuli have frequently been paired with fear or anger-provoking situations.

Since one of the goals of evaluation for therapy should be to assist the child in discovering and planning to make maximum use of his potentials while he is working through his pathology, it behooves us to explore more fully the area of personality potential as an adjunct to planning for therapy. This has the advantage of not only opening up an untapped area of development and maturation for the cerebral palsied child, but also may serve to minimize many emotional tensions through negative conditioning.

Kaufmann, in a recent article, points out the following:

A *highlevel* wellness for the individual . . . is: An integrated method of functioning which is *oriented toward maximizing the potential of which the individual is capable,* within the environment where he is functioning.

It therefore involves: (A) direction of progress *forward and upward toward a higher potential of functioning,* (B) an open ended and ever expanding tomorrow *with its challenge to live at a fuller potential,* and (C) the integration of the whole being of the total individual — his body, mind, and spirit — in the functioning process.[28]

Looking toward spontaneous communication and personality development in terms of strengths and potentialities has some very important advantages in terms of future planning for therapy. First, cerebral palsy children and their parents have a very limited view of personal strength potentialities. They can write prolifically about the weaknesses and disabilities which the child has, but feel extremely inadequate in describing his strength areas. More attention to strengths and potentials of the child may help parents and others to accept the child with a higher level of esteem and even to utilize to a greater degree those strengths and potentialities which are available but are being bypassed or ignored.

A second advantage in considering resources for greater personal development lies in the fact that the *therapist's* own concept of the child may be influenced significantly by his image of the child's potential assets and this may have a decided effect upon the way in which *he* relates and the *frankness* with which he can convey an accepting, understanding, and sustaining attitude.[19]

Thirdly, speech and language, being highly voluntary and manipulative in nature are classified as primarily "operant" types of behavior. Operant learning depends upon creative and spontaneous searching and exploration.[33, p. 181] The cerebral palsied child who is constantly anxious about his pathologies may have little desire for exploration, searching and spontaneity. The encouragement of operant motivations in the child will be fascilitated by enriching him with as many successful operant type experiences as possible.

Some of the "personal resource" areas where strength and potentialities can be explored have been suggested by the *Otto Inventory of Personal Resources.*[37] Selected parts of this inventory may be adapted into a questionnaire type of survey.

Social Speech: Closely related to psychological readiness in speech therapy and subsequent to development of freedom and better control in the use of the voice are the more direct activities of aiding the child to become more skillful in social speaking situations. This includes social skill development as well as increased ability in the use of language as a social tool.

Stuttering during the use of oral language is frequent among cerebral palsied children—more frequent than among the normal population. Similarities between general rhythm disorders found in cerebral palsy and those of stuttering are rather striking. Differential diagnosis of stuttering blocks and spasms resulting from neuromuscular involvement of the muscles of articulation is often difficult. Regardless of whether the unusual rhythm observed is merely developmental stuttering or an organic rhythm disorder, therapy of the two remains very similar. Secondary tensions have been found in the rhythm disorders of the athetoid. These are a result of his consciousness of his difficulties in rhythm and muscular movement and of his efforts to force their control. Speech training in coordination and rhythm will help the child overcome his rhythm problems.

An indirect approach is recommended to aid the young child with rhythm disorders. All of the principles outlined for the primary stutterer are applicable to the cerebral palsied stuttering child.[24] Conferences should be held frequently with parents. Reductions of family tensions and anxieties which are intensified as a rule in the world of cerebral palsy, should be effected through carefully planned techniques of counseling. The secondary stutterer should be counseled in such a way that he understands his problem better. He should be encouraged to change his perfectionistic goals, if such exist, from the desire to *overcome* his stuttering to the desire to *be able to stutter well and acceptably.* He should be given an opportunity to express freely and without guilt his repressed feelings and anxieties, if for no other reason than to help him recognize, define and understand them more fully.

Social situations of varying emotional stress have a definite effect upon the social performance of the cerebral palsied person. Even if he is not a stutterer, it is easier for him to talk to some people than to others. The amount of tension and incoordination is proportional to the amount of his emotional stress. Possibly one of the reasons for this is that cerebral palsied children, like stutterers, have conflicting goals. They fear to do things that they cannot excel in doing, yet they wish to accomplish most in those areas where they are most handicapped. One cerebral palsied person in college who had a very severe speech defect and was fearful of difficult speaking situations, wanted nothing more than to become a radio announcer.

The need for a total rehabilitation program for the teenager and adult, including a counseling program, is very real. It is difficult enough for a normal teenager to understand himself and his role in social situations, but the day by day buffeting in normal social experiences which guides the normal youngster in his attempts to conform adequately to shadings of interpersonal relationships are greatly lacking throughout most of the early life of the cerebral palsied child. In order for him to develop an adequate introspective system, he must be taken through these situations either in real or structured life settings. Normal or acceptable behavior must, in some way, be experienced by the cerebral palsied child before he really understands what it is.

Graded social situations, structured to provide success experiences are an important part of speech and language therapy, and may be accomplished with the help of understanding and cooperative children in school, church, or community groups. Much of the "oddness" of the cerebral palsied child is due to the peculiar social role he is forced to play by the reactions of other people. Children who associate with him must be made to understand this. They should be encouraged to react to the child in a way that will alleviate attention given to his "peculiarity" and to emphasize his normal abilities and likeable personal traits. Mere acceptance in a social group may, in itself, remove some of the stigma surrounding the social behavior of the cerebral palsied child.

Much of the group reaction to cerebral palsy stems from traditional, preconceived notions handed down from the time of Little. People reject things they don't understand, but once the barrier of nonacceptance is overcome in a social group, the afflicted child will be better understood and accepted *for what he is.* This is one right and privilege that cerebral palsied children have perhaps not completely enjoyed heretofore.

In the structuring of social situations, the therapist should not ask the other children involved to accept the cerebral palsied child for what he is not. Rather, they should be informed realistically about his assets and liabilities. It should be pointed out both to the cerebral palsied child and his peers that all people have some weaknesses and peculiarities; where some people are weak, others are strong and vice versa. A realistic attitude, with this built-in humanistic element of understanding will remedy much of the social problem.

Many social skills can be learned in speech therapy. Instruction in etiquette should be a part of the speech therapist's program. Emphasis should not be placed upon what the *cerebral palsied child* must do around others, but rather upon what *people* normally are expected to do around *each other.* The CP should be permitted to observe other children who are socially interacting and see how the principles of etiquette are commonly practiced.

He also has to be taught not to make unreasonable demands upon his friends and associates. He has always had to depend, to a certain extent upon other people. Training in self-help usually makes him more independent physically, but training in emotional and social self-help is often overlooked in the habilitation program. He should be taught the principles of courtesy and should be allowed to observe the extent to which normal people impose on others. If he really wants to make a more normal adjustment, he will try to imitate those things done by the normal person.

A most frustrating thing for the cerebral palsied child is the significance we place on the time element in communicative and other activities. Parents and peers are prone to dislike waiting to listen. Even when a child is talking with friends and neighbors of the family, parents find it much easier to say for him what he intended to say, rather than to let him struggle through and stand the chance of causing discomfort to the listener. It is not so much that people detest waiting—they do not when they know it will help the child—but they often lack insight and think they are helping him more by not making him struggle. When the child is cut off in his conversational efforts by more competitive persons —around the dinner table, for example—he may feel a lack of competitive ability unwarranted by his actual disability; his motivation will be reduced and he may develop a "give up" attitude. He will not feel as much a part of the family, and these feelings may develop also in his school classes.

Johnson states that one of the best criteria for appraising improvement of social development is concerned with the following:

> (The) verbal output — the cerebral palsied person's speaking time . . . It is to be expected that, other things being equal, and allowing for understandable exceptions, as a cerebral palsied child grows up socially and as a personality, he will increase his speaking time.

Some of the major criteria of social adjustment may be pointed to as:

> group membership, school activities, sharing of hobbies, number of acquaintances, and "closeness" of friends . . . Over all, a lively interest in people and places as they are to be experienced in the reading of books, magazines and newspapers, in listening to radio and watching television, as well as in more direct ways, is clearly conducive to good social adjustment for the cerebral palsied. The very fact that the cerebral palsied are limited . . . in their ability to . . . be active makes all the more essential a systematic and persistent effort to enrich their relationship with other persons.[23]

If special allowances and opportunities are made for the cerebral palsied child to express himself successfully, and if people are willing to wait and listen, he may be more relaxed and thus able to achieve greater success in being understood. He will definitely feel more a part of the communicating group.

Role playing, geared to the ability of the individual, is an effective tool in the development of social finesse. Careful evaluation of the social prognosis of the child is very important before he attempts to imitate the role of some mode. The goal of social efficiency rather than social perfection, should be created. It must be remembered that all social interactions stem from the effort to fulfill the basic needs of acceptance, recognition and other such drives. If the behavior of the child can be changed to provide a degree of satisfaction of these drives, the chances for *more adequate* adjustment can be increased. The achievement of this change has to be carefully planned and guided by the cooperative efforts of the speech therapist, the psychologist and other members of the therapeutic team. The child or adult who makes abortive attempts toward a more adequate adjustment without any insight, knowledge or guidance usually ends up in a psychiatric ward or clinic.

REFERENCES

1. BLUMBERG, M. L.: Vital capacity, and related therapies in cerebral palsy. *Cereb. Palsy Rev., 16:*23-25, 1955.
2. BOBATH, B.: A new treatment of lesions of the upper motor neuron. *Brit. J. Phys. Med., 2:*26-29, 1948.
3. BOBATH, B.: A study of abnormal postural reflex activity in patients with lesions of the central nervous system. *Physiother., 40:*259-267, 295-300, 326-334, 368-373, 1954.
4. BOBATH, K., and BOBATH, B.: A treatment of cerebral palsy based on the analysis of the patient's motor behavior. *Brit. J. Phys. Med., 15:*107-117, 1952.
5. BOBATH, K., and BOBATH, B.: Tonic reflexes and righting reflexes in the diagnosis and assessment of cerebral palsy. *Cereb. Palsy Rev., 16:*4-10, 26, 1955.
6. CHOINIERE, R. L.: A survey of speech therapies for the cerebral palsied. *Speech Monogr., 18:*238, 1951.
7. CRICKMAY, M.: *Description and Orientation of the Bobath Method with Reference to Speech Rehabilitation in Cerebral Palsy.* Chicago, National Soc. for Crippled Children and Adults, Inc., 1955.

8. DENHOFF, E., and ROBINAULT, I.: *Cerebral Palsy and Related Disorders.* New York, McGraw-Hill Book Co., 1960.

9. DIXON, R. P.: An exploratory investigation of the effects of the chest-abdomen respirator on the breathing and speech coordinations and the judged speech intelligibility of children with cerebral palsy who display abnormal breathing patterns and speech difficulties. *Speech Monogr., 23:*140-141, 1956.

10. DOLL, E. A.: *Measurement of Social Competence.* Minneapolis, Educational Test Bureau, 1953.

11. DORINSON, M.: Antidrool mask for children with cerebral palsy. *J. A. M. A., 155:*439-440, 1954.

12. EGEL, P. F.: *Technique of Treatment for the Cerebral Palsied Child.* St. Louis, C. V. Mosby Co., 1948.

13. EVANS, M. F.: Children with cerebral palsy. In *Speech Problems of Children,* ed. by W. Johnson. New York, Grune and Stratton, 1950, pp. 158-189.

14. FROESCHELS, E.: *Dysarthric Speech.* Magnolia, Mass., Expression Company, 1952.

15. HARDY, J. C., *et., al.:* Surgical Management of palatal paresis and speech problems in cerebral palsy. *J. Speech Hearing Dis., 26, 4:*320-325, 1961.

16. HARRINGTON, R.: *The Respirator as an Aid to the Control of Breathing Dysrhythmias in Cerebral Palsy: A Report of Research in Progress.* New York, United Cerebral Palsy Assns., 1950.

17. HIXON, T. J., and HARDY, J. C.: Restricted motility of the speech articulators in cerebral palsy. *J. Speech Hearing Dis., 29, 3:*293-306, 1964.

18. HOHMAN, L. D.: Help the cerebral palsied child grow up. *Crippled Child, 24:*20-21, 1947.

19. HOLLIS, F.: *Case work — a psychosocial therapy.* New York, Random House, 1964.

20. HUBER, M.: Letter to the parents of a cerebral palsied child. *J. Speech Hearing Dis., 15:*13-16, 1950.

21. JACOBSON, E.: *Progressive Relaxation.* Chicago, University of Chicago Press, 1938.

22. JOHNSON, W.: *People In Quandaries.* New York, Harper and Brothers, 1946.

23. JOHNSON, W.: Adjustment problems of the cerebral palsied. *J. Speech Hearing Dis., 21:*12-17, 1956.

24. JOHNSON, W., *et al.: Speech Handicapped School Children.* New York, Harper and Brothers, 1956.
25. JONES, E. I., HARDY, J. C., and SHIPTON, H. W.: Development of electrical stimulation in modifying respiratory patterns of children with cerebral palsy. *J. Speech Hearing Dis., 28, 3:*230-238, 1963.
26. KABAT, H.: Central facilitation: the basis of treatment for paralysis. *Permanente Foundation M. Bull., 10:*190-204, 1952.
27. KASTEIN, S.: Speech hygiene guidance for parents of children with cerebral palsy. Paper read before the meeting of the Cerebral Palsy Society of New York City, Inc., 1949.
28. KAUFMANN, M.: High-level wellness, a pertinent concept for the health professions. *Ment. Hyg., 47: 1:*57, 1963.
29. KEATS, S.: *Cerebral Palsy.* Springfield, Illinois Thomas, 1965.
30. LeFEVRE, M. C.: A rationale for resistive therapy in speech training for the cerebral palsied. *J. Except. Child., 19:*61-64, 1952.
31. MARLAND, P. M.: Speech therapy for the cerebral palsied based on reflex inhibition. In *Speech Therapy, A Book of Readings,* ed. by C. Van Riper. New York, Prentice-Hall, Inc., 1953, 235-238.
32. McDONALD, E. T., and CHANCE, B.: *Cerebral Palsy.* Englewood Cliffs, N. J., Prentice-Hall, Inc., 1964.
33. MOWRER, O. H.: *Learning Theory and the Symbolic Processes.* New York, John Wiley and Sons, Inc., 1960.
34. MYSAK, E. D.: Pilot study films of a neurophysiological approach to cerebral palsy habilitation. Newington, Conn., Newington Hospital for Crippled Children, 1960.
35. MYSAK, E. D.: Pilot study films of a neurophysiological approach to cerebral palsy habilitation. Part II. Newington, Conn., Newington Hospital for Crippled Children, 1962.
36. MYSAK, E. D.: *Principles of a Reflex Therapy Approach to Cerebral Palsy.* New York, Teachers College, Columbia Univ., 1963.
37. OTTO, H. A.: The personal and family strength research projects: Some implications for the therapist. *Ment. Hyg., 48, 3:*439-450, 1964.
38. PALMER, M. F.: Studies in clinical techniques: II. Normalization of chewing, sucking and swallowing reflexes in cerebral palsy: A home program. *J. Speech Hearing Dis., 12:*415-418, 1947.
39. PALMER, M. F.: Speech disorders in cerebral palsy. In *Proceedings Cerebral Palsy Institute,* ed. by M. Abbott. New York, Assoc. for the Aid of Crippled Child., 1950, pp. 47-64.

40. PERLSTEIN, M. A.: Principles of therapy. In Symposium on Cerebral Palsy, ed. by F. L. Darley. Washington, D. C., Speech and Hearing Assoc. 1962, pp. 30-36.
41. PIAGET, J.: *The Language and Thought of the Child.* New York, Harcourt, Brace and Company, 1926.
42. PLOTKIN, W. H.: The usefulness of the electro-lung in modifying the breathing and speech of seven athetoid children and a respirometric study of their rest breathing patterns. Unpublished Ph.D. dissertation, Northwestern Univ., 1957.
43. REDL, F., and WINEMAN, D.: *Controls From Within.* Glencoe, Illinois, Free Press, 1952.
44. RUTHERFORD, B. R.: *Give Them a Chance to Talk.* Minneapolis, Burgess Publishing Company, 1956.
45. TOYNBEE, A.: Conditions of survival. *Saturday Review, XLVII:* 35-24-26, 193.
46. WESTLAKE, H.: Muscle training for cerebral palsied speech cases. *J. Speech Hearing Dis., 16:*103-109, 1951.
47. WESTLAKE, H.: *A System for Developing Speech with Cerebral Palsied Children.* Chicago, National Society for Crippled Children and Adults, Inc., 1951.
48. WESTLAKE, H. and RUTHERFORD, D.: *Speech Therapy for the Cerebral Palsied.* Chicago, National Society for Crippled Children and Adults, Inc., 1961.
49. WILSON, F. F.: A study of effect of a superimposed respiratory pattern on the breathing and speech of eight athetoid children. Unpublished Ph.D. Dissertation, Northwestern Univ., 1956.
50. WOLBERG, L. R.: *The Technique of Psychotherapy.* New York, Grune and Stratton, 1954.

Chapter VI

SHAPING ADEQUATE SPEECH, HEARING AND LANGUAGE BEHAVIOR

MERLIN J. MECHAM

IN TERMS OF REINFORCEMENT learning theories, behavior learning includes at least three primary aspects: (1) Conditioning discriminative stimuli, (2) differential reinforcement of successive approximations of the desired behavior and (3) chaining or sequencing behavioral patterns. These aspects cannot easily be isolated in behavioral training, nor can the complexities of communication be "unfolded or expanded" in each of these aspects separately. However, it is common to present procedures for discrimination and perceptive training separate from those used in developing more adequate production, and such is the case in the present chapter; a section is included regarding developmental patterns in communication. Thus the suggestions presented are arranged roughly in terms of the general principles of learning theory but application of any operant-conditioning techniques in therapy is left entirely to the option, industry and ingenuity of the therapist.

TRAINING IN AUDITORY PERCEPTION, DISCRIMINATION AND RECEPTIVE LANGUAGE INTEGRATION

Discrimination is said to have developed when a response has been extinguished in the presence of one stimulus and maintained in the presence of another.[7] Before discrimination can develop, sensory intake properties of the end organs must be normal or the stimuli must be modified. But the actual process of listening requires much more than mere reception and discrimination of stimuli. It involves highly complex analyses which are influenced by past experiences and which at the same moment become a part of the individual's experience. We shall discuss sensory reception, discrimination and receptive language integration, in that order, in terms of how they may be better utilized in the total listening process.

Sensory Acuity: Since a large number of cerebral palsied children suffer from hearing problems, it is felt that some of the general principles involved in hearing therapy should be discussed as applicable to cerebral palsied children. The CP child having a hearing loss needs all of the auditory care and training that any child having a hearing problem needs. Hearing losses may range, among hard-of-hearing children, from a mild loss of 15-25 decibels to medium and severe losses of 25-60 decibels. A child with an average loss of over 60 decibels would require the special attention accorded a deaf child.

In *auditory training,* the objective is to enable the child to make the best possible use of his residual hearing. This may be achieved both through amplification and through training the child to listen and discriminate more selectively and accurately.

Hearing aids are commonly used as the means of amplifying sound. The use of the hearing aid, however, may present problems with many of the more severely involved cerebral palsied children, especially the athetoids with excessive involuntary movement and those cerebral palsied children who fall frequently, e.g., the ataxics. Danger of damage to the ear of the child and to the hearing aid precludes the use of an aid with some children, but the child who is unable to wear an aid can be helped by amplifying the sounds "free field," by closing the distance between him and the sound source or by talking directly into the child's ear, etc. Sounds may also be fed to the child *via* padded ear phones and a special amplifying unit. Fitting the child with a hearing aid and training him to use it should be done only under the careful supervision of a competent audiologist.

If the listening intelligibility of the child is appreciably reduced, *speech reading* should accompany speech conservation and auditory training. O'Niell and Oyer[16] discuss the various methods of speech reading that have been developed and become popular down through its history. In order to teach speech reading, the therapist should have had reasonable training in speech reading methods and practice. In planning instruction in speech reading, the therapist should concern himself primarily with the careful selection of subject matter, with the development of the lesson materials, and with his manner of presenting the speech-reading materials to the child. Each speech-reading session should be devoted to a single topic. Lesson materials should be composed of whole units geared to the skill level of the child. Many children will be able to learn to speech-read more rapidly than others. Whole meaningful phrases should be presented together with rich visual and kinesthetic stimuli to help in cueing the child. Again, success experiences are important in motivating and building self-confidence in the child. The therapist should speak the materials to be speech-read in as interesting and normal a manner as possible, without grossly exaggerating lip movement and facial gesture. Informality will create a more normal and stimulating interpersonal association between the child and the therapist.

Speech-reading is apparently facilitated if action currents take place in the speech musculature of the reader. Learning to speech-read may be difficult if such currents do not take place. Since there are constant irregular discharges of action currents from the reciprocal speech synergists in the athetoid child, it is difficult to conceive that he could ever learn to speech-read or talk.[17] The same holds true for one whose tonicity is excessively increased, as in the spastic. It is therefore essential that the spastic or athetoid child remain in as relaxed a condition as possible before speech reading training is attempted.

Sensory Perception: While the answer to the question of how much can be done to correct perceptual aberrations in the brain injured is still quite theoretical, there is considerable clinical evidence which suggests that some degree of amelioration is possible. Procedures for improving the cerebral palsied child's perceptual abilities should be geared toward helping him proceed through steps of normal perceptual maturation. It is believed that perception, like any other activity, is largely learned. Not only does this learning involve visual, kinesthetic, and proprioceptive facilities, but it is also thought to be affected by the child's language concepts and emotional orientations.

Perception through the various sensory avenues has meaning

for the child only as it becomes associated with his life activities. As life experiences and activities of the average child expand and become more complex, so likewise do his perceptual skills. The child first perceives on the level of objects, their gross differences and relationships. With increased exposure and awareness, finer discriminations are made with respect to these objects and relationships. As the child matures, his perceptions encompass more abstract experiences and processes which have to do with not only the physical world around him, but also his interpersonal relationships with others.

Beginning with the more concrete level with the cerebral-palsied child, perceptual habilitation should be begun with as few variables as possible at first and then the number of variables is gradually increased as progress is made. Training in discrimination should be graduated from the most dissimilar to the finer differences.

The following list of areas for concrete perceptual training may be found helpful in increasing the child's perceptual readiness for communication skills. A given child may need help in one or any combination of these areas of perception.

1. Form or shape perception. *Matching* activities are undertaken first in which a given form or shape is constantly in the child's stimulus field. From a choice of two, three or four stimuli, he is to designate which is the same as the given form or shape. As the child becomes sucecssful in matching, he is encouraged to *copy* the given form or shape while it is within his stimulus field. As he becomes able to master this level of perceptual activity, he is encouraged to learn to *identify* the given form or shape wherever it is found in relation to a group of two, three, or four other forms in the stimulus field. As a final step in the concrete perceptual training for form or shape, the child is encouraged to become able to copy the original shape from *memory* after it has been removed from the stimulus field. Care should be taken that on each of the above levels of training, the number of variables are known and controlled. It is not unusual in early matching of forms (circle, square

and triangle — match the square) that children fail because one square varies in size from another.

2. Color perception. The activities of training should proceed through three of the graduated levels of difficulty mentioned above, i.e., *matching, identifying* and *memorizing.*

3. Color-form perception. Stages of activity for this are the same as number two above.

4. Letters. This is a more complex process of form perception and goes through the four training stages, *matching, copying identifying* and *memorizing.*

5. Auditory sound perception. This would proceed through the stages of *imitation, identification* and *memorization* (recall). Training in identification relies rather strongly on visual perceptive abilities, since the child listens to a sound and then selects the source of its origin out of several possibilities. Perception of gross sounds which are commonly heard, such as those found on the Utley training record, should be mastered before any training is given in auditory word or phonetic perception.

6. Sensory discriminations in other than visual or auditory fields, such as: (1) form discrimination by feel, (2) identification of objects by touch and (3) identification by taste, smell, proprioception, etc., should be given to children who have difficulty in these areas.

Brain-damaged children may be prone to listen and attend to those sensory stimuli which have little relevance to them or the immediate situation. For this reason, some training in selective listening and figure-ground organization is important. The child may spend a few minutes each period in listening for certain sounds made by the wind or birds or various animals, and so on.

Utley's record and the book of pictures entitled *What's Its Name?* have proved to be valuable in training for selective listening of brain damaged children.[22] It is recommended, however, that a stencil be used in the picture book which will allow only the picture in question to appear, especially if the child is very distractable, since several pictures appear on a page.

Music therapy has been felt by many to be a useful adjunct to physical therapy, speech therapy and psychotherapy in the treatment of the cerebral palsied. One author reported that he found that the emotional impact of music acted as a definite aid to the development of sensory perception and mental activity.[19] In remedial education, music is being used increasingly in special schools and centers in England and abroad and is beginning to attract interest in America.

Phonemic Discrimination: Even in children with apparently normal sensory acuity and perception, before any work on sound production is attempted many children need to be given extensive training in the recognition and discrimination of the sound or sounds to be produced. Auditory discrimination between speech sounds is but an extension of the grosser discrimination between words and phrases within which the sounds are found. Likewise, discrimination between words and phrases is an extension of the ability to discriminate between the gross sounds of one's environment. Zedler[26] suggests that it is unwise to ask a child to analyze a word until he is given experience in perceiving the word within the larger thought unit, the sentence. For this reason, it is suggested that listening-training be given in the form of interesting stories at first, in which the child can be taught first to listen for words within context and then, gradually, for the sounds within words.

An orientation program of gross listening is helpful before formal work on stories is given. This may include many listening and guessing games which can be devised to emphasize identification and discrimination of familiar sounds such as bells, whistles, animal sounds and people's voices. Such training creates a listening awareness in the child and increases his interest and attentiveness. It can later be used to help the child link the speech sounds being taught with sounds in his own environment; for example, the m sound can be linked with moo and may be labeled the "cow sound." Zedler's *Tommy Stories*,[26] containing a separate story for each consonant sound, are useful in the auditory training program for speech sounds. After a story has been read or told, games can be created utilizing words containing the speech sound and the story may be acted out by the children. Flannel-board games also can be used as follow-up activities in listening training. Records such as the following are helpful in auditory training for speech sounds:

1. Elaine Mikalson: *Speech Development Records for Children.* Pasadena, California, Pacific Records Company, AC-120.
2. Charles Van Riper: *Fun with Speech.* Wilmette, Ill., Encyclopedia Britannica Films, 1952.
3. Jean Utley: *What's Its Name?* Danville, Illinois, The Interstate Printers and Publishers, Inc., 1950.
4. John Tracy Clinic: *Learning to Listen.* Capitol Records Company.
5. J. J. Thompson: *Say and Sing.* Jeri Productions, 3212 Glendale Blvd., Los Angeles 39, California.
6. Louise B. Scott: *Talking Time.* St. Louis, Webster Publishing Company, Missouri.
7. Marie E. Roger: *Time to Relax.* Jeri Productions, 3212 Glendale Blvd., Los Angeles 39, California.

Careful analysis of the child's experiential background should be made before associative ear-training activities are introduced, and such activities should be geared to the experiential background and interest level of the children in the group.

Receptive Language Integration: The receptive aphasoid child needs to get stimulation with audible symbols in association with their visual counterparts. If the child recognizes visually, a process of conditioning may enable the child to gradually achieve auditory skills of recognition. An example of this is given below.

Have the following objects, either real or toy, in a box or in some other convenient place where they can be kept out of sight: car, house, table, chair, dishes, doll, wagon, dog, airplane, book, pencil, comb and apple. *First,* present these objects one at a time, in the child's visual field where he can see both your lips and the object and say their names several times. Say their names slowly but without exaggerated lip movement. Repeat this procedure until you feel the child is familiar with the names of the objects. *Second,* present the objects again two at a time. Name only one of them and bring the one named closer to the child, discarding the other into the box. Repeat this procedure several times. *Third,* place the objects before the child two at a time and name one, allowing the child to see the name being formed on your lips. Take his hand and help him passively pick up the object which you named. As you repeat this procedure over and over you will probably see the child's visual attention move to the object being named. If this is consistent, you may be sure that the child has learned to recognize the names of the objects on your lips and perhaps even auditorily. At this point, present the objects two at a time, naming one, and encourage the child to pick up the object which is named, by himself. *Fourth,* when he does this fairly consistently, place a card in front of your lips and repeat the same procedure; this time, return to the passive grasping stage, as in step three above, and proceed until he is consistently able to auditorily recognize the name of the object and actively pick it up. In order to make steps three and four more interesting, the child may be encouraged to place the objects which are named into a small, brightly colored box on the table, or, each time he is successful, give him a gold star in his personal scrapbook.

As the child becomes able to recognize the names of the objects listed above, additional familiar objects should be gradually added to the collection. With new objects, one must be careful to go through all four steps in order to establish the proper conditioning necessary to insure success experiences for the child. Objects and toys being used should be realistic, and brightly colored. One may refer to the list of nouns on the basic vocabulary list in Appendix A, in choosing additional toys and objects.

After the child learns to recoginze the names of several objects auditorily, the therapist should move into the more complex step of teaching him to recognize simple instructions. In addition to lip movement, the child should be able to observe simple pantomimes in association with simple sentences appropriate to the pantomimic action.[3] It is easier to begin with simple directions such as "Pick up the pencil," "Open the book," "Hand me the apple," "Put the toy chair in the box," etc. These should be repeated over and over, and if necessary, the child should be taken passively through the correct responses to the verbal commands and encouraged to take over the response as rapidly as he is able to do so successfully. As the child gradually masters appropriate responses to commands, as he sees them on the lips and in pantomime, the visual cues should be eliminated in order for the child to learn to replace them with auditory recognition. Again, the reduction of visual cueing should be done gradually enough to provide for more successful experiences than failures. It should not, however, be done so slowly that it produces boredom.

As the child achieves auditory recognition, he should be taken from the level of mere recognition and categorization to higher levels of understanding. Instructions may be introduced which are more abstract, yet closely related to the child's daily life activities, e.g., "The doll is hungry. Let's feed the doll." "Let's take the doll for a ride," etc.

Sensory avenues through which the child can most readily achieve and which are most appealing to the child should be used in sensory training and conditioning for language. This will facilitate the use of impaired avenues. Careful evaluation of the relative facility with which the child can utilize his various sensory avenues is an important prerequisite to planning therapy. A multisensory approach should be used as much as possible, but there is usually one or two sensory avenues which have the most basic appeal to the child and by which he can learn more readily.

In general, it is best to begin training in visual skills for reading after the child has acquired some skills in listening and speaking. For the child who has visual agnosia or aphasia, it is often profitable to utilize kinesthetic and tactile reinforcement in teaching words to be read. One child learned to recognize a word by tracing it with his finger. When the word was presented to him visually, he would begin to write it in the air and immediately the word was identified.

Sensory aphasoid children seem to require more time to absorb material and will respond more readily if a certain amount of intensification and repetition of sensory stimuli is given.[5] Discernment must be used, however, and repetition should not be used to the point of boredom or distraction. Auditory stimuli may be enlarged; for example, large pictures, blocks or toys rather than average sized ones should be used. Intensification of stimuli should be reduced to normal as therapy progresses.

INTEGRATION OF GENERAL BEHAVIOR

Throughout the literature, it has been stressed that a major problem of the brain injured child is his tendency toward bizarre behavior. This is a problem which the therapist must approach early from the standpoint of integration for communication. Non-adjustive behaviors frequently found which have a disintegrating effect upon communication include reduced motivation, abstracting ability, attentiveness, inhibition and adaptive flexibility and increased tendency toward catastrophic response.

Increasing Motivation and Abstracting Ability: Motivation is dependent partly upon the child's awareness of a need for improved skills and partly upon the child's anticipatory feelings that he can be successful. In group therapy with a little aid from the therapist, the children may develop an awareness of the comparative abilities and skills of the various members of the group. They may even develop competitive attitudes in their desires to be recognized and accepted by the group. Stimulation for competition and intergroup criticism should be controlled to the extent that it is constructive and motivating. If not controlled, it may add to the frustrations of certain children in the group and decrease their motivation and desire to participate in the group situation.

Training in classification and categorization in individual therapy will give the child an opportunity to think more abstractly about differences or relationships in terms of their categorical meaning in his life experiences. Many of the suggestions in the section on perceptual training may help the child in his abstracting ability; these may be extended into higher realms of abstraction as the child progresses in his perceptual achievements. Care should be taken not to deviate too far from the *practical* in training activities which are designed to aid in perception and abstract thinking. One therapist, for example, was fairly disappointed when he had spent considerable time teaching an aphasoid child to match, sort and classify different consonant letters and found the child completely unable to recognize these letters when they were observed within word symbols.

Increasing Attentiveness, Inhibition and Adaptive Flexibility: Distractibility, disinhibition and perseveration are commonly indicated as being accompaniments of brain damage.

Strauss and Lehtinen suggests that whenever a child is found to be *hyper-distractible,* i.e., engages in forced responses to outside stimuli, the environmental surroundings should be simplified to the point of eliminating or minimizing distracting visual and auditory stimuli other than the educational stimuli being used.[19] Myklebust suggests a small sound-*treated* room with no pictures.[15] (He suggests that an extensively sound-*proofed* room, however, has adverse effects on the aphasoid child.) The distance is gradually increased between the therapist and the child from two feet to four feet to six feet and finally to normal proximities. It should not be assumed that every CP child is pathologically inattentive. If a child is plain "bored" with the activities of the class, he may be very inattentive. In this case, it should not be the physical environment but rather the course activities which must be modified to meet the child's needs. Sometimes it is necessary to reassign the "bored" child to a class with children who are more stimulating and challenging.

Disinhibition is somewhat different from distractibility. The disinhibited child is distracted by stimuli which arise from within his own organism. He is impatient and unable to "wait" normally for expected events to occur. The child with this problem has abnormal difficulty in waiting activities and demands that expected events occur "now." The child who displays this type of behavior chronically should not be overly exposed to "expectancy" situations. He should not be told in advance what is going to happen, at least, not until he gradually learns to inhibit his impatience toward expected events.

Preservation is related to distractibility and disinhibition in that it prevents the child from voluntarily managing or reacting appropriately to those stimuli which help him attain a particular ultimate goal. The child who perseverates usually does so in situations which call for adaptations or responses which he is unable to make. He therefore persists in a previously successful behavior in an attempt to maintain equilibrium and unity with his environment.

The approach to helping the brain damaged child with one or more of these three problems is mainly an individual one. Myklebust suggests the principle of firmness with acceptance and without anger.[15] Sometimes the use of mild restraint is all that is necessary to help achieve behavioral integration.

One must learn to know the level of tolerance of the CP child. He may suffer from these symptoms only under certain emotional or stress situations, or he may suffer from them chronically. Stimulation should be within the limits of the child's ability to maintain behavioral integration. The child may either have to be moved from the immediate group environment into a modified environment, or the group will have to maintain a calm, quiet and orderly atmosphere. Gradually, stimulation should be increased to allow the child to increase his ability to react appropriately, but stimulation should always be within his range of successful responses.

Avoiding Catastrophic Responses: Adjustments needed to satisfy special physical needs imposed by the condition of cerebral palsy are often easily recognized and made available. We cannot always be as aware of special adjustments needed to adequately "tend to" abnormal emotional needs imposed also by the same handicap. It is easy, for example, to see that a child needs a special seating arrangement if he cannot remain upright in the sitting position. It is not so easy to see what adjustment is needed for a child who has extreme difficulty feeling a sense of inclusion or "sameness" in his environment and at the same time feeling a sense of importance and individuality for what he can do.

Eisenson states that if the catastrophic response occurs during the course of therapy, it signifies that the situational demands, at the moment, have exceeded the patient's ability to produce an appropriate and integrated response.[5] If and when it occurs, either a change of activity or reduced demand of performance is indicated. The therapist should avoid the catastrophic response in the child whenever possible. A watchful eye on precursive signs such as increased irritability, disinterest, sweating, severe headaches and dizziness, may cue the therapist as to dangers of the catastrophic response. Careful observations of areas and levels of activity in which the child meets with enough successes to increase motivation and reduce the need for abortive behavior will be of value to the therapist during the course of training. If failure to perform stems from distraction, disinhibition or inability to abstract, activities should be modified so as to minimize the effects of these disturbances. If failure has resulted from an intense arousal of autonomic "reaction syndrome," this effect can be countered by helping the child to feel *included, acceptable* and *important* in spite of his inabilities.

EXPRESSIVE LANGUAGE INTEGRATION

Since cerebral palsy and aphasia are nosological in origin, many cerebral palsied children also have difficulties in language learning and usage. Drill on individual sounds or letters is of little benefit to the brain injured child. The approach should be geared toward eliciting productive configurations of simple and concretely meaningful words.

Whole configurations should be taught first on words which the child can use to indicate his most urgent needs or satisfy his most important desires. Reasonably recognizable word configurations should be accepted and rewarded as actual speech. Berry and Eisenson exhort a functional and realistic approach to the aphasoid child in this respect.

> The first words a congenitally aphasic child is directly taught should . . . probably be related to food, to his own name, to the names of persons with whom he lives, and to the names of tools he must employ. Further vocabulary building should continue, at least in the early stages, along strictly functional lines in terms of the child's everyday life.

> In order to encourage all possible efforts at speech, a liberal attitude must be taken towards pronunciation. Any approximation of a verbal utterance should be accepted as correct. If the

child hears other children and adults whose pronunciations are correct, in time more accurate pronunciation may be expected. In any event, correction of pronunciation or of articulation should not be attempted until the habit of oral speech is clearly established and the desire for accurate speech is motivated. Too early an effort at correction may discourage attempts to speak. This, by all means, is to be avoided.[3]

Many concrete experiences in associating words and their meanings should be provided for these children. For example, as the word "ball" is said, the ball is touched by both child and therapist. If a real ball is available, it should be used rather than a picture. There are many realistic toys and objects that can be used in therapy, such as cars, toy animals, dolls, dishes, etc.

Frequently, the cerebral palsied finds it difficult to say phrases of any great length. Because they are made to feel hurried, some of them try to force through whole blocks of words without regard to phrasing. They talk as long as they can squeeze out words. Breathing training, counting and voice sustaining may be incorporated at the time that training is carried on in phrasing and sentence building. One helpful technique is to begin with short phrases and then gradually introduce longer ones. The ability of the child to say these in one breath can be charted and improvements can be noted as therapy progresses.

Nucleus Experiences: Most higher processes of language functioning depend upon transcortical integration of various sensory or receptive avenues. First among the steps to be taken in helping the child achieve transcortical integration is recall or initiation of verbal symbols according to the purposes for which these symbols were intended. A nucleus vocabulary involving concrete words should be employed in basic oral language development activities. The use of a nucleus vocabulary is essential in order that the child may be bombarded with stimulation of the vocabulary within his daily life activities. Although drill as such, in transcortical integration serves little or no purpose, frequent exposure to the symbolic stimuli which the child must learn to store and recall spontaneously, when the occasion arises, is very helpful. Regardless of type of communication being taught, short units of symbolic material should be used and their length should be increased gradually, as the child is able to handle them. Symbol association should proceed from the real object or situation to pictures of object or situation and then to the written or spoken vocabulary representing the object or situation.

A nucleus vocabulary, based on frequency of usage, will insure utilization of familiarity and frequent practice opportunity as aids in language development. (See Appendix A.)

Multiple meanings of words should be taught gradually in harmony with the child's experience background. The child may understand that a ball bounces, but he may not know what "throw the ball" means until he has experienced throwing the ball or seeing it thrown. There are many rich experiential activities which the teacher or therapist can employ for the purpose of enabling the child to give organization and meaning to the words and phrases which he is learning.

Cerebral palsied children who have transcortical difficulties are often limited in flexibility of extent and variety of oral language function. If a child learns to use a word in one phrase, for example, it is often necessary to work over and over with the use in a different phrase. Use of the same words in different phrases should not be done within the same experiential situation. In teaching the use of the word "hand," for example, one should not teach "I clap my hands" and then "I write with my hand" in the same therapy unit. "I clap my hands" will be more readily learned by the child in an experience which calls for clapping the hands. "I write with my hand" should wait until the writing period when writing is actually taking place. The same is true in the instance of teaching the use of "eyes" in the phrases "I blink my eyes," and "I read with my eyes."

Structured Experiences: Wherever possible, socialization should be incorporated into the training program early. The level of difficulty of social experiences should be geared to the ability of the child. There is usually a need for structured social experiences in the beginning so that social adequacies may be improved and success experiences increased.

As a rule, group singing and vocalizing activities are very

stimulating to young, delayed speakers. These activities may not only aid the cerebral palsied child in rhythm and voicing, but also in interpersonal and group activity which is so important in social speech. Group singing activities tend to reduce the conspicuousness of each member of the group; children who are shy or inhibited in respect to group participation are more likely at first to participate in this type of activity than in conversational speech. Some of the songs which cerebral palsied children seem to enjoy are "Row, Row, Row your Boat," "Jingle Bells," and "Old MacDonald Had A Farm." Here again, voicing of the tone should be of primary importance.

Nonspeaking children should not all be placed in the same group; there should be a mixture of speaking and nonspeaking children. This will give the children an opportunity to observe each other's problems and yet stimulate each other to achieve in various aspects of communication. Group activities should include situations which call for interpersonal relationships.

Since cerebral palsied children do not usually learn well through drill techniques, the use of these techniques is limited and should be confined to those situations where game spirit is one of high motivational level and propositionality is low. As a matter of fact, the greater the teacher's ingenuity in devising a game situation out of the perceptual and other types of "drill," the more effective the techniques will be, especially with young children.

Sequencing: Serial training has been found by many to be effective with a person who has poor transcortical integration.

> Children . . . with amnesia involvements need certain types of approaches which are called round-about techniques. These are methods permitting the damaged cortex to function on the tasks at hand.
>
> Such devices actually have produced language functions that would be impossible otherwise; similarly with learning. For example, facts placed in definite series can be learned when they *cannot* be learned in isolated sequence. During the war we learned a great deal about this kind of work with veterans.
>
> In teaching numbers, let us suppose a child cannot recognize a seven when he sees it. He can recognize a six, but he is

frustrated when seven is presented. If this is placed in a series, he can learn 1 2 3 4 5 6 7 8 9 10 much more easily than he can learn 7. And the child can be shown to know 7 if he is taught to count it internally to himself . . . If he is asked, "What's this?" he will reply, "seven." If one inquires how he arrived at that answer, he always says, "ten, nine, eight, seven," which we did not teach him. As a result, we were able to decrease by two or three months the time spent with our veterans, just by reversing these series when we arrived at fluency. It is an interesting phenomenon. This illustration from numbers, of course, is only an example of many other devices in other portions of the language process.[18]

Jargon speech and jumbled grammar can likewise be approached through techniques of serial training. Expression of things learned in sequence such as months, days, numbers, the alphabet and swearing, often become what is termed "automatic" speech. Nursery rhymes, poems and finger plays are a higher form of serial learning and grammatical structure is one of the highest forms of serial training. In the English language, for example, a word never begins with *ts,* the verb almost always follows the subject, the subject usually comes at the beginning of a sentence and adjectives almost always precede a noun. These arrangements are learned early in a child's speech and become automatic. It is not until we get into late grade school or high school that we learn the *why* of these arrangements. They are learned serially and just become an automatic part of one's expression.

Modality Association: In gaining transcortical integration, the child must receive associative cues from all sensory avenues possible in order to learn to recognize and understand the greater symbolic meaning of heard or written symbols. Concrete experiences may be of great assistance in association with very abstract symbols of language. The aphasoid child may readily be cued for the appropriate recall of the word "dog," for example, if, when he learns the word, he associates it through conditioning with the memory of the feel of the hair of the dog or the sight of the dog. He may be more able to recall a word if he has learned, through the process of conditioning, what it felt like to trace the word with his finger or pencil.

As a child gets older, language building in writing and reading may facilitate development in oral language and vice versa. When skill in writing and printing is developed, he should write the word as it is said and as the object or picture of the object is shown. The Dolch picture cards and later the Dolch sight phrase cards[4] are good, not only for the development of reading, but also for oral language development.

If the child has more difficulty in transcortical integration in one aspect of communication, for example, letter reversals in writing, it may be helpful to work on serial training of the word configurations auditorily, then to combine writing of the words simultaneously with auditory stimulation.

A rather detailed program of *associative* training has been developed by McGinnis[11] which may be helpful to cerebral-palsied aphasoid children, even though the method was developed primarily as a result of working with children in a school for the deaf. The *associative method* centers primarily around the following seven steps of training.[10]

1. The child produces in sequence from the written form the sounds composing a noun.
2. He matches the picture, of the object represented by this word, to the written form of the word.
3. He copies the word and articulates each sound as he writes the letter (s) for it.
4. He repeats the word aloud after watching the teacher say it and matches the object or picture to the written form of the word. (While the child watches, the teacher articulates the word aloud, first broken into a sequence of separate sounds, then smoothed into the word unit. The child articulates the word in the same manner. Then he identifies the picture or object named by the word and says the word again, both broken and connected) .
5. The child says the name of the object from memory. (The teacher presents pictures representing nouns already taught and the child must say the name of the object without the aid of lipreading, auditory pattern, or written form.)
6. The child writes the word for the object from memory, articulating each sound as he writes the letter (s) for it.
7. The child repeats the word spoken into his ear and matches

the picture to the written form of the word. The procedure here is identical to that in Step Four except that the child does not watch the teacher; he receives an auditory pattern only. The auditory step is usually last, in order that the child may have as much experience as possible with the word before he is called upon to recognize it auditorily.

The specific procedures outlined in these seven steps constitute only the initial portion of the entire program for aphasic children.

Although the clinical usefulness of this method has been reported by Monsees,[14] Kleffner[10] and others, its application to cerebral palsied children with aphasoid symptoms has not been fully explored.

DEVELOPMENTAL SCHEDULES

In the normal population, maturity is seen to evolve through various stages from complete dependence to semi-independence and independence. Most authorities agree to the usefulness of developmental schedules in evaluation and appraisal but little stress has been placed upon the facilitative effects of developmental sequencing of response patterns in the development of language and speech. An understanding and use of developmental sequencing in therapy helps one to capitalize upon the current "maturational readiness" stage and helps minimize any ill effects stemming from "premature" teaching.

When materials are given to the cerebral palsied child before he is ready for them, he is apt to experience repeated failure in the situation. Such failures are not conducive to the development of a desire for communicating. It is very important for the child to establish and maintain a high degree of confidence in the response situation. A systematic program of language geared to the child's readiness will help accomplish this end. There is no reason why the cerebral palsied child cannot learn to communicate with pleasure providing the experiences in communicating are not frustrating to him and providing he achieves a mental age for communication experiences. In many cases, however, certain aspects of the communication process have been presented to the child long before he is ready and a negativistic attitude toward communicating has been the natural result.⁹

Intellectual Capacity and Oral Communication: In general, oral communication follows certain maturational levels which correspond to advances in mental age. Therapeutic efforts in aiding the severely retarded cerebral palsied child in the development of oral communication should reflect the importance of keeping the child's level of communicative achievement abreast with his general level of social competence. A profile of various aspects of development can be used as an index to guide one in planning a program of speech and listening training for a particular child. If the child's achievement in the communication area is considerably below his achievements in other areas on a developmental scale, there is definite need for detailed evaluation and therapeutic planning.

It has been fairly well established that children normally begin to talk at approximately twelve to fourteen months — *mental* age. Various levels of social competence are achieved in oral communication as the mental age of the child increases. Before the child's second birthday, he uses short sentences and has a vocabulary of twenty-five words or more. This is not mere "parrot talk;" it is propositional. He also uses a great deal of jargon which may continue for three or four additional years. Auditory-memory span increases from two to six digits between the ages of two and one-half and ten years. This increase is accompanied by an increase in ability to turn out progressively longer words and longer sentences. Toward the end of his second year, the child is using up to three words per sentence but sentences at this age, for the most part, are functionally complete and grammatically incomplete. Before his third birthday he gives a simple account of his experiences and tells stories that can be understood. During the third year the child begins using pronouns and plurals and verbalizes his toilet needs. By the end of the fourth or the beginning of the fifth year he begins learning nursery rhymes, names of colors, names of coins and he relates fanciful tales. By the time he is eight years of age, he is able to count to one-hundred, retell familiar stories and can define meanings of several words. By this time he still uses around 20 per cent simple sentences, 40 per cent functionally complete but structurally incomplete sentences and about 40 per cent of his sentences are complex, compound or contain prepositional phrases.[13] By his tenth year, the "average" child retells jokes and short stories, uses the telephone independently and produces all of his speech sounds correctly. He uses the telephone in a practical way; he looks up the number, makes the call and carries on sensible, purposeful conversation. He does not usually attempt long distance calls at this age, however; any automatic dialing may be difficult unless he has had special help in the mastery of dialing. By sixteen years he is able to use intelligent and persuasive speech in the discussion of current events and politics.

If oral language development is significantly delayed in respect to the rest of the child's developmental profile, play activities and auditory stimulation should incorporate a vocabulary which is meaningful and needed by the child in his activities of daily living. The vocabulary used should be concrete, should have inherently the greatest potential for being intelligible, and should be used jointly by therapist, teacher and parent to insure ample stimulating experiences for the child. The nucleus vocabulary should form the basic tool for oral language training.

Principles underlying the acquisition of language are closely related to those involved in acquisition of concepts and values derived directly from experience. "As the concept forms in our minds we learn symbols for the whole concept and for each of its parts or qualities and these symbols become part of the concept also."[24]

Thus, if labels are not supplied in experience-settings, but are taught separately and apart from experience, such as in the case of drill lists, they have little functional meaning or practical value.[12]

IMPROVEMENT IN SPEECH PRODUCTION

The training program for shaping more adequate communicative behavior can be greatly facilitated by utilization of the principles of differential reinforcement and successive approximations. Since methods of reinforcement and criteria-changes necessary for successive approximations depend upon the individual child and his total productive and/or "need contingencies," only general circumstances which have proved clinically conducive to development of more adequate patterns of expression can be described. Application of differential reinforcement and adjustment of criteria for successive approximations toward "goal" performance is left to the initiative of the clinician.

Voice Training: The voice can be analyzed into its various components, including pitch, intensity, duration and quality. It is possible to take each individual component and analyze it to see whether it is deficient. It is also possible, even in the cerebral palsied, to work with each defective component individually. However, with a severely involved cerebral palsied child, segmentation of various voice characteristics is difficult. Evans[6] has stressed the importance of working with the speech behavior of these children as a whole. The voice of an athetoid child may be perfectly normal if he assumes one particular posture, and completely absent if he assumes another.

It is frequently noticed that the athetoid may have periods of abnormal tension in the larynx, especially under periods of emotional or situational stress. The voice may be jerky, may crack, or may fail completely in the middle of the word or sentence, and, as a result, speech comes out in a series of isolated words or incomplete word groups.

Efforts should be concentrated on relaxation. Ability to relax is a skill; development and mastery of the skill can result only from repeated experience. Various methods of achieving relaxation have been discussed in a previous portion of this text. Once an atmosphere of relaxation has been created, speech and voice are produced in accompaniment with relaxation.

Cerebral palsied children as a group tend to be "silent children."[23] Reward should be given for the slightest effort to produce voiced sounds. Positive reaction to adult attention is prominent in very young children. If the child's repeated efforts are well rewarded, the various vocal skills may become easy and natural for him. Success-experiences in successive approximations may create in him a desire to do more vocalizing.

The imitation of animal sounds such as "moo," "bow-bow," "baa," and "maa," which are composed of the bilabial sounds and vowels is good for very young children because these sounds are easy to produce. Unless the cerebral palsied child has a serious neuromuscular difficulty which prevents voice production, he will respond readily and vocally to these animal imitations because they are concrete and interesting. Toys, representing the various animals, should be used in conjunction with these "imitation" games.

Variation in the voice is usually a major problem for the cerebral palsied child, especially the spastic. Greater variation may be obtained if the child is made conscious of (and is able to discriminate auditorily) gross variations. He may be taught to produce the voice alternately very softly and then very loudly in order to hear and feel differences in intensity. An older child may be taught to "go up the stairs" with the pitch of his voice, by first starting with only two "stairs" — the very bottom one and the very top one — then one by one, the number of "stairs" or pitch steps in between can be increased. The "stairway" may then be made smooth like a slippery-slide and the voice may learn to slide up one side and down the other. Gross variations in voice may be incorporated into fingerplays or other speech activities; and then, gradually, finer variations can be mastered as greater skill is developed.

It must not be forgotten that during all of these voice procedures, the child has to overcome muscular, perceptual and emotional imbalances which his condition has imposed upon him. Developing anything near normal speech for him is a tremendous task, although it rarely even challenges a normal child. It is not easy for him to make adjustments in a great many areas of competition with a world which is much more physically, perceptually and emotionally intact than he. For this reason, it is wise to help the child adjust his goals within the realms of his endurance. He must learn to content himself with *efficiency* of function rather than *all* or *none* perfection.

Improvement of Articulation and Intelligibility: A thorough articulation analysis of the child who has a functional language usage will reveal defective sounds and the ways in which they are defective. Substitutions, distortions or omission of sounds from the child's speech, whether organic or functional in nature, will have an effect upon the intelligibility of his speech.

One of the first and foremost objectives in correcting the articulation errors of the CP child is the establishment of correct motor patterns for production. The fact that the child has articulatory errors is evidence that he already has a functional vocabulary upon which to work. Movements designed to correct distortions will perhaps be compensatory in nature. Those designed to correct substitutions and omissions will be quite new and different from old patterns they are designed to replace.

Berry and Eisenson stress the importance of coordination of respiration with phonation and articulation in speech. Production of the p sound can be obtained by having the child "puff" out the flame of a candle with the explosion of the lips. The b sound can be added by having the child turn on the "motor" (voice) as he does the p sound. Other plosive sounds can be taught by a modification of the same procedure with the use of different parts of the articulation mechanism. Fricatives and sibilants are taught by restricting the exhaled breath stream in various ways in accordance with the conventional methods of teaching speech sounds.

In the correction of articulatory errors, the therapist is confronted with the problems of which sounds to work with first, and which method will be most effective in obtaining the correct sound. If the child needs success experiences and motivation, it may be wise to teach first the sounds easiest for him to produce. These will vary from one child to another, depending upon the nature of his muscular involvement and the motor patterns already established. As has been mentioned previously, those sounds requiring tongue-tip and fine, coordinated movements are, in most cases, the most difficult to produce. The p, b, and m sounds are perhaps the easiest sounds for most children to make. Other sounds, in order of chronological development and possibly in order of their difficulty of production are $h, w, t, d, n, k, g, j, f, v,$ $\int, t\int, d_3, 3, \int, s, z, hu, r, \theta$ and the blends.

There are certain sounds which tend to deter intelligibility. Attention to the production of these may be minimized in therapy and those which enhance intelligibility considered of prime importance. The sounds and their effect on intelligibility are described in Chapter II.

The following methods have been used in establishing correct patterns of sound production after appropriate ear training has been given. They are described in the order of frequency of their use in most clinical situations. It is suggested that if the first method is not effective, the second one should be resorted to, and if that one fails to produce the desired results, the third one should be attempted. With cerebral palsied children who need a multisensory approach, a combination of the three methods may be useful.

The *stimulus-response method* incorporates visual, auditory and kinesthetic avenues of stimulation. In this approach, the therapist and children seat themselves in front of a mirror, and the therapist repeatedly stimulates the children with the sound to be worked on. The children are encouraged to listen to it and watch the therapist's face as it is produced. They then, in turn, try to reproduce the same sound. The success of this method depends upon many things, among which are the attentiveness and cooperative attitude of the children as well as the degree to which their visual, auditory and kinesthetic senses are intact. Defective function of the visual and auditory feedback mechanisms may render the stimulus-response method ineffective. However, it should be given adequate trial. Some children, those with special problems, may respond to these activities better in individual therapy sessions.

The *phonetic-placement* method may incorporate the techniques employed in the stimulus-response method but has, in addition, verbal instructions by the therapist on how to place the articulation mechanism. Such suggestions as the following are often used: "Watch the tongue! Keep the tongue back. Close the lips tightly and then make them explode." It is most important not to confuse the children by calling too much attention to the parts of the anatomy or using technical or complicated phonetic placement descriptions.[8]

The moto-kinesthetic method, developed by Young, may be used in conjunction with either of the above methods or by itself. This method is particularly effective if the touch and kinesthetic mechanisms are intact. It often holds the attention and concentration of the brain-damaged children where other avenues of sensory stimulation do not. The method employs manipulation of the articulation and other speech musculatures through the actual movements of speech production. Complete directions on the application and use of the techniques involved can be found in Young and Hawk's book, *Moto-Kinesthetic Speech Training.*[25]

Suggestions and techniques for teaching the production of sounds have been elaborated in various sources. As the sounds are developed and incorporated into words, the words should automatically become more intelligible.

One of the most difficult tasks with cerebral palsied children is to get them to habituate the sounds in their everyday speech activity. As soon as a child is able to produce the given sound in isolation successfully and easily, he is ready to incorporate it into a broader speech pattern, such as a word or phrase. Speech situations should be carefully structured so that the child's response is limited to the speech pattern containing the new sound.[1]

The technique described below, for increasing the intelligibility of words, has been used with teenagers and young adults and found helpful by the author. The same procedures can be adapted for use with younger children. Usually, the cerebral palsied person can say a word more correctly when he makes a concentrated effort to say it in isolation and to get all the sounds correct than when he says it in connected discourse. To attack this problem, the therapist picks out and notes the sounds of the most unintelligible words in the person's speech over several sample speech periods. The sounds affecting the intelligibility of the word (defective sounds) are worked on by direct therapy and are labeled "cues" in intelligibility. Whenever the person is talking or reading aloud and the therapist hears one of these words being badly produced, the therapist says "huh." By prior agreement, the word "huh" sets off a series of activities on the part of the patient. First, the person thinks of the word that he has just said; second, he recalls the "cues" in the word, and finally, he repeats the word, making special effort to produce all the "cues" in the word correctly.

To insure that he is working with a nucleus vocabulary that is best suited to the person, the therapist uses only words found in the areas of familiarity which are most suited for the person. A vocabulary which has been worked out for cerebral palsied individuals can be found in Appendix A. A nucleus vocabulary such as this has a decided advantage in that it tends to reduce the number of alternative choices in the reception of a message, thus reducing chances of error in reception and increasing speaking intelligibility.

Carry-over (resulting from this particular technique) from isolated word production to production in spontaneous speech has been fairly encouraging, and intelligibility has been improved in most patients. From time to time, the cerebral palsied person, in the course of normal conversation, hears the word "huh" from other people and, if conditioned well enough, will recall and go through the steps of picking up "cues" in the words which were not understood. A further goal in this kind of therapy is to create an anticipation on the part of the cerebral palsied person of the words which give him the most "trouble," so that he may keep cues well in mind during the original production of the word in discourse. This will eliminate unpleasant and time-consuming word repetition in his attempts to become better understood.

REFERENCES

1. BACKUS, O., and BEASLEY, J.: *Speech Therapy with Children.* Boston, Houghton-Mifflin Company, 1951.
2. BERKO, M. J.: Some factors in the perceptual deviations of cerebral palsied children. *Cereb. Palsy Rev., 15:* 2:3-4, 14, 1954.
3. BERRY, M. F., and EISENSON, J.: *Speech Disorders.* New York, Appleton-Century-Crofts, Inc., 1956.
4. DOLCH, E. W.: *Picture-Word Cards and Sight Phrase Cards.* Champaign, 111, Gerrard Press.

5. Eisenson, J.: Therapeutic problems and approaches with aphasic adults. In *Handbook of Speech Pathology,* ed. by L. E. Travis. New York, Appleton-Century-Crofts, Inc., 1957.

6. Evans, M. F.: Children with cerebral palsy. In *Speech Problems of Children,* ed. by W. Johnson. New York, Grune and Stratton, 1950, pp. 158-189.

7. Holland, J. G., and Skinner, B. F.: *The Analysis of Behavior.* New York, McGraw-Hill Book Company, Inc., 1961.

8. Irwin, R. B.: *Speech and Hearing Therapy.* New York, Prentice-Hall, Inc., 1953.

9. Kirk, S., and Johnson, G. O.: *Educating the Retarded Child.* New York, Houghton, Mifflin Co., 1951.

10. Kleffner, F. R.: Aphasia and other language deficiencies in children. In *Speech and Language Therapy with the Brain-Damaged Child,* ed. by W. T. Daley. Washington, D. C., Catholic University of America Press, 1962.

11. McGinnis, M. A. *Aphasic Children.* Washington, D. C., Alexander Graham Bell Assn. for the Deaf, Inc., 1963.

12. Mecham, M. J.: Developmental schedules of oral-aural language as an aid to the teacher of the mentally retarded. *Ment. Retard. 1,* Dec., 1963.

13. Miller, G. A.: *Language and Communication.* New York, McGraw-Hill Book Company, Inc., 1951.

14. Monsees, E. K.: Aphasia in Children. *Volta Rev.,* October, 1958.

15. Myklebust, H. R.: Aphasia in children — diagnosis and training. In *Handbook of Speech Pathology,* ed. by L. E. Travis. New York, Appleton-Century-Crofts, Inc., 1957.

16. O'Neill, J. J., and Oyer, H. J.: *Visual Communication for the Hard of Hearing.* Englewood Cliffs, N. J., Prentice-Hall, Inc., 1961.

17. Palmer, M. F.: Speech disorders in cerebral palsy. *Nerv. Child, 8:* 193-202, 1949.

18. Palmer, M. F.: Speech disorders in cerebral palsy. In *Proceedings Cerebral Palsy Institute,* ed. by M. Abbott. New York, Assoc. for the Aid of Crippled Children, 1950, pp. 47-64.

19. Palmer, M. F.: Personal communication.

20. Rutherford, B. R.: *Give Them a Chance to Talk.* Minneapolis, Burgess Publishing Company, 1956.

21. Strauss, A. A., and Lehtinen, L. E.: *Psychopathology and Education of the Brain-injured Child.* New York, Grune and Stratton, 1947.

22. UTLEY, J.: *What's Its Name?* Danville, Ill., The Interstate Printers and Publishers, Inc., 1950.
23. WESTLAKE, H.: *A System for Developing Speech with Cerebral Palsied Children.* Chicago, National Society for Crippled Children and Adults, Inc., 1951.
24. WOODRUFF, A. D.: *Basic Concepts of Teaching.* San Francisco, Chandler Publishing Co., 1961.
25. YOUNG, E. H., and HAWK, S. S.: *Moto-kinesthetic Speech Training.* Stanford, Stanford Univ. Press, 1955.
26. ZEDLER, E. Y.: *Listening for Speech Sounds.* New York, Doubleday.

Chapter VII

PSYCHOLOGICAL AND LINGUISTIC IMPLICATIONS OF BRAIN DAMAGE IN CHILDREN

MARTIN J. BERKO

As WE SEE IT, the clinician working with brain-damaged children faces a rather unusual dilemma: he must be able to recognize and react appropriately to the fact that the child with whom he is working is a "special child" and at the same time, a *child* whose needs for security, acceptance, success, *frustration tolerance* and *discipline* are essentially the same as they are for any child. All too often in the clinical situation, we have observed orientations which tend to ignore one or the other of the "two faces" of the brain-damaged child. In the earlier years, before the heavy outflow of publications dealing with the symptomatology of childhood brain damage, the motto of most clinics seemed to be "Tender Loving Care." This was a philosophy that implied that the child's main needs were security, absence of pressure and protection from the cruelties of the normal world. To some extent, this was a good philosophy in that it kept the child relatively happy while he was in school, eased some of the parental problems in caring for the child, and, largely as an incidental dividend, sometimes managed to teach him something. This orientation persists in many minor clinics today, particularly in those with well-meaning, but minimally trained or nonprofessional personnel.

However, with the recent outpouring of literature dealing with "brain injury syndromes," "perceptual problems," etc., and with the concurrent "raising of professional standards" among clinical personnel, there has been an ever-increasing awareness that "Tender Loving Care" was not enough. This, in the majority of cases, resulted in the attempt to incorporate modern clinical knowledge in clinical practice, and has to a great extent improved the habilitative proficiency of most disciplines. Unfortunately, in many instances, however, this vastly improved knowledge of the

144

brain damaged child as a clinical entity has tended to dull the clinician's awareness of the child as a *child*. Various clinicians and various general clinical orientations are guilty of this to differing extents, and in differing ways. At the individual level the major problem often lies in the clinician's preoccupation with the child's symptoms, to the detriment of his establishment of a warm interpersonal relationship with the child. At the clinical organization level, we often see the development of "programs" which are so intent upon the tasks of reducing hyperactivity, establishing neural "dominance," or whatever the focal concern of the clinic happens to be, that they establish routines which force the child to function in situational structures which are completely divorced from anything the child must learn to tolerate in the real world, and which often impose upon the families of such children "home programs" and "regimes" and "practice sessions" which are completely unrealistic in terms of time demands and behavioral restrictions placed upon parents and siblings, and which, in turn, result in family tensions, increased parental guilt feelings when they find themselves unable to meet the demands of "the program," and, perhaps most unfortunate, an *enhancement* of the child's role as the "outsider," or the "burden," or as the focal point of friction within the total dynamics of the family structure. Regardless of the theoretical efficacy of such programs in the approach to the special clinical needs of the child, they are detrimental and self-defeating when they ignore the child *as a child,* or when they disregard the role of the child within his family.

The foregoing should not be regarded as questioning the value of modern clinical techniques, nor as an attack upon family responsibility or family participation in habilitative programs. These are both good and *necessary* if any sort of actual habilitative achievement is to be expected. What we are arguing for here is simply the paramount necessity of the realization that the brain-damaged child is, first of all, a *child,* and that therapeutic programs have value only to the extent that they enhance his ability to live as other children do. Any approach which isolates a child from his potential environment, which does not assist him in making social and emotional adjustments to his family and to his peer groups, any program which fails to supply the child with information and social experience which is related to life in the normal world, is of little functional value in terms of total life adjustment even if it is successful in achieving certain circumscribed goals, such as locomotion, speech, or the reduction of hyperactivity. This is perhaps a seemingly radical, "far out" concept. Yet we have seen too many a child whose newly-acquired ability to walk simply *increased* his potential social liability because he lacked awareness of physical dangers and now had to be watched constantly lest he walk into traffic or tumble down stairs. We have seen children who had developed "huge vocabularies" in terms of their ability to name objects or pictures, but who were unable to answer simple questions, such as "What do you wear on your head?" because of the speech clinician's failure to realize that teaching picture-naming was not tantamount to teaching *language concepts* and that the child's ability to associate verbal and pictorial symbols was not by itself a socially meaningful behavior nor one which helped him to understand the world about him. In short then, we view the function of the habilitative program, in all its various aspects and modalities, as a broadly-based, coordinated attempt to bring the child into realistic contact with his social and cultural environment, and to provide him with the linguistic, informational, social and emotional tools which will enable him to interact with the social and cultural environment to whatever extent his general potentialities will eventually permit.

THE GENERALIZED BRAIN DAMAGE SYNDROME

We view the task of the habilitative program as an attempt to provide the brain-damaged child with the linguistic, informational, social and emotional tools which will optimize his ability to cope with the world in which he lives. In the case of the motor-impaired brain-damaged child, the physical tools must be added. However, we view cerebral palsy as a subdivision of the general brain damage syndrome, differentiated from it only because the motoric disability is the most obvious or most immediately identifiable in severe cases. This makes the habilitative task different from that presented by the aphasic child, or the organic mental retardate, but only in terms of the degree of emphasis which must be placed on the motoric aspects of the total problem.

Attempts to define the brain damaged child in terms of a group of "signs" and "symptoms" have met with only limited success. The pioneering work of Doll,[19] Palmer,[65] Strauss and Lehtinen,[81,82] Werner[92] and many others[13,17,18,27] has very strongly indicated that brain damaged children display a certain community of behavioral aberrations which tend to identify these children as a diagnostic group. However, as Birch[12] suggests, the logic underlying the derivation of the variously suggested lists of symptoms is not entirely satisfactory. Some of the signs were derived from observations of adults with known brain damage. Some were derived from the behavior of post-traumatic, brain-injured children, and some from postencephalitic children with *presumed* brain damage. Since these behaviors were in many ways similar to those with known brain damage, brain damage was presumed to be the causal factor. This, in itself, is perhaps logically defensible, albeit not rigorously scientific. However, the difficulty with this approach was further compounded in later years when various other authors derived further "signs of brain damage" from the behavior of "childhood aphasics" and other aberrant children whose brain damage was either merely *inferred* on the basis of predisposing prenatal and neonatal factors, such as toxic pregnancies, high fevers during infancy and infantile bumps on the head which may or may not have caused brain damage. This compounding of inferential data eventually leads, in some instances, to the derivation of "brain-damage signs" from the observation of children for whom there was no actual evidence of brain damage other than the fact that their behavior was similar to the behavior of other children who were *presumed* to have brain damage. The logical absurdity of this approach is obvious. Furthermore, as Birch indicates, medical evidence that children exhibiting the behaviors ascribed to brain damage *actually* do have brain damage is poor; and conversely, many children with clear-cut neurologic or anatomic evidence of brain damage *do not* exhibit the behaviors presumably characteristic of such damage.

As a result of the foregoing history, we must question the appropriateness of the label "brain damaged" as applied to the etiologically heterogeneous group of children to whom this term is applied. At least, if we are to continue to use this term, we should be aware that "brain damage" is simply a *behaviorally descriptive term* and not one which legitimately describes a physiologic entity. It must be recognized that when we speak of brain-damaged children, we are speaking of a group of children having similar *behavioral* characteristics, and who respond in similar ways to numerous specialized, educational and therapeutic approaches. Some of these children, such as those with cerebral palsy, and those suffering from palpable or provable brain lesions arising from severe head trauma, surgical removal of tumors, etc., are *known* to be brain damaged. Others, such as the "childhood aphasics," the "minimally brain injured," etc., are simply *inferred* to be brain damaged because they exhibit behaviors similar to those *known* to have brain damage. With these restrictions in mind, we shall proceed to outline a behavioral symptomatology which we shall use as a means of identifying the group of children under consideration. We want to emphasize, however, even at the risk of redundancy, that these symptoms, while occurring in many children with known brain damage, are not, as we view them, necessarily *caused* by brain damage, nor do they in any way *prove* the existence of brain damage. Their usefulness lies simply in the fact that *they define a behavioral population who have needs for specialized educative and therapeutic techniques,* and clinical failure to recognize the presence of these "signs" will result in generally poor, if not damaging, therapeutic programming.

In the presentation of the following list of "clinical signs" we are borrowing quite freely from Palmer, Strauss and Lehtinen and many others. However, the particular selection, description, and interpretation of these signs are our own, and drawn from direct clinical observation of several thousands of these children over a period of twelve years. In the main, these signs are those commonly exhibited by children with cerebral palsy and other known brain damage, but are also noted in the so-called "childhood aphasics" and "minimally brain injured."

Attention Defects: "Brain-damaged" children present a wide variety of attention disturbances. *Hyperirritability of attention* refers to the difficulty displayed by many of these children in selecting one stimulus complex out of a broader field of stimuli. In our view, this represents a sort of "generalized figure-ground confusion" in which normally "closed" or "good" stimulus information is not automatically isolated. This is basically a problem of inadequate stimulus selection, in which the "ground" aspects of the stimulus complex tend to impinge upon the "figure" aspects. This deficiency in stimulus-selective behavior results in what has generally been referred to as "distractibility." Children with this difficulty find it difficult to restrict their attention to any given set of stimuli. They live in a confusing world in which the sound of the teacher's voice is no more compelling or focalizing than the sounds of the traffic passing in the street outside, or in which the writing on the blackboard is just another of the hundreds of things they see, each demanding attention, each detracting from the degree of concentration available for the performance of the task which should be the center of attention.

In our experience, we have found that hyperirritable attention is to a very considerable extent, trainable. The Cruickshank[16] approach represents an early insight into the trainability of attention. Limiting the availability of distracting stimuli to the child by clearing the room of all objects which are not central to the task presented, plain and unadorned clothing of clinicians, soundproofing of classrooms to eliminate extraneous noise, special lighting of circumscribed work areas, etc., all are excellent means of eliminating distracting influences and restricting attention to specific tasks. This is generally a necessary first step in establishing focus of attention, but it is only a first step.

The child in the normal world does not function in situations in which stimuli are presented in majestic isolation. The child must actually be given the opportunity to *learn* to select stimuli out of heterogenous matrices, to attend to specific stimulus events in spite of potentially confabulatory and disruptive background inputs. What we advocate here, is to *begin* with the "stimulus isolation" approach which is basic to the establishment of specific attention. However, this approach must be followed up by attempts to gradually increase the child's tolerance for background or noncentral information inputs. Once specific attention is established for single, focalized inputs, potentially distracting stimuli should gradually be brought into the situation while the interaction between student and clinician serves as a vehicle for maintaining attention upon the task at hand. The key here is motivation: the task of the clinician is to keep the child so busy, and so interested in what he is doing, that his own involvement in the situation serves as a "screen" for extraneous stimuli. Admittedly, this is no easy task for the clinician; but it can be achieved if the clinician can project himself into the situation with such vibrancy and such force of presence that the child's interest is maintained at a high level. As must be obvious by now, we regard attention as a form of *behavior* which is stimulus-controlled, and, as are all behaviors, modifiable and trainable. The simplest level of modification is related to control of stimulus inputs. More difficult is the modification of behavior through the teaching of stimulus-selectivity and discrimination. Yet, this later step must be achieved if any meaningful and lasting modification of attention pattern is to be achieved.

In addition to the general problem of hyperirritable attention, there are a number of more specialized forms of attention deficits. A commonly-recognized one is *general hyperactivity*. The specific manifestations of general hyperactivity are of course to a great degree controlled by the child's physical potentialities. The wheelchair-bound cerebral palsied person is not going to gallop about the room, whereas some of the less physically disabled children may. However, regardless of physical condition of the child, there is one pervasive factor: this hyperactivity is not something the child *wants* to do. This is a compulsively driven behavior which is often as distressing to the child as it is to the clinician. The mobile child who runs around the room and can't seem to stick to anything for more than a moment or two, or the wheelchair-bound child who must fidget and squirm and grab at everything in sight, is not "misbehaving": he is displaying an extreme stress reaction to his inability to achieve selective focus of attention.

Control of hyperactivity is achieved in much the same manner as control of hyperirritable attention: limitation of distracting influences, limitation of the actual amount of physical space available for exploration, etc. In many cases, very hyperactive children actually seem to function more adequately under direct physical restraint. This statement may disturb some of our "free-expression oriented" clinicians, but there is sound logic behind this. In the first place, the maximally hyperactive child is not really "expressing" anything other than his complete frustration with his lack of ability to organize his environment. The imposition of physical boundaries, whether by placing the child in a very small and barren room, or by holding him in your lap, or even by tying him to his chair with a broad restraining strap around his waist, effectively imposes "ego-space" and body-image boundary limitations which simplify the stimulus selection process for the child, give him a sense of physical security and thereby reduces his tendencies toward hyperactivity. Once again, however, restraint and stimulus deprivation are effective only as first steps in the reduction of hyperactivity. Once circumscribed focus of attention is achieved, it is necessary to gradually expand the child's tolerance for more loosely structured situations while *retaining* the basic "ego-boundary" and body image orientations. In good clinical practice, this is the point at which highly "space-structured" motor activity games are instituted. These activities should begin at extremely simple levels: Activities such as simply having the child "march" around the perimeter of a barren room, trailing his hand along the wall as he goes, and learning to "stop" and "go" at a given signal, or very simple games in which clinician and child roll a ball back and forth while standing at opposite ends of the room are excellent beginning activities at this level.

The clinician should understand that we are interested neither in teaching the child to march, nor in teaching him to bowl. What we are doing is giving the child simple, "perceptually uncluttered" experience in functioning within a spatially-ordered environment. And, as Held[41] and Reisen[70] have clearly demonstrated, the development of spatial cognizance, and the ability to function appropriately within the boundaries of spatially-ordered environments, are highly dependent upon experiential motor interaction with spatial factors. These reports are also supportative of Berko's[7] 1954 postulation that many of the "visual perceptual defects" noted in severe cases of cerebral palsy had their basis in inadequate or bizarre motor experience, and were not necessarily related to neural lesions in any of the visual systems. But this is part of another tale.

There is a third type of attention defect which we shall call *drifting attention*. Although this is noted in some brain-damaged children, it is also noted in children with severe emotional disturbances, in the child with severe endogenous mental retardation and in many chronically-ill children of various etiologies. Its general manifestation is that of weak or brief focus of attention. However, unlike the distractible or the hyperactive child, the child with drifting attention is one who is *not* hyperreactive to stimuli. Characteristically, this is the child who seems to lack the ability to follow through with a simple activity. He may, for an example, pick up an object, such as a form from a formboard, and then simply hold it in his hand, or let it drop to the floor, while he seems to "drift off into his own little world." Children displaying this type of behavior should always be singled out for careful diagnostic study: They may be epileptoid. They may be severely autistic, or very grossly mentally deficient; and a full analysis of medical, intellectual and emotional status should be begun as soon as this type of behavior is noted as a consistent pattern.

We have chosen to discuss attention disturbances first because we believe that the amelioration of this area of difficulty is a basic prerequisite to the general success of all habilitative programs. In our own clinical experience in the observation of several thousand cases, we have generally noted that many of the other "signs" of brain damage which a child appears to have when first examined, particularly some of the so-called "perceptual difficulties" and "abstracting problems" seem to disappear once stable patterns of attention are established. Obviously, one might argue that our reasoning is faulty, and that the improvement of perceptual and abstracting processes is what *permits* improvement in the organization of attention. This may be true at later stages of therapy; but on the basis of our own experience, the establishment of stable habits of specific attention must occur before any real improvement is made in other areas.

Deviant Propositionality: For the purpose of this discussion, we shall define a "proposition" as a conscious, sequentially planned, goal-directed act. This is contrasted with an act which is either "nonpropositional," or of "lowered propositional value," either because it is not goal-directed, or because its execution has, through habit and practice, become more or less "automatized," and now requires little or no conscious sequential planning and guidance. Another characteristic of a proposition is that its "level of propositionality" is to a considerable extent controlled by situational and environmental factors which are somewhat independent of practice effects and are closely related to what the layman calls "situational pressure." A few brief examples will help to clarify this entire concept: A common greeting one receives from a casual acquaintance hurrying along a college hallway is "How are you?" and the usual response is "Fine" ("O. K." "Great," or something to that effect). One generally responds in this manner even if he has a cold, a toothache, or a sore foot. "Fine," in this case, is an "automatized response" and has no propositional value. If, on the other hand, one were to respond, "I have a headache and my foot hurts," this would be "propositional speech." Propositionality is a characteristic of motor acts other than speech, also. The average boy of five or six years rather painstakingly learns the steps of making a single knot, then two bows, then making the second knot of the two bows. The adult reader of this book, simply ties his shoe, and unless the shoestring breaks probably pays little or no conscious attention to *how* this is done. To the five-year-old, the tying of the shoe is a highly propositional act. To the reader, this same act has little or no propositionality. One aspect of propositionality, then, is the level of integration, and level of attention required for the performance of the act.

A second aspect of propositionality is related to the *situational context* in which the act is performed; and many activities which are performed at varying levels of *non*propositionality in some contexts may become highly propositional in others. The average man pays little or no conscious attention to lip, tongue and jaw movements while speaking. Yet, if he were suddenly requested to address a large audience, he would very likely find that the act of speaking is one which now requires careful attention and a good deal of conscious control of lip movements, etc., in order to achieve the type of speech which he deems necessary to convey his message to the audience. Similarly, the experienced automobile driver rather unconsciously goes through the relatively complex routine of inserting the key into the ignition switch, shifting into neutral, depressing the starter. . . . etc., *ad infinitum*. The experienced driver does these things almost without awareness of the execution of a highly sequentialized performance. Yet, if he were being examined for a chauffeur's license, he might suddenly become extremely aware of each step, and might even become rather flustered, and might even find his hand trembling slightly as he inserts the key, or he might forget to release the handbrake.

Now, accepting Goldstein's concept of brain damage resulting in generalized impairment of integrative and organizational capacity,[32] the implications of propositional deviations for the training of the brain injured child become obvious. Due to their motor, perceptual and attention problems, as well as to a long social history of failure, negative social reactions etc., complex behaviors for the brain damaged child tend to "automatize" more slowly than for the average child. The child with cerebral palsy, with stiff or shaking hands, may *never* completely "automize" the act of tying his shoes. Moreover, even though he may learn to do this fairly well when he is alone, he may fumble or fail at it if he is being hurried or watched. This slowness in the automatization of behavior often pervades all of the activities of the brain-damaged child. Returning to our normal speaker who has difficulty speaking before an audience, consider the child who has actual motor difficulties in speaking: How much more difficult when *he* has to speak to a group of people!

Actually, deviant propositionality can be a pervasive force in *all* of the activities of the brain-damaged child. Propositional effect on the organization of behavior is a *normal* phenomenon. *Deviant* propositionality refers to the marked exaggeration of this effect in the brain-damaged child. Clinicians called upon to demonstrate a child's ability to perform some task, such as performing a few simple arithmetic problems, or reciting a short poem are often surprised that the child is now completely unable to do something which he had been doing very easily in therapy for some time. In our clinical experience, we have found no "sure cure" for deviant propositionality. For the retention of circumscribed, short-term tasks, "overlearning" seems to be an effective way to guarantee that the task will be accessible to the child even when he is under pressure. However, a *generalized* reduction of propositional deviance appears to be a long term process which is also dependent upon a general reduction of the child's overall communicative difficulties. In fact, deviant propositionality seems to be one of the most persistent of all the "signs" of the brain damage syndrome. What is most commonly noted is that, in a long term clinical program, the *level* of propositional activity can be very markedly raised, but that, for a given behavioral modality, the susceptibility of propositional organization to situational pressures is difficult to reduce.

The implications of deviant propositionality in the training situation are extremely complex, and are perhaps most conveniently discussed in conjunction with the consideration of another behavioral entity, *catastrophic behavior*.

Catastrophic Behavior: Palmer[65,66] and various other early writers tended to define catastrophic behavior, as did the present writer, as a specific or unitary sign. We can no longer accept this viewpoint, and must look upon catastrophic behavior as a loosely defined cluster of nonadaptive reactions to situational stress. Before going into this, we must briefly return to a consideration of deviant propositionality. We have defined the *level* of propositionality, inferentially at least, in terms of the level of cortical integration at which a given act is organized. Nonpropositional or "automatized" behaviors are relatively "reflexive" in terms of organizational or integrative levels. As propositionality is increased, progressively higher levels of cortical integration are called into play, and the greater is the conscious ego involved in the performance of the act. Here we see the development of a "vicous circle" for the child: His nervous system is so organized that there is relatively little automatization of behavior. Thus he is forced to function at relatively high propositional levels much of the time. This continuous stress on the child's higher-order integrative abilities forces him, if he wants to interact with his environment, to be continually "alert," in a "readiness state" and highly ego-involved in the totality of his behavior. Thus, almost every demand for action and every new situation is a potential threat to the child's security. Now, we have already stated that one aspect of propositionality is its responsiveness to situational stresses, and that performances well within the level of a given child's integrative abilities in one situation may become propositionally beyond the child's integrative capacities when situational pressures increase his ego-involvement in the act. Catastrophic behavior occurs when situational demands raise the propositionality of an act to such a point that the child is no longer able to react to it in an adaptive manner. It is at this point where we see extreme manifestations of the *affective* disturbances generally associated with brain damage.

One of the most readily recognized affect disturbances commonly associated with brain damage is *emotional lability and reactive inappropriateness*. The brain-damaged child is one who laughs readily, cries easily and is prone to temper outbursts. These reactive behaviors tend at times to be inappropriate, both in terms of mode of expression and in terms of duration and intensity. This appears to be a rather generalized affect disturbance, not always related to propositional stress; but propositional stress appears to intensify the manifestation of the disturbance to a very marked degree. Under relatively low propositional levels, the child with emotional lability and reactive inappropriateness is the one who "gets the giggles" in the classroom, who cries in response to a slight reprimand, who may strike out physically at classmates in response to an unintentional shove or some friendly teasing. Inappropriate reactive expression is also manifested at times in terms of the actual expression of the "wrong" emotion.

The child may begin to laugh uncontrollably in response to a reprimand, or cry when he is happy. The clinician's awareness of patterns of this type is extremely important if usable clinician-child interactions are to be maintained. The child who laughs when telling about his mother's serious illness is not necessarily "schizoid." The child who bursts into tears while the teacher reads him an amusing story is not necessarily demonstrating a lack of comprehension.

By "catastrophic reaction" we mean an intensive display of emotional lability or reactive inappropriateness which is manifested when the child is faced with a situation which is beyond his capacity for propositional integration. The reaction may have any of a great variety of forms. The most readily recognized and dramatic form is the overt emotional outburst: screaming, crying, physical attacks on the clinician, throwing objects about the room, etc. This is a signal that, for one reason or another, the child has been pushed into a level of propositional stress which he is totally incapable of handling, that his level of frustration tolerance has been surpassed, and that something in the classroom or in the speech lesson, or in the organization of the play period is completely "wrong" for this child. All clinicians should be aware that catastrophic reactions are somewhat like "built-in programming error detectors." In general, they signal the fact that the propositionality of the situation is too high. They also may at times indicate other types of clinical errors. These will be discussed later in this chapter.

Fortunately, in the child's "built-in programming error detection system" there are a number of "warning signals," and if the clinician is alert to these, he need not wait for "all hell to break loose" before he realizes that something is going wrong. One of these signals is *vasomotor lability*. Depending on the site of the neurological lesion (and on whether or not there actually is a lesion), vasomotor lability need not *always* indicate a potential catastrophic reaction. According to Grinker,[34] vasomotor lability may be a clinical sign of some forms of subcortical damage. Vasomotor lability refers to a generalized instability of the child's homeostatic and vegetative functions. In the clinical situation, this may be manifested in any of a number of ways which are immediately observable to the clinician: sudden perspiration or "claminess" of the skin, sudden "flushing" and/or pallor and highly unstable respiratory patterns and pulse rates are the surface signs of vasomotor lability. In some children, these are fairly consistent patterns: that is, they are "normal" for them. In other children, these patterns are the "early warning signals" of a catastrophic reaction. Thus, once again, we see, at least by inference, the overwhelming necessity that the clinician *know the child* and know *how to look* at a child. Simply knowing the textbook symptomatology is not enough. The adequate clinician is one who knows "what it says in the books," knows intimately the behavior range of the *particular* child with whom he is working, and has the capacity to make correct inferences about what is happening in the immediate situation by correlating the two sources of information.

Another "warning signal" is *perseveration.* Again, this is a sign with a number of ramifications, some relating to catastrophic behavior and some relating to various intellectual and emotional problems. We shall attempt to sort these out later; but meanwhile let us consider the relationship between perseveration and catastrophic reactions. Perseveration refers to the child's tendency to repeat a given behavioral reaction unit when such a reaction is no longer appropriate in relation to the natural progression of input stimuli or situational demands. For example a child may be giving adequate responses to a simple picture-naming task, until he comes to a picture of a cup, which he names correctly. Following this, however, each successive picture is also called "cup." Or, a child may be required to draw a row of alternate geometric patterns, such as X O X O X O X O. Instead he produces: X O X O O O O O. With a little checking, the clinician may discover that the child has no difficulty in *differentiating* between "X" and "O," nor has he any difficulty in *counting,* or in *drawing;* he simply has difficulty in making rapid and appropriate shifts in response integration; and this is what is generally referred to as perseveration. Once again, the identification of the behavior depends upon the clinician's awareness of perseveration as a clinical sign, and also on his ability to *know how to look* at what the child is doing. Is he just being stubborn? Is he not able to perceive the difference between "X" and "O?" Can he perceive the difference, but have a visual-motor difficulty which prevents him from consistently drawing them differently? Is he *perseverating?* The knowledgeable clinician is immediately aware of all these reasons why a child may produce X O X O O O O, instead of X O X O X O X O, and immediately runs a variety of brief, perhaps impromptu tests to determine what is happening.

We have, then, increased emotional lability, vasomotor lability and perseveration as signals associated with the onset of a catastrophic reaction pattern: and we know that the catastrophic reaction is an indication that the child has been forced into a situation with which he cannot cope in an adaptive manner; or, in other words, a situation in which the level of propositionality is too high. Obviously, the appropriate clinical reaction is to "lower the level of propositionality." But what does this mean? Basically, it means a restructuring of the communicative or interactional situation in such a manner that the child is able to cope with it. We have already discussed the problem of attention defects and means by which a reorganization of various environmental factors can improve attention and reduce hyperactivity. The problem we now must face is: What are the behavioral factors contributing to situational propositionality, and how are these factors dealt with in the clinical situation? Within the general heading of the "brain injury syndrome," this brings us to a consideration of linguistic and general intellective functions.

Linguistic and General Intellective Functions: Once again we feel that we must restate our position on this matter. What we are about to discuss here are a group of *behavioral characteristics.* These characteristics are found in motorically normal children who display attention disorders, deviant propositionality and catastrophic tendencies. They are also noted in children displaying the aforementioned signs, and who also have cerebral palsy or other clearly demonstrable evidence of injury to the central nervous system. Some of these signs are also reported by Head,[37] Nielson[63] and Goldstein,[32,33] in their classic studies of adults with medically proven brain pathology. We must reiterate, however, that the questions of a direct causal relationship between brain injury and these signs, and of the appropriateness of the use of these signs as diagnostic indicators of brain damage where such signs occur in the absence of direct physiological evidence of brain damage, are to a large degree, unsettled. Nevertheless, the fact that these behaviors are often noted in cerebral palsy and in other forms of provable brain damage, and the fact that they are responsive to a given set of clinical techniques and educative procedures, seem to justify their inclusion in the description of a diagnostic pattern which, by history and common usage has come to be generally known as the "brain injury syndrome."

Among the linguistic and general intellective characteristics commonly ascribed to brain damaged children, *deviant abstracting and categorizing processes* hold a position of importance. In our own clinical experience, this seems to be the most pervasive, most generalized and intellectually most limiting factor. Classical descriptions of this aberration are to be found in the clinical reports of Goldstein.[33] In our own clinical experience these patterns are noted repeatedly both in the cerebral palsied child, and in the nonmortorically handicapped child with presumptive brain damage. One of the most common difficulties in this area appears to be extreme concreteness and rigidity in concept formation. Here we find children whose concepts of "alike" and "different" tend to be circumscribed by an inability to linguistically handle more than one categorical concept at a time, and by difficulty in differentiation of the central and the incidental characteristics of objects. Thus, a big ball and a small ball have no common characteristics for such a child, and the fact that, regardless of size, both are *balls* is a concept which must be *taught*. This lack of generalization seems to be one of the major blocks to learning in these children. The fact that, in their linguistic development, generalized categorizational concepts develop slowly, and sometimes only with a great deal of specialized teaching is probably the central factor which isolates the brain-damaged child from his environment, and makes the world a confusing, disorganized place when he must attempt to deal with it on a symbolic linguistic level. Added to this concretization and lack of generalization, we also note a tendency for abnormal, deviant processes of abstraction and generalization. In most cases this takes the form of improper identification of the definitive characteristics of objects and situations, or, perhaps more accurately in some cases, difficulty in selecting the *most* definitive categorizational factor out of a hierarchical order of possible classifications. This is not to be confused with the simple low-level abstractions of the very young child, but is rather a bizarre, linguistically confused process. Any young child may tell you that horses and cows are alike because they both have legs; and a considerable degree of linguistic sophistication must develop before the generic concept "animals" is evoked by a question regarding the similarity of horses and cows. But when horses and cows are alike because "They are not people," or because "We don't have any at home," there is an obvious pathology in concept formation.

The differentiation between pathology and simple low developmental levels is a difficult task, and one which generally should be left to the clinical psychologist whose knowledge of normal developmental sequences is inherent in his training. However, a general knowledge of developmental sequences is a tremendous asset to any clinician working with handicapped children. In any intelligently organized clinical program, normal developmental levels and sequences must define the educative and therapeutic goals, and it is difficult to see how any realistic planning or systematic treatment organization can be done without a thorough knowledge of what may be expected from the normal child. (Obviously, all classroom teachers cannot be clinical or developmental psychologists; but they should all know enough about normal developmental sequences to be able to see the futility of trying to teach reading to a child who lacks simple form discrimination or the ability to differentiate vertical from horizontal lines.)

Deviant patterns of abstraction and categorization are not limited to verbalized classificatory functions and higher-order abstractions. In severe cases, bizarre patterns may be noted at relatively simple levels. Inability to synthesize relatively low-level concepts are readily demonstrated with some of the Goldstein-Scheerer-Weigl Tests of Abstract and Concrete Thinking.[33] One subtest presents a set of geometric forms of equal size across their maximal dimensions. The set consists of three basic forms: triangle, circle and square. Each form is duplicated in four primary colors: red, yellow, green and blue. The examiner asks the child being tested to arrange the forms in "groups that go together." Normal responses include either grouping on the basis of form (all circles in one group, squares in the next and triangles in the third) ; or groupings might just as readily be made on the basis of colors — all reds, yellows, blues and greens. When the first normal repsonse is obtained, the examiner then asks "Can you group them in some other way?" If the form grouping response has been obtained first, the child can readily *shift* to a color grouping response. The child demonstrating deviant patterns of abstraction and categorization may often given very aberrant responses to this type of test. In the extreme cases, we may find that the child is completely unable to cope with the situation in any manner, and may either produce a disorganized, "senseless" reaction, or he may react catastrophically. This type of reaction, again, is one which calls for immediate investigative procedures on the part of the clinician. A mark on a score sheet which indicates a failure is not sufficient for an adequate diagnosis. The clinician has the additional responsibility of determining the processes which contributed to the "failure." As with the question of perserveration, we are again faced with the necessity of taking appropriate measures which will enable us to correctly identify the meaning of the noted reaction. The fact that the Color-Form Test is a test of abstracting and categorizing function, plus the fact that the child has "failed" the test, does not, in any way, justify a *prima facia* conclusion that abstracting and categorizing difficulties were the basis of the failure. Once again, the results of any specific test must be correlated with other information about the child before any conclusions can be made regarding the *meaning* of the test response.

When faced with a catastrophic reaction, or a "senseless" reaction to any test procedure, the clinician's next step is to find out exactly what has happened in terms of the child's linguistic and general intellectual functions. Our point here, is that tests are diagnostic *tools;* they are *not* diagnoses. A diagnostic procedure is one which simply uses "test results" as the raw materials from which diagnostic evaluations are constructed. Returning to the child who produced aberrant responses on the Color-Form Test, an analysis of what has actually transpired can be achieved only if the clinician analyses the various components of the performance on a molecular basis. The quickest way to do this is to break the task down into its various elemental functions. Can the child match forms? Can he match colors? Does he match colors and forms easily, but become confused only when color and form are presented *simultaneously,* and he must choose one basis of selection? It is only when this "triad" of hierachical functions are separated out, that one can validly infer that a "senseless" or a catastrophic reaction to a test of abstracting and categorizing functions implies that the child actually does have difficulties in abstraction and categorization.

Discounting "complete failures" on tests of abstraction and categorization, the brain-damaged child may produce a number of other types of aberrant reactions which are more readily identifiable as being indicative of difficulty with abstract and/or categorizing behavior. One common type of reaction indicative of abstracting and categorizing difficulty is inability to maintain a particular "set" for a simple abstracting task. For example, in the Color-Form Test, the child may begin to sort the objects on the basis of color, but will then shift to a form orientation before completing the color series. The converse of this pattern may also occur. On the same test, one often notes an *inability* to shift from one orientation to another when such shifting *is* appropriate. In other words, the child may perform adequately in grouping the test objects either on the basis of color or of form; but, once having completed one orientation, becomes confused or disorganized when asked, "Can you group them in some other way?" In other words, then, subtended under the generalized heading of deviant abstracting and categorizing processes, is the more specific reaction type, which we have termed *conceptual rigidity.*

It is important to be able to differentiate conceptual rigidity from simple perseveration, although, admittedly, such differentiation is sometimes rather tenuous. Simple perseveration is generally a reaction to propositional pressures and may be manifested in any of a large variety of situations. The factor which identifies it as simple perseveration is that what is observed is simply a repetition of a previous behavior *unit*: The child identifies a picture of a cup with the word "cup," then continues to respond with the word "cup" to the succeeding pictures in a series. Conceptual rigidity, on the other hand, refers specifically to an inability or great difficulty in *shifting* between categorizing or general abstracting orientations.

Another type of abstracting difficulty commonly noted in brain-injured children is that of making abstractions or categorizations which are "'correct" inasmuch as they do show some systematization or integration of stimulus factors, but the factors selected are not those which would be commonly recognized as the prime determinants for abstracting or categorizational systems. Early, we gave the example of the child who responds "They are not people," to a question regarding the similarity of horses and cows. This is the type of reaction presently under consideration. Note, first of all, that this is not entirely a "wrong" answer: Most assuredly, horses and cows are *not people*. However, the quality of being "not people," is not the quality which, in our culture, most readily determines the similarity between horses and cows. It must also be noted that this type of aberration of intellectual functioning may be manifested at a number of levels, and in a variety of ways. One common "model" of problems of this type may be found in a child's reactions to the Color-sorting subtest of the previously mentioned Goldstein-Scheerer-Weigel Tests. This subtest presents the task of sorting a large number of skeins of colored yarns. The yarns vary both in hue and in saturation. That is, there are reds, yellows, blues, greens, and a number of other colors. Then, for each color, there are skeins with varying degrees of color intensity, or saturation, ranging from pale pastels to very vivid hues. When a normal child is requested to "Put these in groups that belong together," his first response is, generally, to make groupings of the more saturated reds, blues, browns, greens, etc. Then, if he is urged to "Find some more that go with these groups," the normal child usually proceeds to extend or "generalize" his original selection patterns down through the less saturated colors of the same hue. In the brain damaged child, a rather different pattern of selection is often seen. The brain-damaged child may make his original selection, not on the basis of hue, but rather on the basis of *saturation*. Thus, greens, browns, blues, etc., may be lumped together, with the degree of saturation or intensity of color being the primary basis of selection. Note that this is not a "senseless" or "wrong" selection. It is, rather, *a selection based upon a factor not commonly treated as a primary basis of selection.*

In other cases, the brain-damaged child may actually make his first selection on the basis of *hue,* picking a *few* heavily-saturated reds, blues, etc. However, when asked to "Find some more that go with these," he becomes puzzled and frustrated, or he may react catastrophically. In other words, what we see here is primary selection on a proper basis, but inability, or poor ability to *generalize.*

In summary, the abstracting and categorizing difficulties take a number of forms which are readily recognizable, but are not in any sense mutually exclusive. At the most severe level, we find virtually no abstracting or categorizing functions. At this level, however, performance failures yield only inferential data concerning the child's abstract functioning, and cannot identify the child as one who has a specific abstracting and categorizing problem. These data are relatively meaningless unless they are correlated with other factors known about the child. At a slightly higher level, we find children who can make simple selections, such as grouping on the basis of color or form, but the selection process breaks down when the child must select from a somewhat more complex stimulus. In other words, the child can make normal selections on the basis of color or form, but only when a very limited choice of colors or forms are offered. Another type of abstracting and categorizing dysfunction is one in which the child makes *meaningful* selections, but makes them on the basis of factors which are not *generally* used or recognized as the prime determinants of abstractive or categorizational processes. Finally, there is a type of dysfunction in which "normal" *initial* selections are made, but there is marked restriction in the *generalizing* aspect of the abstracting function.

From the foregoing descriptions, the ramifications of abstracting and categorizing dysfunctions upon the general learning processes should be self-evident, and should not require intensive discussion. Briefly, however, it may be stated that abstracting and categorizing dysfunctions represent severe impediments to normal patterns of information acquisition for the child. The child with this type of difficulty has a *severe* learning problem in terms of "normal" educative processes. Procedures for overcoming abstracting and categorizing difficulties are lengthy and complex, and fall largely within the realm of the Educational Specialist. From our own standpoint, we view problems of abstraction and categorization as being basically *linguistic* problems; and, in keeping with this, further feel that the correction of abstracting and categorizing problems is fundamentally a matter of specialized teaching of linguistic concepts. Such teaching must have its basis in a general analysis of the child's linguistic functions. In this chapter, we shall present no "formula" or "outline" for such an analysis. On the basis of our own experience, we feel that it is essential that the clinician make some sort of systematic attempt to find out what the child's abstracting and categorizing processes are in terms of general linguistic functions. An excellent outline for the evaluation of such functions has been published by McCarthy.[57] Another test of this type has been published by Irwin and Hammil.[48] These procedures test the subjects' abilities to understand abstract language and to abstract and categorize meanings and references, and to make generalizations. Such outlines and tests are very helpful, although not absolutely necessary in the evaluation of the child's linguistic functions. The clinician with insight should be able to prepare his own outline. What we are basically interested in is determining whether or not a child has the basic linguistic concepts around which abstracting and categorizing functions can be built. For example, does he have basic quantitative concepts, such as "more and less?" Does he sense any sort of relationship or parallelism between "more and less" and "bigger and smaller?" Is he aware of numbers as indicators of specific quantities rather than just as rote numerals? Does he have basic concepts of comparison, such as "same," "different," "bigger," "smaller" . . . . and so forth throughout an extensive list of concepts? We stated earlier that we would not present any extensive list, "outline," or "formula" for evaluation of linguistic concepts in this chapter; but the foregoing are the types of materials which must be considered. Concepts such as these are the basic "raw materials" around which later abstracting and categorizing concepts will be built.

The overall aim of the "language development approach" in the amelioration of abstracting and categorizing difficulties is to give the child the linguistic tools needed in the handling of abstract concepts. Specifically *how* this may be achieved depends highly upon the training and predelictions of the clinician. In terms of our own orientations, the basic process here must be one which is somewhat of a "mixture" of educative and psychotherapeutic procedures aimed at helping the child *interpret his environment within a "normal" psycholinguistic framework.* Much of this work can be accomplished within a clinical "play therapy" or "structured play" approach. Here, the clinician can set up controlled situations which lead the child into psychosocial interactions within a normal linguistic framework; and here, linguistic concepts basic to normal processes of abstraction and categorization can be presented to the child in relatively concrete interactional situations which are readily comprehensible to him at his own level of functioning. The exact methods and procedures will depend both upon the general level of the child's linguistic ability, and upon the specific skills of the clinician. Therefore, the following must be regarded only as a rather *generalized model* of the approach to these problems, and *not* as a specific outline of procedures.

The first step is to determine the general level of linguistic functioning. As previously stated, this can be achieved either through the application of formalized evaluative procedures, such as those suggested by McCarthy and Kirk, Irwin and Hammil, etc., or the advanced clinician can set up his own evaluative procedures. Now suppose simply for the sake of exposition, we find that a child is relatively "abnormal" in all of the abstracting and categorizing functions previously described. What can we do? One very effective approach is to use a variety of classifiable toys and miniature objects around which verbalized play situations can be built. This is generally a very slow and tedious process for the clinician; but its ultimate effectiveness is its own justification. If the child is functioning on a *very* low linguistic level, the first stages of therapy may necessarily consist mainly of training in object recognition and word association. Here objects and pictures are used merely as stimuli to elicit simple identification responses: Show me a cow. Where is the horse? and so on. Where errors are made, they are corrected for the child, but not in manners likely to increase the propositionality of the situation unduly. When errors in identification occur, we have found it best simply to *correct* the child's error, but not to specifically *label* the error. In other words, when the child points to a figure of a cow in response to "Where is the horse?" the clinician *does not* say "No, that's a cow." He simply ignores the incorrect response, points to the horse, and says "There's the horse." If this type of correction is done consistently, the child will gradually begin to eliminate his own errors, and the level of proper identification will improve. Soon after the identification stage is begun, *generalization* should be intrdouced. One need not wait until any specific "vocabulary level" is achieved. As soon as the child has a few (perhaps half a dozen) nouns reliably within his grasp, the process of generalization should commence. Here we might use several different objects within each grouping. That is, varied *colors, sizes,* and *postures,* of horses, cows, cats, dogs, etc. The child is asked to pick out *all* of the horses, dogs, etc., and as he does the clinician interjects descriptive or qualifying concepts: "This horse is *sitting.*" "That is a *black horse.*" "This is a *big* horse" . . . . and so forth throughout each group of objects. During this phase, the noun vocabulary should continue to be extended through the addition of more and more objects to be identified.

When a fairly large number of nouns have been generalized, processes of *conceptual generalization* should be introduced. Here we refer to the transformation of previously-introduced qualifying words into abstracting or categorizing functions. For example, all of the horses, cows, cats, and dogs, are lumped together; and the child is now asked to "Give me all the *black* animals." "Show me all the *little* animals" . . . . and so forth. Note that we are taking a rather huge forward stride at this stage by introducing the fact that descriptive terms may also function as categories, and also that objects having specific names (cow, cat, dog) can also be identified under one *generalized* term, "animals." For the child with severe problems in abstraction and categorization, this huge forward step may be confusing and traumatic; and, at this point, it may be necessary to "back-track" somewhat, in order to reinforce and stabilize earlier steps.

As the child's general language comprehension and ability to abstract and categorize improves and stabilizes at the foregoing lower levels, we move into the more abstract classificatory concepts, teaching that horses, dogs, and cows are all *animals,* that hats, shoes, shirts and pants are all clothing, and so forth. There is no formula by which one can predict how many of these terms must be separately and specifically taught, nor how long they must be taught. What we are doing is giving the child the basic tools which will enable him to cope with his environment at a symbolic level. If he is not too severely retarded, and if he receives sufficient exposure to his environment, he will, after this initial training, begin to "sort things out for himself." That is, once these types of conceptual processes are established, they will begin to "take root" and generalize, so that the child will, as the normal child does, begin to make a normal abstraction and categorization on the basis of what he sees and hears in his environment, so that "everything" need not be specifically taught to him. Constant "checking" and constant reinforcement of basic concepts should be part of the training process; but, given a good start, the rapidity with which many of these children begin to acquire normal linguistic concepts "on their own" is sometimes rather amazing.

With the growth of the child's general ability to deal with linguistic concepts, more advanced (higher-order) abstracting "games" should be introduced. By the time this level is reached, the use of miniature objects, while possibly helpful at times, should no longer be necessary. Here we can rely on pictures; and, at still more advanced stages, it is desirable to try to get along without props of any sort. In the final analysis, the use of *words alone* as meaningful symbols through which the environment can be comprehended and manipulated is our ultimate goal. The objects and the pictures are used as "stepping stones" and "props" on the way to this goal; but true symbolic language is achieved only when such props are no longer needed. This is a tremendously important clinical point: the use of these props considerably simplifies the clinician's task at the early stages of training; but prolonged reliance on the use of "toys" or "visual games" may be self defeating. Of course, the question of "how long is too long" is a rather nebulous one, depending to a great extent upon what the clinician is trying to achieve. However, a good rule of thumb is that the more adept and facile the child becomes in the use of words, the less use should be made of visual props.

The more advanced abstracting "games" should really approximate some of the "verbal comprehension subtests" in the standard psychometric testing devices. Here, we are not interested only in the child's ability to put things in categories and groups, but also in his general ability to understand and deal with his general environment at a verbal level. It is here that we begin to deal with questions of "In what way is a cow like a horse?" It is here that we begin to teach the child to think about things in terms of *functions,* rather than simply in terms of size, shape, color, or species. A great many brain damaged children show little or no linguistic difficulty until this level of abstraction is reached, and it is difficult to identify problems at this level as actually being associated with brain damage, unless other brain-injury signs are also present, and unless the responses are really quite bizarre instead of simply being at a relatively low level of abstraction. Nevertheless, when difficulties are discovered at this area, some attempt should be made to ameliorate them.

It is at this level that boundaries between "language training" and "generalized special education" become indistinct. We feel, however, that the distinction is not really an important one, and that it matters little whether this training is done by the classroom teacher or the speech therapist. In fact, where difficulties in this area are relatively severe, such training might well be a function of several types of clinicians. The general concepts might easily be taught in the group situation as part of a general educational program, while the individual child's particular or unique difficulties be best handled on an individual basis by the speech therapist or the educational psychologist.

Amelioration of these higher level abstracting and categorizing difficulties is perhaps the most challenging and perplexing of all clinical tasks in the habilitation of the brain-damaged child. It is at this level that abstracting behavior, generalized intellectual ability, cognitive functioning, perception, and emotion become almost inseparably intermeshed, and it is only at this level where there may be some justification in "just treating the symptoms" without a clear analysis of the underlying processes. It is at this level that the "unusual," the partially-correct, and the "low-grade" responses seem to crop up sporadically and predictably; and it is here that one is unable to be certain, on the basis of the response alone, whether one is dealing with a specific abstracting problem or general mental retardation. You ask a child "In what way is a ship like a train?" He answers: "They both make smoke." What kind of a reply is this? Clearly, it is not a *good* answer; but does it reflect an abstracting difficulty, or simply low-grade thinking, or lack of experience, or some mixture of any or all of these? To some extent, responses of this type may best be evaluated in terms of standard psychometric testing procedures which will be discussed later in this chapter. Meanwhile, what does the clinician do about difficulties at this level? Largely, it is at this point that the clinician must assume the role of the patient educator, and, somewhat as did the ancient private tutor, embark upon the task of explaining the world to the child, and of getting the child to the point at which he sees and senses the world to the fullest level that his abilities will allow.

At both the classroom and at the individual therapy level, the approach to the type of difficulty we have just described is to bring the child into contact with the world as most people know it, and to get the child to perceive the world, and to talk about it in insightful and appropriate terms. Here is where "Special Education" should become something really *special*. Paradoxically, here is a point or an area where approaches which have long been applied in the education of the "gifted" child become just as appropriate in the training of any other "special" child, whether he be simply "slow," "brain damaged," "multihandicapped," etc. This is where the child's understanding of his world is dependent on what his habilitative program can do for him in terms of broadening and interpreting his life experiences for him. Here is where "project units," field trips, and similar techniques should come into play. It is not the intent of this chapter to cover the broad field of educational techniques. However, we can state that "getting the world into perspective" at this point will depend largely on how much of the world is brought to the child, and how it is interpreted for him. Beyond this, we refer you to the chapter on "Education" elsewhere in this book.

In this section on linguistic and intellective functions, we have concentrated upon abstractional and categorizational problems because of their central and pervasive position in the learning patterns of brain-damaged children, and because a general understanding of these problems is essential to the achievement of effective special education and speech therapy. We shall now very briefly deal with a number of other "signs" which fall within this general heading. We shall mention these items only in a circumscribed manner, inasmuch as they are also treated in other chapters of this book.

Linguistic or "language" disturbances are commonly dealt with in descriptions of *aphasia.* However, since this chapter deals with the concept of a "generalized brain injury syndrome" and does not deal with aphasia except as a part of this generalized concept, we feel that this is the appropriate place for a brief discussion of these signs. As we indicated in our previous book,[58] the dual concept of "cerebral palsy and aphasia," particularly in childhood, has long been irksome to us from a psychological viewpoint. If the brain-damaged child manifests symptoms which are most severe in terms of his motoric disability, he acquires the label "cerebral palsied." On the other extreme, if the brain-damaged child shows very little, or no motor impairment, but nevertheless manifests some of the behavioral signs thus far discussed, he is labeled "aphasic." If he has both a motor disturbance and also shows the behavioral signs, then the term "cerebral palsied and aphasic" is often used. While these clinical descriptions may have useful meanings in terms of defining the child's type of functional disability, they become bothersome when they tend to obscure the fact that *both* entities fall within the more generic diagnostic syndrome, "brain damage."

The foregoing may appear to be a rather trivial comment; but it does have some important implications in the organization and interpretation of long term case history data, and in the selection of subjects in clinical research studies: A severely motor-impaired, speechless child may enter a clinic with a diagnosis of "severe cerebral palsy and possible mental retardation." This is, actually, a valid descriptive classification. The child cannot walk, nor sit up, nor does he have any speech. Thus, he shows few, if any, behavioral signs of brain damage; and his motor impairment (which is obvious and easily evaluated) becomes the basis for the classification. Three years later, the same child may achieve some degree of mobility, some ability to follow simple instructions, and a little speech. It is now noted that he is highly distractible, perseverative, and shows rather bizarre patterns of abstraction and categorization: Thus he is *now* "cerebral palsied and aphasic." Does this mean that he was *not* "aphasic" when he was first seen? Obviously not only do we now have, in the clinical history, a rather strange implication, that the child "became" aphasic during training; but we also find that we must now ask ourselves *when,* or *at what point,* can we draw distinctions, or lines of demarcation between "cerebral palsy," "cerebral palsy and aphasia," and "childhood aphasia?" Obviously, at least from a psychological viewpoint, these distinctions are rather nebulous. It is possible, simply as a matter of convenience, to divide cases into groupings of this type in the manner described in the preceding section. But, as far as any nosological systematization, or case-selective research classifications are concerned, the terms are misleading and can result in symptomatological distinctions which have no reality. For psychology at least, we would prefer to view the entire range of symptoms in terms of the general classification of "brain injured" (for want of a better term), with the realization that, of course, there is a tendency for some cases to show severe motor disturbances, for some to show minor or no motor disturbance but to have varying degrees of behavioral disturbance; and for others to show more or less severe disturbances in both general areas.

In this discussion of language disturbances in brain damaged children, no attempt will be made to relate these signs to any particular type of aphasia (motor, sensory, etc.), nor, indeed, for the reasons just discussed, to any generalized concept, such as "childhood asphasia." We are merely mentioning these signs as part of the general syndrome of brain damage. Their analysis in terms of "aphasia" will be treated elsewhere in this book. Many children with brain damage develop linguistic patterns which show defects in grammar and syntax. Particularly, as Clark[14] states, they have difficulty in the use of abstract words, or words for which there can be little visual, auditory or kinesthetic imagery. Thus, in sentence usage, prepositions, along with some adverbs and other modifiers, tend to be omitted, and sentence structure tends to become "agrammatical," or "telegraphic." Concomitantly, there tends to be, perhaps because of the level of abstraction involved, a persistant misuse or confusion of pronouns. It is important to be aware of this type of reaction, lest a child's essentially meaningful communication go unheeded or misinterpreted by the clinician, resulting in considerable frustration to the child and a general deterioration of clinical efficiency. An illustration of the type of confusion which might arise can be seen from what happens to a simple sentence when these "aphasic-like" speech patterns occur.

The developmental progression of the brain damaged child's speech pattern may often show various types of retardation. We shall not, in this chapter, concern ourselves with the general retardation of speech development which is treated elsewhere in this book, but rather with the more specific types of aberrations of linguistic structure which are often noted in such children. The afore-mentioned concretization of verbal content is often manifested by distortions in grammatical structure in which the child may produce meaningful and appropriate speech, but in which the meaning is evident only if the listener has some insight into the communication pattern being considered. For example, a brain-damaged child may say "Me downtown Momma," which is a highly concretized and "telegraphic" way of expressing "I went downtown with Momma." Similarly, "Johnny do," can be a request that the child needs to go to the bathroom. This syntactically distorted speech can be a source of frustration, both to the child and to those who are working with him at home, or in the clinic. Therapeutic approaches to this type of difficulty are beyond the scope of this chapter. Our main concern is that they be recognized as a form of speech aberration commonly associated with brain damage. With experience, the clinician soon learns to associate what he knows about the child's daily activities with what he learns about the child's linguistic aberrations, and is thereby able to establish a fairly high degree of verbal interaction with a child whose linguistic output is grossly deranged. It should also be mentioned here that many children with relatively severe disruptions in integration of linguistic output may nevertheless have relatively adequate levels of verbal comprehension. In these cases, their inability to make themselves understood is often highly frustrating, and serves as an effective "trigger" for catastrophic reactions which can be highly disruptive to the establishment of an effective working relationship between the child and the clinician. However, the astute clinician gradually learns how to "interpret" these bizarre linguistic responses, thus enabling him to establish a relatively high degree of rapport with the communicatively deviant child. For example, in response to "Me downtown Momma," the clinician might ask "Did you go downtown today?" or, "Are you going downtown tomorrow?" Such questions generally serve to elicit further responses from the child which, although still syntactically inadequate, nevertheless serve to further clarify what the child really *wants* to say: The child may merely nod affirmatively in response to one question, and negatively to the other. Or, he may give a clarifying response, such as "Today go," or, "No today." Responses such as these enable the clinician and the child to communicate with each other even though the child's verbal output is very limited and highly unconventional. The important fact here is that it is the task of the clinician to structure the verbal exchange in such a way that the child can make fullest use of what little communicative ability he has. Insights such as these often make the difference between success and failure of the clinical situation.

Another linguistic aberration often noted in brain-damaged children is commonly termed "anomic" or "amnesic" reactions. In such children there is often difficulty in selecting the proper word for an object. In this instance, the term amnesic, although commonly used, is rather unfortunate in its implication of "forgetting," or "not remembering" the word for an object. Observation of the child's linguistic reactions indicate that this is a gross oversimplification. What appears to happen is not that the child "forgets" the word; but rather that he is unable to call it forth from memory storage under ordinary stimulus conditions. This is rather easily demonstrated in several ways: Shown a picture of a car, house, or any other object, and asked to name it, the child may simply stare blankly, or say "I don't know," or he may give an entirely incorrect response. However, if we lay before the same child a variety of pictures and ask him to *point* to the car or house, he may make unerringly correct responses. Clearly then, the problem here is not simply one of not knowing, or of forgetting a word, but of knowing the word, but in terms of computer analogy, "not having it readily available from memory storage." Another diagnostic clue to this type of disturbance is the child's reaction to the Goldstein[32] "roundabout" technique: Shown a picture of a chair, the child may be unable to name it. The clinician then may say "You sit on a ————," and the child may then immediately respond with the word "chair." This is a well-known speech training device in aphasia, but it is also one which is generally useful in facilitating verbal communication in a variety of clinical settings.

Many brain damaged children have linguistic problems which manifest themselves as disturbances of serial order. To us, this appears to be rather closely related to the anomic problem in that it too is a failure of the information retrieval process, but it is rather specialized in that it seems to be particularly related to the production of serialized information. In many children, this type of aberration is commonly manifested by difficulties in such things as rote counting. The distinguishing factor here is that the difficulty lies not in conceptualization of quantity concepts, but simply in the ability to call forth the appropriate serial order word. A child may be asked to demonstrate simple quantity concepts by placing various numbers of blocks (or similar items) in a box; and he may be able to do this quite successfully, placing on command, 3, 5 or 7 items in a box or on a sheet of paper. Yet, when asked to count the objects verbally, he may say "1, 2, 5, 4, 3, 7." The significance of serial order verbalization difficulties to the processes of education are dealt with elsewhere in this book. They are mentioned simply to alert the clinician to their existence, and as another example of the need for close and discerning scrutiny of a child's performance before evaluative interpretations are made. Finally, in this brief survey of linguistic problems, it should be mentioned that many brain damaged children display the classical signs of "expressive" and/or "receptive" aphasia.

Visual-perceptual Functioning in the Brain-damaged Child: In many ways, the study of the behavioral characteristics of the brain-damaged child during the past twenty years has been dominated by studies of his visual-perceptual processes. An exhaustive review and evaluation of these studies would, of itself, represent a major undertaking which might well result in the writing of a book easily as long as this monograph. Clearly then, our presentation of material relating to perceptual functioning in the brain-damaged child must represent only a very restricted sampling of the vast literature in this area.

Among the earliest studies of visual-perceptual behavior in brain damaged children are the studies of Werner and Strauss[83] and of Strauss and Lehtinen.[82] These studies stressed the presence of the so-called "figure-ground disturbances" in the perceptual characteristics of these children. That this aspect of perception was the first to be studied was perhaps due to the pressures exerted by the "Gestaltist" orientation of perceptual theory through the 1935-1950 period. According to Gestalt theory, one of the basic aspects of all perceptual processes was the inherent neurological tendency of the normal organism to organize arrays of perceptual stimuli into central foreground or "figural" components, and noncentral background (or "ground") components. This was essentially an "organismic" theory of perception, supported by Goldstein[32] and many others, which held that perceptual organization could best be understood in terms of central neural integrative functions. According to this concept, the organization of stimuli into "figure" and "ground" aspects was a primitive function of the central nervous system; and it followed that damage to the C.N.S. reduced its organizational ability. Goldstein stated that defective figure-ground organization could be manifested in a variety of ways, such as the "leveling" of differences between figure and ground resulting in a degradation of the precision with which the figure is perceived, in a lack of stability of figure-ground separation resulting in fluctuating or uncertain figural perception, in complete failure to isolate figure and ground components so that "central" and "noncentral" stimuli are totally confabulated, resulting in totally bizarre and nonveridical perceptions, and finally, a tendency to transpose the perceptual values of figure and ground arrays, so that what is normally the "figure" becomes ground, and vice-versa, again resulting in nonveridical perceptions.

The foregoing concepts led to a large number of studies which need not be reviewed in great detail here. The general strategy of all these studies was to compare the reactions of brain-damaged and non-brain-damaged children on a variety of tasks requiring the isolation of figural stimuli from the "grounds" in which they were imbedded. Werner and Strauss,[83] Strauss and Lehtinen,[82] Miller and Rosenfeld,[60] Dolphin and Cruickshank[21] and many other workers devised many ingenious tasks to test figure-ground organization. In one study, the subjects were presented with two Marble Boards (similar to the familiar boards of the "Chinese Checkers" game), one on which the experimenter had constructed a mosaic pattern by placing variously colored marbles in the holes, and another board upon which the subject was to reproduce the pattern. In order to test the effect of background impingement upon the central figure, the Marble Boards had imprinted upon them an intricately structured background pattern which could easily be confabulated with the central figure which had been constructed of marbles. Using normal, endogenously retarded and brain-damaged subjects matched for age and IQ, it was demonstrated that the brain-damaged group tended to reproduce figures which showed significantly greater confabulation with the background pattern than did either of the control groups; that is, the normal and the endogenously retarded groups tended to construct patterns which followed the general outline of the stimulus presented, while the brain-damaged group tended to produce disorganized patterns in which the placement of the marbles often tended to "wander off" into a pattern given on the background of the board, thus suggesting, in the brain-injured group, a strong tendency for background impingement upon the perceptual organization of foreground figures.

During the past twenty-five years virtually countless variations of the above study have been done. In some, the subjects were required to detect drawings of objects which were masked by random background patterns. In others, subjects were required to locate a central figure, such as the numeral "4" within a matrix of adjacently connected angular lines. In all studies of this type, children with brain damage showed significantly poorer performance than did matched controls of normal and/or endogenously mentally retarded children. The prevalence of figure-ground disturbances in brain-damaged children has received the longest and most concentrated attention, and is a well-established fact. However, figure-ground disturbances do not explain all of the perceptual aberrations noted in these children, and a number of other areas must be considered.

Drawing largely upon the studies of Berko,[7,8] Miller and Rosenfeld,[60] Dolphin and Cruickshank,[21] Birch and Bortner[13] and Helle Nielson,[62] a great deal of evidence has been gathered which indicates that figure-ground disturbances are but one of many visual-perceptual disturbances noted in brain damage. Among the most commonly noted disturbances reported, we find aberrant patterns of Gestalt integration. We refer here not to figure-ground difficulties, but to failures in figural discrimination, poor closure and lack of integration of part-whole relationships even in situations in which figure-ground relationships do not seem to be a factor. Berko[7] noted that children with cerebral palsy made ten times as many errors in attempted placement of forms in the Seguin Formboard as did a group of normal controls, matched for age, sex and intelligence. This would suggest that poor form discrimination, independent of figure-ground relationships is a characteristic of the brain damaged child. It should be noted that in this study, although the experimental subjects had cerebral palsy, none of them had severe motor difficulties, and their errors in form placement could not be attributed to their minor motor problems.

Disturbances in perceptual analysis and perceptual synthesis are commonly noted difficulties in brain damaged children. Given, for example, a picture of a square as a model, plus a variety of test lines of various lengths and angles, brain damaged children show significantly poorer levels of performance in their ability to *select* which of the several test lines would be needed to reproduce a given geometric figure or model than do matched groups of normal or endogenously retarded children. Conversely, given a model of a partially completed drawing, plus a choice of several additional parts, the brain damaged group shows a great deal of difficulty in selecting which of the additional parts would be needed to complete a "good" geometric form, such as a circle, triangle or square.[12,13]

This very brief survey of the types of perceptual defects noted in brain damage has thus far stressed visual perception as a unitary, or unimodal function. Most of the studies thus far treated deal only with a rather naive type of experimental format in which the subject is presented with a variety of visual stimuli, and asked to report, generally in terms of some sort of matching, or reproductive, task, what his visual impressions are. Valuable as such studies may be in the demonstration of some types of perceptual difficulties noted in brain damage, they fail to tap a vast area of perceptual functioning. In 1954, Berko[7] suggested that visual perception, that is, perception of the visual world, was not a function of the visual system in isolation, but rather, that the ultimate mode of visual perception was to a large degree affected by the functional integrity of the perceptual system as a whole, and the degree of interaction between the various perceptual modalities. In the intervening years, the ramifications of this concept have spread in several directions. We do not wish to imply in any manner that our article, appearing in an obscure midwestern journal, stimulated the ramification of research in this field; but we do feel that we were among the first to recognize the importance of this area of perceptual behavior to the whole problem of visual perception in the brain-damaged child. In the original article, we simply raised questions of whether visual-perceptual disturbances in brain damaged children must, as had often been implied, be directly related to neurological lesions in the visual systems, whether the bizarre motor responses which some brain-damaged children gave to visual tasks could realistically be lumped into one *single* concept of "visual-perceptual disturbance" without some qualifying nosology, and finally, whether the limitations and aberrations of *motor* functioning in the cerebral palsied may, at least partially, account for their apparent defects in visual perception. Sadly, we merely asked the questions, and let the matter ride, in deed, if not in thought. Fortunately, however, other workers have supplied us with what seem to be some of the answers.[75,76]

The question of whether or not "visual perceptual deficits in brain damage" could, on the basis of response patterns alone, be subtended under a single nosological heading has recently received considerable attention from Birch and his associates.[12,13] They point out, quite astutely that the simple fact that a child is unable to make an adequate copy of a drawing actually may tell very little about the type of perceptual disturbance which causes the defect, or indeed, whether it is a visual perceptual problem at all.

Birch,[12] as did Berko some ten years earlier, emphasized the potential importance for the development of normal perceptual processes of the cortical integration of sensory information arising from various input modalities. Birch cites a number of studies indicating that brain-damaged children are often able to recognize and match geometric forms, but, even though they have no severe paralysis, cannot adequately *reproduce* the same forms through motor activities, such as drawing. Bortner and Birch[13] demonstrated that many brain damaged subjects who were unable to reproduce block designs were nevertheless able to discriminate between their own reproductions and the model, and to indicate specific, detailed awareness of the incorrect aspects of their own reproductions. Clearly then, a "perceptual test" which tests only the subject's ability to reproduce visual stimuli may give some highly misleading impressions regarding his perceptual functioning.

It would then follow, that the general model for the evaluation of perceptual functioning should always include at least two major aspects; pure recognition or discrimination, and reproduction, which is perceptuo-motor, rather than a "purely perceptual function." In other words, any really meaningful analysis of perceptual processes in brain damaged children must make some form of differentiation between failure or distortions at the discriminative level, and perceptual-motor failures which may have extremely important influences on the child's habilitative needs, but which may not in any way be associated with deficits at the "visual" level of perceptual behavior. Failures in discrimination are failures at a more primitive level of neurological organization and demand a more basic and stringent type of training in simple things such as basic form recognition and differentiation, whereas perceptuo-motor difficulties in the absence of discriminative difficulties suggest a considerably higher level of cortical integration. In Bortner and Birch's study of thirty brain damaged children, only 19 per cent of the cases showed primary discriminative failures, while 81 per cent showed perceptuo-motor difficulty while having relatively normal discriminative ability. Evidence of this type indicates the extreme importance, in terms of habilitative program planning, of making a clear distinction, wherever possible, between true visual-perceptual failure and perceptuo-motor difficulty.

During the past twenty years, a large and involved controversy has arisen over the basic nature of perceptual development. To treat this matter with even minimal adequacy would be a monumental task, and one far beyond the intended scope of this book. Very briefly stated, there appears to be a highly and minutely graduated scale of opinions, ranging, from one extreme which states that all perceptual information is "given" in the visual stimulus array presented to the eye, and that perceptual development is merely the selecting out of "constancies" or "invariants" which specify the facts of the world about us, and that "perceptual learning" is merely the increase and refinement of discrimination or "detection" of specifying invariants, to the other extreme position which states that all perceptual development is a matter of associative learning based upon experience. If one does an exhaustive survey of the literature, he can find ample support for either extreme stand, and for all shades of opinion, and all modifications of theory between the two polar extremities. Therefore, we shall not even attempt any sort of review of this material, stating only our own viewpoint (which, at the risk of appearing somewhat sophomoric, must be an eclectic one, and therefore probably rather unimpressive) which is that "everybody seems to be a little bit right."[9,10,29,30,31,38,40,41,49,61,69,85,86,87]

Our own viewpoint, while eclectic and lacking in theoretical elegance is nonetheless quite complex. We feel that it must be presented here because it has widely ramified implications for the training processes which should be used with the brain damaged, and particularly with the cerebral palsied. We agree, on the one hand, that much of the information about the visual world about us is "given" in the patterning of stimuli presented to the eye, and that facts of shape, depth, texture and distance are "built-in" to the interactions between our nervous system and incoming stimuli. On the other hand, we feel that the *meaning* of what is perceived is learned both in terms of associative processes and in terms of a progressive sharpening of discriminative processes. Secondly, we strongly believe that, in spite of the time-honored concept of stimulus-receptor specificity, the "total perceptual process" as we choose to call it, transcends the boundaries of specific sensory modalities; and what we see, hear, smell, feel and taste, is not the result of a simple chain of reactions between the appropriate receptor and its cortical projection, but rather, any given perception is the product of the total interacting array of sensory inputs at a given moment, plus the residuals of past environmental interaction. In other words, we feel that the concept of circumscribed sensory modalities must inevitably be replaced by a concept of a "total perceptual-interactive system" in which vision, for example, may be modified by proprioception, kinesthesis, haptics, audition and so forth. For example, the array of light presented to the eye from a spherical object differentiates it from a flat, or cubical object. This is a function of neural organization, and permits some discrimination of shape. But to the child, fully meaningful cognitive perception of the quality of sphericality is much more than this and involves the interaction and higher order integration of all the sensory modalities. The real "meaning" of sphericality is the result of the interactive processes of all the modalities of the perceptual system. It is the result of *interaction* between the object and the individual which permits cortical integrations which give a clear and precise definition of the object. It is not merely a matter of passive sensory intake, but is an *active* process in which the total sensory and integrative system of the individual must participate, must *actively experience*.

It is, within the format of this theory, the total sensory interaction between the individual and the object, which provides the individual with clear, sharp, intermodally-integrated perceptions. This intermodal integration of inputs represents a higher level function which permits the individual to extract meaningful data from the sensory array given in the environment. For example, the perception of "fire" would not be possible without such sensory integration. Fire contains the sensory elements of vision (color and light refraction), cutaneous sensations (heat), olfaction (smokey odor), etc. Yet the perceiver of fire receives not a mish-mash of sensory impressions which he must consciously associate and analyze, but one total complex of input data which specifies "fire." True enough, the perceiver eventually learns that any one of these cues may specify the possibility of fire; but this is a later cognitive process. Returning now to our earlier example of sphericality as a visual quality, the normally active child, *through active experience,* soon learns that the quality of sphericality includes a haptic element (the ball *feels* round), and moto-kinesthetic or proprioceptive element (he can *roll* the ball), an auditory element (the ball makes a distinctive sound as it rolls). Let not the reader assume here that we are reverting to Titchnerian sensationalism to explain perceptual processes. We are *not* claiming that these are separate "sensations" which somehow get agglutinated into a perception, but rather that the active participation of all sensory elements is what gives a high degree of clarity, specificity, constancy and uniqueness to visual perception.

The importance of *active sensing* in the perceptual processes has received practically no attention in the literature pertaining to the rehabilitation of brain-damaged children. Experimental psychology has a seventy-year-history of studies of individuals under artificially-imposed optical distortion.[22,23,24,39,44,50,77,78,79,80]

Space does not permit a survey of these studies. The general format of these experiments involves subjects wearing various forms of optical lenses which distort the visual field: transposing left to right fields of vision, inverting lenses which make everything look upside down, transposition plus inversion, etc. The subjects were required to wear the lenses over protracted periods of time (a few days, to over a month), while performing various tasks. The general results of the studies were that various types of *adaptation* to atypical visual inputs were possible. In some studies, the subjects became progressively less aware of the perceptual distortion until the world "looked" normal when in fact, the retinal images were inverted or transposed. In other studies, the world continued to look upside-down, or laterally transposed, but complex motor tasks which could be done with great difficulty or not at all when the distorting lenses were first worn became progressively easier, and in many cases, approached the same level of performance achieved by the subject under normal optical conditions.

The above studies seem to raise some extremely important and complex questions regarding the nature and the functional dynamics of visual perceptual problems in the brain injured, and particularly in those with cerebral palsy.

We do not wish to imply here that visual distortions imposed upon normal observers through the use of optically-distorting prisms are equivalent to the perceptual disturbances associated with brain damage. Nevertheless, some of the information produced by the visual distortion studies may have important implications for the understanding of perceptual functioning of brain injured children. The basic question in which we are presently interested is that of the apparent persistence of visual perceptual difficulties in brain damaged children. Lashley,[52,53] in his many extirpation studies with rats and monkeys, repeatedly demonstrated that damage to the visual cortex results in only temporary derangements of visual perception in these animals. We do not wish to involve ourselves in the pros and cons of the "equipotentiality" argument here; but we do wish to point out that in many cases, normal adults after trauma to the visual cortex, depending on the extent of the injury, show varying degrees of recovery of visual adequacy and perceptual normalcy. Our argument here is simply that while brain-damaged children show varying degrees of perceptual disturbance, such disturbance need not be assumed to be a direct correlate to cortical damage, nor necessarily to the subcortical structures of the visual system. This in no way ignores the fact that cortical damage, and damage to subcortical visual tracts and relay points, can and does cause visual and visual-perceptual disturbances and that some of these may be irreversible. What we are arguing however, is that both the Lashley studies and the numerous optical displacement studies seem to suggest that perceptual disturbance, whether neurologically or optically generated, seems to be amenable to a great deal of compensation, or normalization, and, as we shall see later, further imply that perhaps some forms of perceptual deviations in the brain damaged, and particularly the cerebral palsied, may have etiologies which are not fully determined by the site of the neurological lesion.

First, regarding the fact of *adaptation* to prismatically imposed visual distortion, recent studies by Held and others[42,43,44,45] indicated that adaptation to visual distortion, that is, the development of the subjects' abilities to interact with the physical environment in a normal manner while wearing distorting lenses was greatly affected by their opportunities for motor interaction with the physical environment. In the typical experiment in this area, two groups of subjects wear distorting lenses which invert or laterally transpose the visual environment. Simple tasks, such as walking along complex paths, following pencil and paper mazes, etc., are presented. In pretest sessions, one group is lead passively through the task several times. For example, they may be wheeled along the test path in a wheelchair, or their hands may be passively guided through the maze. The second group is given an equal number of trials in which they themselves actively explore the path or maze. Invariably, the "active exploration" group shows rapid adaptation, learning to make correct turns in the pathways and mazes in spite of the imposed optical distortions. On the other hand, the passive group, regardless of how many times they are lead through the task, show no adaptation, no "learning" when finally given the opportunity to perform the tasks actively; and regardless of how much previous passive experience they are given, do not achieve the performance proficiency of the *active* group until they are given as many active trials as the latter. In other words, passive exposure to visually distorted fields contributes nothing to adaptation. It is not until the body is involved with motoric, self-generated, interaction with the distorted environment that any real adaptation can occur. There is, then, a vast difference, in terms of potential neurological organization, between passive and active visual experience. According to Von Holst's theory of *re-afferent stimulation*[45] it is the proprioceptive and kinesthetic feedback from one's own spatially-oriented compensatory movements which ultimately correlates initial visual impressions with a "feel" for spatial reality and for full appreciation of the relationships between spatial direction and bodily motion. When such feedback is disrupted, either by lack of experience or by neural disruption of proprioceptive-kinesthetic feedback tracts, *the development of* visual-motor integration and spatial perception are grossly retarded, and adaptation to optically distorted environments is virtually impossible.

The implications of the foregoing in terms of visual perceptual functioning in brain damaged children, particularly in those with severe motoric disabilities, are vast, and have complex ramifications. First, assuming that some perceptual disturbances in brain damaged children *do* arise from direct injury to the "perceptual" areas of the cortex, we should assume, both from Lashley's animal studies, and from the degree of recovery of perceptual functions in adults with known cortical damage, that some degree of recovery, or normalization should occur automatically, that this automatic normalization does not seem to occur in brain-damaged children, without complex and extensive training, may be explainable in two basic ways. The first explanation, a well-known one, may be found in Lashley's own studies of cortical ablation in animals [51,54,55] in which he showed that perceptual functions which were developed *before* ablation were relearned quite readily. However, if ablation was performed before the animal had an opportunity to have much perceptual experience, the acquisition of perceptual abilities remained quite slow and difficult throughout the life of the animal. Possibly then, we can extend this finding to a suggestion that children suffering prenatal damage to the visual cortex may show visual-perceptual problems which are relatively resistive to amelioration. However, as Birch and others[12,34] have indicated, postmortem brain studies of children with known perceptual difficulties show little correspondence between perceptual difficulties and the loci of the brain damage, with, indeed, many cases showing no evidence of lesion to the neural structures known to be associated with visual, and visual-perceptual functions. How then, do visual-perceptual malfunctions occur in the absence of palpable lesions in the visual-perceptual systems? In the cases of the nonmotorically handicapped, this question could present us with considerable difficulty. Therefore, let us return, for the moment, to our earlier distinction between *primary visual-perceptual disabilities* and *breakdown in perceptual-motor ability*. It may be well, at this point, to reiterate and clarify this distinction. In referring to primary visual-perceptual difficulties, we imply failures in basic perceptual organization, in discriminative functions and so forth. By perceptual-motor difficulty, we refer to a much more subtle type of defect in which basic perceptual organizational and discriminative functions are unimpaired, but, due to cortical damage to areas other than the perceptual cortex, these visual perceptions cannot readily be transposed into motor activities: The child has, then, what is generally referred to as "apraxia."

There is, we find in speaking to clinicians, a great deal of confusion regarding the type of functional breakdown represented by apraxia. The commonly expressed error is that apraxia, being termed a perceptual-*motor* dysfunction, is somehow related to paralysis, to some failure of efferent innervation. While such confusion is perhaps understandable, nothing could be less accurate. Apraxia is not paralysis, even though many apractic behaviors superficially do resemble paralytic dysfunction. The fact, however, is that the apractic child (and this is where things do get horribly confusing) may or may not have a motor paralysis. However, the paralysis can generally be orthopedically diagnosed and demonstrated. Apraxia refers to a disorder in motor functioning in which the individual has the basic motor capability to perform a motor act, but is unable to plan the act at an ideational level, or transpose a visual impression into an appropriate motor conterpart or sequence. Such apractic conditions might readily be misconstrued as being primary perceptual disturbances if appropriate diagnostic procedures have not been applied. Appropriate diagnostic procedures for the differentiation of apraxia and basic visual-perceptual difficulties may be exemplified by models such as the following: If a child can match, identify from memory, or otherwise show good recognition and differentiation of visual stimuli, but, in the absence of demonstrable paralysis, is unable to copy simple drawings, or is unable to fit simple puzzles together, even though he is able to indicate that he *knows* where the parts should go, he is demonstrating an apraxia. In the clinical situation, some children's performances with the old Goddard or Seguin formboards, give excellent examples of apraxia. Given the forms, removed from the board, the child may readily place the circular form in the appropriate recess. But with forms, such as the star, or the cross, in which placement requires rotational orientation in order to get the form to *fit* into the recess, the apractic child may immediately bring the form to the proper recess, but then fumble about, not knowing quite how to *turn* the form so that it will fit into the hole. Now, it is this type of situation, repeated perhaps dozens of times each day through the child's routine of normal activities, which can cause what was merely an apraxia in the early life of the non-motor-handicapped child to develop into a serious primary visual-perceptual deficit in later perceptual development.

This degradation of apraxia in early life to severe primary visual-perceptual difficulties as the child grows older, has a twofold basis. One lies in the basic learning processes, and the other in the processes of central neural organization. We stated earlier that we hold to an eclectic theory of perceptual development which admits that both learning and central, automatic organization of input stimuli contribute to perceptual development. The problem of apraxia, within this theory, is that apraxia can be disruptive to both central organization and discriminative learning. Without going into learning theory, we will simply take as a maxim, that learning of any type, even the development of perceptual discrimination, is at least partially dependent upon reinforcement, upon the constant association of action with result. The old maxim, "The burnt child dreads the fire," might well be amended to "The repeatedly burnt child learns to dread the fire." It is the *constancy* of interaction that enables the organism to organize its environment into meaningful, predictable units of information. If, for example, contact with fire sometimes resulted in a painful, burning sensation, sometimes in a pleasant cooling sensation, and sometimes with no sensation at all, the burnt child would *not* learn to dread the fire: He would learn only to be terribly confused by it. Now, this is somewhat analogous to what the apractic child faces in his perceptual development.

As a generalized example, let us return to the apractic child and the formboard. He sees the circular form and the circular recess, and very easily places the form in the hole. Then he picks up the star form, locates the star recess, and then discovers that, for some reason completely beyond his understanding, *the star form does not fit* into the recess that looks like a star. In how many ways might this type of situation be repeated in the early life of the apractic child? He tries to copy a square, but it come out looking like a circle. He turns his tricycle to avoid collision with a wall, and steers it directly into the wall. In short, the apractic child lives in a bizarre world in which he may see things as others do; but seeing does not give him much help in reacting appropriately. As time passes, and while other children are learning to make ever finer and more subtle perceptual discriminations and distinctions, the apractic child is learning that what the world looks like to him often does not give him the cues which tell him how to react appropriately to a given stimulus array, and that what he sees does not always enable him to make a motor response of the appropriate type. Gradually, as non-apractic children are developing higher and more complex levels of visual discrimination, the apractic child, due to the absence of a pattern of constant and stable relationships between the way the world looks, and what happens when he reacts to it motorically, fails to develop higher levels of perceptual discrimination and attention, fails to increase his alertness to perceptual detail, and thus eventually may fall far behind the non-apractic child in his total development of visual perceptual skills so that, as far as higher levels of visual-perceptual organization are concerned, primary visual-perceptual deficits may develop even though there is no lesion to the primary visual-perceptual system.

If apraxia may be responsible for later development of primary visual-perceptual difficulties on a learning basis, it may be reasoned that it may be equally disruptive to perceptual development in terms of neurological organization. In accordance with the theories of Von Holst[45] and Hebb[38] and supported by the experimental studies of Held and his associates[41,42,43], some of which were quoted earlier in this chapter, perceptual organization, particularly, higher orders of discrimination, spatial perception, the automatization of correct interaction between visual input and motor reaction, the clarification and sharpening of form discrimination, etc., *is* highly dependent upon the association of visual stimuli with the reafferent proprioceptive feedbacks generated when one attempts to deal with the visual environment in terms of motor response. If we view apraxia as distorted or unstable, or nonveridical reafferent feedback, as false information regarding one's own body schemata, disruption of visual-perceptual function in terms of failures or retardations of central organization can easily be understood as a natural concomitant of apractic disturbances, and some insight may be gained regarding the ways in which brain damaged children may have severe primary visual-perceptual disturbances, even when there may be no lesion to the visual cortex or its associated structures.

With a few minor changes in emphasis, the dynamics of perceptual disturbances in the cerebral palsied may be approached in a manner similar to that which was outlined above. We again must question the extent to which normal perceptual development can occur in children who suffer prenatal, or very early postnatal lesion to the visual cortex and its associated structures. However, Reisen[71,72] and Lashley[52,54] both indicate that while perceptual development and adaptation in lower animals occurs more readily when the lesion occurs after the animal has had some perceptual experience, considerable perceptual development may occur, even with prenatal lesion. As we have previously indicated, one of the key factors in perceptual adaptation, and perhaps in all forms of perceptual learning, is *active interplay* with the visual environment. Now, in the case of the severely motor handicapped child, that is, the child who cannot walk, who has little or no use of his hands, or the one who may have considerable mobility, but whose motor patterns are highly erratic, variable, and unsystematically patterned, the opportunity for active motor interplay with the visual environment, particularly interplay which produces patterned constancies of visual-motor interaction is extremely limited; and it is this limitation which may retard both perceptual-neural organization in children with lesion to the visual-perceptual cortex, and perceptual—discriminative development in motor handicapped children without such damage. The term, "patterned constancies" was used here for the first time, and may require some explanation, although we have hinted at its meaning several times within the latter sections of this discussion.

By "patterned constancies," we simply mean a stable and dependable complex of interrelationships between visual stimulation and the informational feedback from the responses which they evoke. In the visual-perceptual development of the normal child, this occurs automatically. The neonate begins to pattern his visual-motor constancies soon after birth: He soon learns that certain movements bring his hands within his visual field. Later, he learns that objects can be brought into view, or located, by certain head movements, that reaching in a certain direction enables him to touch an object, that certain types of finger movements permit him to pick up the object, etc. Later, in crawling, and in learning to walk, he learns to control his direction of movement, to judge distances, and to avoid (or contact) obstacles. At first, all of these activities are gross and inaccurate. But, with maturation, accuracy and precision increase, and the child develops a stable pattern of visual motor interactions and central neural integrations which establish his relationships with the visual world at a level of stability which enables him to make judgments of distance, size, shape and of his own bodily relationships to his surroundings in such a way that seeing becomes the natural, automatic guide for doing. By contrast, the child who has no motoric ability, or the one whose motor control is erratic, either has very limited opportunity for such development, or finds that visual stimuli provide poor guidelines for behavior: He reaches for an object, and knocks it over. He steps toward his mother, and bumps into a wall. At other times, he does grasp what he reaches for, or does get to his mother. But there is no constancy, no dependability. Thus, basic spatial orientations develop more slowly, and consequently, the finer visual discriminatory processes remain retarded or underdeveloped. In this way severe motor disabilities may retard perceptual development, both in children with lesions to the visual-perceptual cortex and its associated structures, and in those who have no such lesion. We feel that this is at least a partial explanation for the rather frequent lack of correspondence between postmortem information regarding the loci of cortical lesions in children who were known to have severe visual-perceptual problems. Visual perception is a complex process involving the neurological and experiental functioning of the total organism; and, while damage to the visual and visual-perceptual cortices and their associated structures undoubtedly play some part in the perceptual processes of some brain-damaged children, comprehension of the perceptual processes of such children can never be achieved solely by study of the localization of brain functions, and certainly not by searching for simple and direct relationships between brain lesions and perceptual problems.

Throughout this chapter, we have touched only occasionally and lightly upon matters pertaining to therapeutic procedure. Where we have, it was generally done simply as a way of clarifying or demonstrating some aspect of the symptomatology under discussion. In dealing with perception, we hesitate to attempt any outline of amelioratory procedures. However, the theoretical orientation given here contains some major implications for a therapeutic approach, and it might be appropriate to comment briefly upon some of these implications.

In terms of the foregoing discussion, it would seem to be implicit that visual-perceptual training in brain-damaged children would have to be oriented toward activities which facilitate the basic processes of general neurological organization, establish or enhance intermodal sensory integration, and help clarify or define (or stabilize) the child's visual-motor interactions. Training in discriminatory processes may also be necessary; but discriminational learning will proceed more rapidly if primary stress is placed upon facilitating the basic organization and interaction of the total perceptual system. We feel that too often, in many clinical situations, "visual-perceptual training" simply means training in visual discrimination, and that such training basically consists of learning to match forms, or to copy drawings within a training framework of simple repetitive practice, verbal correction, and more practice. There is nothing terribly wrong with this. Discrimination practice *should* be part of perceptual training; but it is by no means the whole of it, nor even the correct starting point unless we are dealing only with children who already have highly developed and fairly normal perceptual abilities, and need only a little sharpening of their discriminative ability. But, perhaps even here, visual discrimination might possibly be more rapidly facilitated by the inclusion of a more holistic approach.

By "holistic approach," we mean the involvement of the total organism in the visual perceptual processes. Many clinicians complain that brain-damaged children lack "visual focus" or "visual attention," and that this is at the root of most of their learning difficulties. However, what many fail to realize is that the development of visual focus and attention is an active, integrated process, and cannot be effectively taught merely by telling the child to "look at what you are doing." The act of "looking at what you are doing," in normal children, is the result of visual-motor maturation and integration; and, except during some specialized instances, such as when confusing or distracting stimulus situations arise, becomes an essential and involuntary part of normal motor behavior. This is a maturational process. The normal young child shows less stability in this type of integration. But, after a few years of moving about in the world, reaching for objects, avoiding obstacles, etc., *looking* and *doing* become one integrated act. Of course, some highly specialized forms of "looking and doing" take a considerable amount of conscious practice and learning, even in normal, healthy, individuals. "Keeping your eye on the ball" in playing golf is a specialized behavior which has to be practiced at a conscious level. But aiming one's eyes in the direction one walks, looking at the object you reach for, looking at the picture as you draw it, or at the letters as you write is a result of normal visual-motor maturation in the normal child. It begins very early in life. Normal infants reach for their mothers' faces, look at their bottles as they begin to feed themselves, reach for the toys they watch dangling over their cribs, etc. *Looking* and reaching, *looking* and grasping, *looking* and getting where one wants to go, becomes part of the child's neural organization, part of the visual-motor behavior complex very early in life. The reasons why this type of development may not occur, or may occur terribly slowly, in some brain injured children have already been discussed. The question which naturally follows is, "What can be done to facilitate the development of the general perceptual system in the brain damaged child?" We can offer no "cookbook solution," no "recipe for training." We can, however, suggest a few fundamental principles.

The first general principle (and this applies to both the cerebral palsied and the non-motor-handicapped brain-damaged child) is to permit him to receive as much *active motor experience* as possible. Ideally, we might hope that diagnosis of brain damage is made in early infancy, since the earlier the training can begin, the better are the prospects for relatively normal development. We shall, therefore, develop this outline on the basis of the assumption that the child reaches the clinic relatively early in life. However, even if the brain-damaged child does not begin to receive training until the age of five or six years, the same general principles with some adaptation to allow for the child's maturational status still apply. This is particularly true of the severely motor-handicapped child. If such a child, at the time he enters training, has little physical mobility, and a concomitant history of limited environmental experience, the general training outline need not differ to any great extent, even if it does not begin until relatively later in life. True, the later the beginning of training, the poorer are the chances for normal perceptual development. But we have seen a few instances in which considerable perceptual development occurred, even though training did not begin until adolescence.

We spoke previously of the importance of "active motor experience" in perceptual training. This does not imply simply unguided or random activity, although this should also be part of the program. Fundamentally, however, we refer to the provision of a sequence of experiences which facilitate, or, in some cases, recreate the visual-motor and intermodal sensory integrative experiences inherent in the developmental patterns of the normal child. These activities and experiences, in order to be fully effective, must cut across various clinical and educational disciplines, and, in a clinical setting, should receive some attention in the classroom or preschool socialization group, as well as in such disciplines as occupational therapy, physical therapy and speech training.

The early steps in training should be aimed at establishing stable relationships, or stable interactional patterns between the child's body and the perceptual environment. In other words, the first step is to establish within the brain-damaged child an "internalization" of the fact that, regardless of whether or not he has a severe motor defect, certain constancies exist between what he sees, and what he does with his body. The exact nature of how this can be achieved cannot be outlined very specifically here, since procedures must be tailored to fit the individual needs of each child. In general, however, the aim must be to help the child isolate some basic relationships between himself and the world about him.

Where this process should begin is a matter of judgment for the clinical staff. What we will present here is an idealized outline of what order of procedures would be followed, assuming that a child has virtually no visual-perceptual skills. It would not *harm* any child, regardless of his state of perceptual development, to be taken through all of the procedures, but some degree of clinical judgment must prevail in determining if the particular activity is beneficial to the child, or how long the activity should be continued. One principle, however, should be borne in mind: that of *overlearning*. The fact that a child reacts normally within a structure "sometimes," or "usually," is not good enough. We are seeking *stable* relationships between the child and his environment; and relationships cannot be considered stable unless (barring very unusual or distracting situations) the child *always* demonstrates an ability to react in a normal manner to a given visual-motor setting.

The lowest level of active visual-motor integration is simple visual attention to moving objects. Such attention can be more rapidly achieved if the child is actively involved with the object on a motoric level. In the very young infant, or in the older child who is so severely disabled that his motoric development is at an infantile level, the first training should be in gross manipulation of objects. Here, for example, many of the toys generally used to amuse infants may be used at a clinical level. Such items as swinging rattles and bells are useful here. Assuming that the child can hear, he will reflexively *look* and *reach* in the direction of the sound source. The normal infant will generally strike out rather randomly, hitting the rattle or bell, generally by chance at first, derive some pleasure, both from the physical contact with the object, and from the sound. After some time, in the normal child, the randomness of the reaching activity decreases, and the child begins to search for the object with his eyes, and strike out at what he sees. This is a normal maturational process and the lowest level of visual-motor integration. Clinically, some adaptations can be made which will *facilitate* this basic integrative process in the brain-damaged child: After some brief experience with the random activity and random pleasurable contact described above, the clinician begins to manipulate the target object in such a way that the child strikes it *only* when he is *looking* at it. In other words, the situation is structured by the clinician in such a way that no pleasurable reinforcement of a movment can occur unless the sought-after object is within the child's field of vision. Conversely, (and this is particularly true with the motor handicapped child), sometimes the clinician should reverse the process, bringing the object into contact with the child's hand *whenever* he focuses upon it. The creative clinician should be able to devise any number of variations of this technique, and we will not elaborate upon possible variations. Obviously, the aim here is to establish, at a very primitive neurological level, the integrated perceptual-motor act of *looking* and *reaching*, or looking and touching. It is at this very primitive level that we can begin to establish in the brain damaged child a central neural organization in which visual focus has some functional value, as a means by which the child achieves some control of his environment.

The previous discussion used infants or very severely motorically disabled children as "models" in the training processes. However, as most clinicians have experienced, visual attention is sometimes absent in the older non-motorically brain damaged, or in the less severely cerebral palsied. Establishing visual attention here follows the very same principles. The materials used may have to be altered somewhat: Perhaps reaching for a piece of candy and getting it only if one looks at it is a more effective type of stimulus situation for the older child. But the principle remains the same: Looking and reaching are rewarded; reaching without looking precludes the possibility of reward. As we stated earlier, this section is not intended as a "cookbook," nor a manual of procedures. We are simply presenting some basic principles in perceptual-motor training, and trust to the ingeniousness of the individual clinician to adapt procedures which fit the principles in each individual case.

With the emergence of rudimentary central neural processes of visual attention, perceptual-motor development begins to ramify in many directions simultaneously. The linguistic constraints of our language demand that we present these ramifications and developments in some sort of order. However, this does not imply that, once visual attention appears, further perceptual motor development is a step-by-step process in which one step must be entirely completed before another begins. Quite to the contrary, visual-motor development, and visual discriminatory development constitute a complex of overlapping and simultaneously interacting processes from which mature and normal perceptual development emerges. By this, we mean simply that one cannot say that first comes visual attention, then visual motor integration becomes a fully developed function and so on — up through fine visual discrimination. Following the rudimentary development of visual attention, other facets of the visual-perceptual-motor-integrative system become complexly and inextricably interrelated. By presenting the various components in a particular order, we simply imply that certain types of developments must manifest themselves before later developments can be expected to take place; but *never* that one facet is "completed" before another is begun.

The early development of the "looking and reaching" aspect of visual-motor integration sets the stage for a more complex level of visual-motor development, that of simple spatial and directional orientation in relation to one's self. This is not to imply that *all* spatial perception is learned. Indeed, Watson,[88] and later Gibson and Walk[31,86] give ample evidence that stimuli which represent height, or the possibility of falling, evoke fear reactions in infants and young animals who would have had no experience with falling. Nevertheless, the child's total appreciation of spatial relationships, and particularly his understanding of the personal implications of the relationship between what he sees, what he does, and what happens to him, is modified by his motor interactions with the visual environment. In the normal child, this is part of normal maturation: As the normal child's sphere of activities increases, as he crawls, walks, climbs, falls, etc., he very rapidly develops a "cognitive map" of the world in which he lives and with maturation, he is able to make ever finer discriminations of distance and direction. At the same time, his form perception becomes more specific, and visual perceptions blend with other modalities to form the total perceptual system. Visual arrays may specify the difference between a sphere and a cube; but the child, in his normal experience quickly learns that a ball rolls when it is pushed, while the cube merely slides. He learns that spheres and cubes feel differently, that the spheres held in the hand give a haptic perception of "roundness," while cubes have edges. Visual textures have haptic meanings: Roughly textured arrays are rough to the touch: "Textureless" or "glossy" visual arrays are smooth. Slanted surfaces, when one walks along them in one direction, give rise to motokinesthetic sensations which are quite different than when one walks along them in the opposite direction. The importance of all this is that the normal perceptual system is highly intermodal in terms of the types of information it imparts to the intact nervous system, and this totality of information is processed by the nervous system in such a manner that inputs from one sensory modality supplement, amplify, and clarify inputs from other modalities. It is this inter-modality of sensory information which, through central integrative processes, provides the normal individual with a totality of information which gives ultimate meaning and stable reality to perception. Concomitantly it provides the individual with a system of internal cross-checks which, in the case of visual perception, are automatically used to help clarify ambiguous percepts: There are finely graded differences in light reflection between a toy plastic bowling ball and a real sixteen-pound wooden bowling ball, even when the two are identical in form, size, and surface color; but to the person who has never handled either the toy or the real ball, these visual differences, if they are noticed at all, give the *passive* observer no clue regarding which of the two balls is real. However, the active observer can easily differentiate the two balls by lifting them. Having done so several times, the differentiations in light reflection become more noticeable, and also convey information which immediately permits differentiation on the basis of visual cues alone. Thus the active motor experience not only heightens his awareness of visual cues, but also gives them meaning. This is a rather dramatic and contrived example of how motor experience can sharpen visual discrimination to the point where visual properties which may at first be totally unnoticed can, through appropriate motor inter-action, become so clear and compelling that they now provide enough information to vividly clarify a previously ambiguous percept. There are undoubtedly thousands of examples of the effects of perceptual intermodality in real life. The granular structure of a lump of uncast glass, and a lump of ice are quite similar, and convey little meaning to the individual who has had no physical contact with either. But, once having *touched* each, the visual differences become both sharp and meaningful.

Returning once again more specifically to the problem of visual-perceptual and perceptual-motor development in the brain-damaged child, the achievement of visual attention must be followed by the development of a general schemata of the relationships between the child's "ego," "self," or "body image" (we need not concern ourselves with the differing nuances of the psychological implications of the varying terms) and the visual world in which he lives. Actually, this training was already begun, being an inherent part of the visual attention ("looking and reaching") type of training. The next step is that of expanding structured visual-motor experience to a much wider sphere. At this point, the child must begin to have *active* structured experiences in exploring the world around him. Techniques here present no great problem with the non-motor handicapped, but may call for some creativeness, and perhaps a little "faith" in working with children with severe motor handicaps. There are two major aspects to this level of training. The first has already been stated, i.e., to establish a stable schema of relationships between the child as a focal point, and the visual world. The second is the establishment of a neurological organization in which visual stimuli become central in motivating and guiding motor behavior. Once again, we can offer no "recipe," but only indicate in a generalized, schematic manner, some approaches which might be employed to achieve these goals.

At this stage, we need to work both in terms of locomotion and manual activities. This may seem to pose insurmountable barriers for children with severe motor handicaps; however, these barriers become less frightening, and less deterring, once we understand what it is that we are trying to accomplish. We are not concerned here with teaching children to walk, or to use their hands (although these techniques could be highly useful in such therapies) ; but we are primarily concerned with establishing within the neurological organization of the child a schema which informs him that certain types of visual stimuli infer certain constancies, or meaningful "cues," about the world in which he lives, and that he can and should depend upon these cues to guide his behavior. We want the child to internalize the fact that certain types of visual stimuli indicate a horizontal surface which will support him, and permit him to transport himself across it in some manner if he wants to reach the proximity of a distant object. We want him to come to know that another type of visual stimulus indicates an impediment to movement: Or, more simply, that one can move across floors, but will crash into walls, and that the things you can move across always have certain visual aspects about them, but the things you crash into have other visual aspects. These visual aspects are constant and dependable properties, and must be attended to if you want to get along in the world.

At the clinical training level, the implication here is the need for active physical exploration of the physical world by the child. In reference to the child with cerebral palsy, exploration should begin as early as possible, even if the child is grossly handicapped. Wherever possible, such a child should be taken from his bed, or wheelchair, (with medical approval) and be placed on the floor, and be allowed to roll, tumble or crawl about in whatever manner he can. The value of such visual-motor experience will far outweigh the bumps and bruises he may receive. As early as possible, for both the cerebral palsied and the non-motor handicapped brain injured, visual control of direction of locomotion, and visual control of manipulation, should be brought into play patterns at various levels. Simple activities, such as walking or crawling toward a desired toy placed variously in a corner of the room, midway along a wall, or in the center of a room, are excellent visual-motor developmental activities. The "run and fetch" games which so delight normal eighteen to twenty-four month old children are normal parts of childhood play, but they also serve as the basic framework in the development of visual-motor integration and later perceptual skills.

Before pursuing this further, we wish to correct an unintentional implication which seems to be finding its way into this presentation. By the stress we are putting upon the importance of motor activity in perceptual development, we may appear to be suggesting that we hold to a rather circumscribed (and perhaps outmoded) "motor theory of perceptual learning." This is an implication which must be corrected. Obviously, where central neural integrative functions are not disrupted, motor activity may, under certain conditions, play a relatively minor part in perceptual development. There is a great deal of information "given" in visual stimulation alone; and, where central neurological organizational capacity is undisturbed, the immobile individual can probably achieve a good deal of perceptual organization, although such organization would probably be enhanced and accelerated by mobility. However, in cases of brain damage, where presumably there is a degradation of neurological organizational capacity, active contact with the world assumes a greater level of importance in perceptual organization. Finally, as we have been stressing all along, the normal child, through his normal developmental experiences, develops intermodal perceptual organizations in which motor activity plays an important role. It follows, therefore, that the more "normal" the general sensory-motor experiences of the brain-damaged child can be, and the more sources of sensory data he has available to him for incorporation in his general perceptual system, the greater are his possibilities for relatively normal visual-perceptual and visual-motor development. Hence, we stress motor activity as an important factor in the perceptual development of the brain damaged child, not because we believe that there can be no visual-perceptual development without motor activity, but because we believe that motor activity normally does play a role in normal perceptual development. On the other hand, we definitely do not feel that motor activity, *of itself,* that is, motor "patterning" devoid of association with the entire gamut of sensory experience, has any real value in perceptual organization. Motor experience helps to organize and clarify visual experience, *but only when such motor activity is performed in interaction with visual activity. Motor activity clarifies visual perception; it does not create it.*

We have already given a few examples of how locomotion and manipulation help clarify and bring specific meaning to the visual world. Through locomotion, the child internalizes the spatial relationships between his body and the world around him. Through manipulation and locomotion, shapes and textures are more rapidly differentiated, and more quickly given specific meaning. Clinically, this means that for optimal visual-perceptual development, the child should be given broadly based experience in active exploration of the world. Within the limits of common sense and medical prudence, the brain-damaged child should be exposed, as soon as possible, to every form of active sensory experience. Some of this experience should be of a random, exploratory nature. He should be given opportunity to crawl, walk, tumble, bump into things, roll balls, lift objects, feel things which are

hot, cold, rough, dry, wet, etc. Once visual focus and attention
are established, every new sensory experience will help clarify
the meaning of the visual environment. However, random, or
"free" experience is not enough. There are things that the clinician can do in a structured situation which will accelerate visual-
motor integration and visual discrimination.

We have already described the very simple "look and reach"
games for the development of visual attention. The importance
of "run and fetch" games has also been discussed. Along these
same lines, throwing and catching games can be important aids
to perceptual organization. The simple game of rolling a large
ball back and forth along the floor between the child and the
clinician helps establish hand-eye focus and a sense of direction.
The child soon discovers that "looking where he is rolling" generally gets the ball to the clinician, who will then return it. Concomitantly, "keeping your eye on the ball" generally lets you
catch it as it comes to you, while "not looking" allows the ball
to get away. Crude drawing games are also very important at this
level of perceptual development. The fact that an implement
can be used as an extension of one's own body was a discovery
that took several hundred thousand years in the history of human
evolution. It is also quite a grand discovery, and a great forward
step in the perceptional development of the child. Children
should be given the opportunity to scribble with crayon and
paper, or to pile things one upon another, as early in life as possible. The discovery that the way one moves his hand determines
whether or not the block will go on top of the pile, and that one
can make different kinds of lines on a paper by moving one's
hand in different ways, is a slow discovery for the normal child.
To the brain-damaged child, it may be excruciatingly slow, and
the earlier such experiences are begun, the better are the chances
for relatively normal perceptual development.

This exceedingly long section on visual perceptual functioning in brain-damaged children has been essentially theoretical in
orientation, has dealt largely with the dynamics of visual-perceptual development in relation to visual-perceptual defects; and,
perhaps to the distress of most readers, concludes with a description of only the very beginnings of perceptual training. Classical

perceptual training, that is, specific methodology for training in discriminative functions, in form perception, in prereading skills, however, are covered in very considerable detail in the chapter on "Special Education" in this book. The procedures therein described are natural extensions of the theoretical material presented here. (To some readers, a sense of "closure" might be achieved if the section on perception in the "Special Education" chapter is read immediately after the reading of this present section, even though either section may be profitably read without direct reference to the other.)

Finally, we are fully aware that we have stressed the "intermodal" aspect of visual perception without mentioning that brain injured children may often also have both sensory and perceptual deficits in areas other than vision. We are cognizant of the existence of perceptual difficulties in hearing, and in other modalities, and are aware that these have certain implications relating to the intermodal aspects of visual perception. We hope, at some later date, to treat, in considerable detail, the functioning of the total sensory-perceptual system in the brain damaged child; but this, of itself, would entail the writing of another book. We have chosen, therefore, rather than to treat this immensely complex area lightly, or inadequately, to reserve it for consideration in a separate volume.

General Rigidities in the Brain-damaged Child: General rigidities is a term used to characterize a large group of behaviors having as their basic feature negative reactions to any type of alteration of a currently-operating interactional framework. In affective aspects, a child displaying general rigidities often has difficulty in accepting new situations or minor changes in familiar situations. Such children tend to be emotionally distressed by alterations in their usual daily routines. These are children whose general efficiency is highly dependent upon both spatial and temporal order. They are disturbed by any alteration in their spatial environment. In the intellectual sphere, children displaying general rigidities find it difficult to shift from one task orientation to another. They tend to "carry over" procedures which were effective in the solution of one problem, to new problems or situations in which the previous mode of attack is entirely inappropriate. This is not a perseveration, in the general sense of the term, in that it involves molar rather than molecular behavior segments. A perseverating child may continue to place blocks in a horizontal row on a table after he has been asked to place them vertically. A child displaying conceptual rigidity may tend to continue piling or stacking activity after the blocks which he has been using have been removed and a bead-stringing task has been introduced and demonstrated.

In the psychological testing situation, it is necessary to correctly deal with both the affective and intellectual aspects of rigidities in order to obtain the best possible level of performance from the child being examined. The matter of spatial order arises here, much as it does in the problem of attention disturbance. A child having spatial rigidity will be easily disturbed and distracted by disorderly physical arrangements. He is likely to be disturbed by spatial disorderliness of a nature so minor as to go unnoticed by the normal individual. Test items not immediately and correctly replaced in their containers after use, bits of paper or dust on the examining table, a book out of its usual place on a bookshelf, an improperly-hung blind, or any other lack of complete orderliness may distress the child being examined to the point where he is unable to respond satisfactorily. It should be noted that these manifestations of spatial rigidity are differentiable from those of hyperirritable attention. The hyperattentive child usually reacts to spatial disorder with increased nonadaptive activity. In a similar situation, the rigid child will himself seek to physically rearrange the environment to conform to his drive for spatial order. If permitted, he will generally pick up the distracting pieces of paper and place them in a wastebasket, replace the book in its proper place on the shelf, etc. If his drive for spatial order is frustrated, he may become fidgety, emotionally upset, or merely maintain a distracted attitude and give poor attention to the tasks before him. A child displaying temporal rigidity may be upset by that change in his daily routine which the psychometric appointment necessitated. He may also be upset by the newness or strangeness of the situation. Therefore it is generally advisable that parents or teachers tell the child of the proposed examination a day or two before it is scheduled. The child should be reassured that the experience will be a pleasant one. Wherever possible, brain-injured children should be permitted to visit the examining room, meet the examiner, and be allowed to handle some of the testing materials a day or two prior to the examination so that the strangeness of the testing situation will be reduced before psychological examination is attempted.[4,11,58,59]

In dealing with conceptual rigidities in the psychological testing situation, the examiner's first responsibility is to recognize them for what they are. This is often quite difficult to do inasmuch as the manifestations of conceptual rigidity are at times difficult to differentiate from perseveration and from abstracting failures. The perseverative aspects of conceptual rigidity have been mentioned above. Where perseveration occurs only in response to an induced shift in task orientation, rather than within the framework of a single task, conceptual rigidity is being demonstrated. Abstracting aberrations will be considered in a later reference to the child's inability to make abstractions, or his tendency to make abstractions upon factors which would not commonly be considered as prime situational determinants. Conceptual rigidity, on the other hand, is displayed when a child tends to carry over into a new and different task or test item, an approach which was appropriate to the previous task, but not to the present one. An example commonly noted in brain-injured children's responses to some Stanford-Binet test items may help clarify this point. In Form-L of the Revised Stanford-Binet, one of the items at Year VI requires the child to indicate the past missing in each of a series of five drawings of common items. One item depicts a tea pot without a handle. This is followed by a picture of a glove with a missing finger. A perseverating child may give the correct response to the tea pot item, and then say that the "handle" is missing from the glove. At Year VII, there is an item requiring to tell what is "funny" or "foolish" about each of a series of pictures, each depicting some situational incongruity. None of the incongruities are based upon missing parts. A child displaying conceptual rigidities, having previously mastered the item containing missing parts at Year VI, may now search for missing facial features, missing items of clothing, etc., on the human and animal figures shown in the Year VII item. It should be noted that this is not a "wrong abstraction," but rather a failure to shift from one procedural orientation to another.

Upon encountering conceptual rigidities, the psychological examiner should attempt to determine whether or not the child is able to function adequately at certain previously failed levels if his rigidities are circumvented. Generally, where these rigidities prevent a child from passing a test item at a certain level, he may be able to succeed at that level if the conceptual shift is made for him. Returning to our examples from the Stanford-Binet, if the child is *shown* that the "funny thing" about the first picture in the Year VII series is that a man is walking in the rain with his umbrella held in such a manner that it does not keep him dry, the child may then be able to correctly supply the incongruities in the remaining three pictures. While this "cue" may invalidate the scoring aspect of this test item, it does indicate that the child is capable of making a certain type of abstraction at the seven-year level, and that his performance at this level is at times impaired by his rigidity in concept formation. In a psychological evaluation of a child with cerebral palsy, the acquisition of this type of information about the child's intellectual processes is of considerably greater value than is the establishment of a rigidly-defined IQ score.

Initiatory Confusion and Delay: A behavioral factor loosely associated with rigidity in brain damaged children is initiatory confusion and delay. This refers to the fact that brain injuries which diminish organizational capacity also tend to reduce rapidity of integration. Thus, the child with brain damage generally shows considerable slowness, and confusion in initiation of responses. Such children may often be potentially capable of responding to a visual, or verbal, stimulus, but there may be an unduly long delay between stimulus and response. We are not referring here to response delays due to lack of sensitivity to stimuli (although this may sometimes also be a factor). Rather, the problem here seems to be one of generalized slowness in the ability to organize and execute an appropriate reaction complex. A child may know perfectly well how old he is, but may "just sit and look blank" for a moment when asked his age, not because he has temporarily "forgotten," but because the complex process of becoming cognizant of the question, selecting the correct answer, and organizing the proper motor response to express the answer, takes considerably longer than it does for the non-brain-damaged child. The implications of this type of difficulty will be discussed in further detail in a later section of this chapter.

PSYCHOLOGICAL EVALUATION OF
BRAIN DAMAGED CHILDREN

Basic Considerations: When applied to children, the term "Intelligence Quotient" expresses a *ratio* between the child's *mental age* and his chronological age. This relationship is commonly expressed by the formula:

$$IQ = \frac{MA}{CA}$$

It is obvious that when MA and CA in the above formula are equal, the resultant IQ equals 1.00. In current practice, the decimal point is dropped: thus, where MA and CA are equal, IQ is expressed as 100. Similarly, where mental age exceeds chronological age, IQ is expressed by a figure exceeding 100. Conversely, when mental age lags behind chronological age, IQ is expressed by a figure below 100. For example, a ten year old boy who has achieved a mental age of twelve years has an IQ of 120, while a ten year old having a mental age of only eight years has an IQ of 80.

Generally, it has been believed that, within certain statistical limits, mental age increases at a relatively steady rate throughout childhood. Thus it was believed possible to *predict,* under ordinary conditions, a child's future mental age on the basis of his present IQ score. Assuming, for example, that a child who is five years of age has achieved a mental age of only four years. This child thus has an MA/CA ratio of 4/5 or an IQ of 80. This implies that this *child's* rate of mental growth is four fifths, or 80 per cent of "normal." Accepting this implication, it is possible, within certain limits of statistical confidence, to predict what the mental age of this child will be at maturity or at any specified chronological age between the present and the age at which mental maturity theoretically is reached.

Statistical studies have suggested that, for the general population, IQ scores remain *relatively* stable throughout the life span of the individual. It is this relative stability of IQ that makes it possible to predict the rate and extent of mental development under normal conditions. Thus, a child who has achieved a mental age of only three years on his fourth birthday, has an IQ of 75, and it can generally be predicted that, for example, he will have a mental age of six years when his chronological age is eight, an MA of seven and one-half years when he is ten years old, and a mental age of nine years when he is twelve years old. This relative predictability of future mental age on the basis of present IQ is a basic consideration in many of the educational placement and counselling decisions made in modern educational systems at the present time.

In addition to its predictive aspects, intelligence testing has *comparative* implications. When we state that a child is developing mentally at a rate which is only 80 per cent of normal, we are, in effect, stating that his rate of mental growth is below average, or "slow." Furthermore, there is the implication that, for most children and under normal physical and environmental conditions, the same figure which represents rate of mental development also represents *capacity* or *potential* for mental development.

Numerous statistical studies have established the interpretation of IQ scores in terms which, on a practical basis express levels of "brightness." Various research studies have yielded slightly differing interpretations. In general, however, IQ scores within the range of 95-105 are accepted as implying average mental ability, while decade steps above and below this range express various levels of mental superiority or inferiority. Generally, scores of 70 and below imply definite mental deficiency; and scores of 130 and over express markedly superior mental ability.

While the general concepts of "relative stability of IQ" and of "predictable incremental growth of intelligence" have proven useful as general guides in many academic and vocational counselling situations, research studies have periodically produced findings which do not entirely support these concepts.

Bayley and her associates have repeatedly tested the concept of the relative predictability of the extent of mental development based upon tests administered in infancy and early childhood.[2,3] In their early studies they found that there was virtually no relationship between scores which presumably normal infants achieved on developmental tests during the first few months of infancy, and scores earned at the end of the first year of life. Other workers, most notably Honzik, MacFarlane, and Allen[46,47,1] have produced findings which are in essential agreement with the Bayley studies in that they show a consistently low correlation between mental test scores obtained by infants and scores obtained by the same children a year or two later. There is now rather general agreement that later intelligence levels cannot be predicted from scores obtained on tests during early infancy.

The lack of stability of infant test scores has resulted in the recurrent suggestion that the tests in general use are not composed of the right kind of items; and various efforts have been made to find additional or supplemental items to increase the predictive value of such tests. However, a major difficulty invariably encountered in such attempts is the relatively limited range in infant behaviors which can be objectively observed and recorded. One may observe that a month old infant momentarily focuses on an object dangling before his eyes, or that a sudden, loud noise will elicit a startle pattern. A little later in life he will randomly manipulate a spoon, block or other favored object. Somewhere around the sixth or seventh month he will give evidence of "memory" by becoming distressed when a plaything is removed from his sight, or by "looking for it" if it should accidently roll or fall away from his immediate line of sight. One can also note the progressing variety and meaningfulness of vocalizations, and the developing awareness of strange people and new situations. In making such observations for "test" purposes, the question arises as to which of these activities are forerunners and predictors of later intellectual development.

A standard method of selecting predictive test items is to use later test scores against which to correlate successes on infant test items. Scores earned by infants or very young children on individual test items have been correlated with their later IQ scores, with the items showing the highest correlations being combined into new scales or tests. This method has been tried with varying degrees of success. Anderson[2] compared successes on items under one year with retest criteria at two and five years. Maurer,[56] compared scores on items administered at three and five years of age. Other workers have reported similar studies.[35,64] In general, these studies have shown that predictions made at later preschool ages were considerably more accurate than predictions based upon tests administered very early in life. These findings cast doubt on the measurability of a stable and predictable set of intellectual factors in the very young, and must force some to question the concept of intelligence as a "basic capacity" which expands through childhood at a very steady and arithmetically predictable rate. No attempt will be made here to summarize all of the recent studies of the relative stability or alterability of rates of mental development during infancy or childhood. In general, however, such studies indicate that in normal children prediction of "adult" or terminal IQ levels on the basis of earlier test scores tends to become progressively more reliable when the tests upon which the predictions are based are administered progressively closer to the fifth or sixth year of chronological age.

The relatively poor predictive reliability of intelligence test scores attained by normal children under five years of age would seem to have important implications in cerebral palsy. This poor reliability suggests that tests which are now in common use do not contain items which tap all of the behavioral factors which contribute to the development of general intelligence. It further suggests that intelligence, rather than being a simple or integrated entity, is a dynamic succession of developing and expanding functions, with the later and more complex functions being dependent upon the prior maturation of the earlier ones. If intelligence is a complex of functions developing within a temporal sequence, we must expect that influences which would tend to retard one aspect of development, or otherwise disturb the temporal relationships between various developmental factors, would be reflected by alterations in the rate and general course of intellectual growth. Such influences are plainly evident in cerebral palsy.

Cerebral palsy is a condition in which the various motor, sensory, and intellectual functions are likely to develop at highly individual and differentiated rates. In the normal child, generally three to four months elapse between the time he is able to sit up without support, and the time at which he takes his first few walking steps. In the child with cerebral palsy, the time elapsing between these two events may be a few months; it may be one or two years; or it may be half a lifetime. The normal child, within a span of less than two years, progresses in relatively orderly and temporally predictable steps from random cooing and gurgling, through consonantal babbling, to the use of articulate words and simple phrases. While the speech development of the child with cerebral palsy passes through these same phases, the temporal interrelationships of the various phrases may be vastly different from that of the normal child; the earlier stages may be late in their initiation. Each stage may be prolonged; or any one phase may be disproportionately long in relation to the others. This temporally atypical rate of development may occur in any number of developmental areas.

Accepting the concept of mental development as a dynamic succession of functions, in which later functions are dependent upon the previous maturation of earlier ones, it follows that mental growth in cerebral palsy can often be expected to show the same "incline and plateau" pattern of development as is noted in other areas. That this pattern of mental growth does occur in cerebral palsy was demonstrated by Doll, Phelps, and Melcher[20] over a quarter of a century ago. Their studies of cerebral palsied children at the Vineland Training School indicated that in many cases of cerebral palsy, mental age tended to increase by unequal increments in relation to constant time intervals. Another fact having considerable importance in the mental evaluation of children with cerebral palsy is demonstrated in these studies. The generally accepted mental growth curve, with some qualifications as demonstrated by Bayley and others, rises steadily from birth to about fourteen or fifteen years of chronological age, at which time intelligence as measured by tests such as the Stanford-Binet, tends to "level off" and show no appreciable further growth. The individuals with cerebral palsy studied by Doll, Phelps and Melcher, however, in many cases showed continuing mental growth well beyond the fifteenth year of life.

Our psychometric observations of children with cerebral palsy in training at the Institute of Logopedics strongly corroborates the early findings noted above. Using the 1937 revision of the Stanford-Binet as a basic test instrument, we noted numerous cases of cerebral palsy in which mental age tended to increase in irregular "steps" rather than in the pattern of the smooth incline. This seems to be especially true of children having severe motor or sensory disabilities. The mental growth records of several cases in point are summarized in Table I.

TABLE I
MENTAL GROWTH SUMMARIES OF SEVERAL CASES WITH CEREBRAL PALSY SHOWING ATYPICAL GROWTH CURVES

		Date	CA	MA	IQ
Case J.B.:	Spastic Quadriplegia	Jan. 1950	3-6	2-0	57
		Jul. 1950	4-0	2-1	52
		Jan. 1951	4-6	2-2	48
		Jul. 1951	4-0	2-9	55
		Jan. 1952	5-6	3-8	60
		Jul. 1952	6-0	4-6	75
		Jan. 1953	6-6	5-0	77
		Jul. 1953	7-0	5-7	80
Case D.E.:	Spastic Hemiplegia	Feb. 1951	6-0	2-8	44
		Aug. 1951	6-6	3-9	57
		Feb. 1952	7-0	4-7	65
		Aug. 1952	7-6	5-0	67
		Feb. 1953	8-0	5-4	66
		Aug. 1953	8-6	5-8	66
		Feb. 1954	9-0	6-1	67
Case V.B.:	Athetosis	Mar. 1951	7-0	2-6	35
		Sep. 1951	7-6	3-0	40
		Mar. 1952	8-0	3-5	42
		Sep. 1952	8-6	3-9	44
		Mar. 1953	9-0	4-0	44
Case R.S..:	Athetoid-Spastic (Mixed)	Sep. 1951	34-0	7-2	47
		Oct. 1952	35-1	8-0	53
		Nov. 1953	36-2	8-7	56
		Feb. 1955	37-5	9-3	62
		Sep. 1955	38-0	9-5	63
		Feb. 1956	38-5	9-5	63

It will be noted that the illustrative cases in Table I do not show a constantly maintained ratio between chronological age and mental development. The fact that such patterns of mental growth are very frequently noted in children with cerebral palsy must serve as an indication against using "first test" scores made by such children as the basis for inflexible longterm planning. Even where the individual is of relatively advanced age, as in

Case R. S., above, IQ scores are subject to change. Such changes in
IQ are especially to be expected to occur in cases who are receiving
habilitative training, inasmuch as such training often serves to
ameliorate or correct many of the factors which contribute, in
cerebral palsy, both to retardation of mental development, and
to reaction syndromes which militate against the complete expression of mental ability in standard psychometric situations.

The majority of standard psychometric testing instruments
presently in common use have been standardized on a population
having a relatively homogeneous history of interaction with the
physical and cultural environment of our society.[6] It must be
recognized that regardless of the possible existence of a factor
commonly termed "innate" or "native" intelligence, the performances and responses elicited by intelligence tests are *learned* responses acquired by the individual through his interactions with
the general environment. Thus, the individual's ability to respond
adequately to such tests will be greatly affected by what he has
been able to assimilate from his environmental contacts. Assuming that all individuals tested at any given chronological age have
had essentially the same degree and type of environmental experiences, it is valid to infer that noted differences in performance
repertoires are reflections of differences in "native" intelligence;
i.e., if environmental histories are relatively equal, those individuals who have learned more from the environment in a stated
chronological period are "more intelligent."[7] It must be noted,
however, that children severely handicapped by cerebral palsy
seldom, if ever, have "normal" or "typical" environmental experiences. In the main, such children have had limited, or restricted,
social, cultural, and general interactional experiences.

There are many factors in cerebral palsy which contribute to
the restriction of the life experiences of individuals so affected.
The normal, or "average" child is in daily contact with the cultural artifacts and social patterns which contribute to the general
structure of modern community life. "Experience" for the normal
child begins in infancy. The infant lives in a world of slowly
individuating sensory impressions; visual, auditory, olfactory,
tactile, kinesthetic, and proprioceptive cues which gradually,

through repeated experiential events, acquire specific associations and meanings. In cerebral palsy, where sensory deficiencies and disturbances are frequently noted, contact with the social environment may thus be restricted from very early infancy. As life progresses, the average child draws experiences from ever-widening spheres of interaction. In the early months, the child's sphere of interaction is limited by his lack of mobility and his limited ability to communicate. Somewhere around the ninth month, however, the normal infant begins a rapid expansion of his field of activity. He begins to crawl, and to investigate and manipulate his physical surroundings. He soon learns to perceive and appreciate the physical relationships and personal implications of many of the things in his environment which previously were merely sensory impressions without specific meaning. He becomes aware of spatial depth relationships as he tries to climb, off or onto furniture or stairs. He learns in random play that he can roll round or spherical objects, and makes piles of objects having flat surfaces. He learns to differentiate textures and temperatures, and to avoid discomfort through contact with various objects around him.

Soon after the end of his first year, the average child begins to walk, and thus further expands his environmental experiences. Concurrently, the child's basic patterns of vocal communication begin to expand. The random cooings and babblings of infancy begin to have communicative value, and the child begins to learn that he can to some extent control his environment by specific vocal activities.

Thus it is that the average child progresses into ever-widening areas of interaction. By the time he has reached kindergarten age he has had a multitude of interactions with his environment, and is in daily contact with a world of balls, hoops, cats, dogs, toy cars, real cars, spoons, knives, forks, grocery stores, candy stores, fictional heroes, and other little boys and girls who laugh, cry, sing, tease, boast, pretend and fight. It is these activities, in all their educative ramifications which form the experiential basis for the responses elicited by most tests of intelligence. It must be recognized that regardless of the existence of a factor of "basic intelligence," a child cannot respond adequately to a vocabulary test, a number concept test, a form of recognition test, or a test of any other function unless he has learned through environmental experiences to deal with such factors.

In contrast to the average child, let us consider the child who is brain-damaged. Let us assume, if only for the sake of exposition, that "native" or "innate" intelligence does exist. Could such a child be expected to compare favorably with normal children of similar mental ability when evaluated with a standardized test of intelligence? There are several factors which strongly suggest that he probably could not. If the child has sensory or perceptual disabilities which are often associated with brain injury, his capacity for the acquisition of information through environmental contacts may be affected from early infancy. Such difficulties: hearing deficits, visual and auditory perceptual deviations, kinesthetic and proprioceptive defects may markedly interfere with the early acquisition of basic concepts relative to the immediate environment. The adage, "The burnt infant dreads the fire," implies that the child learns to associate physical discomfort with a definite complex of other sensory impressions. Similarly, the child evaluates and reacts appropriately to environmental stimuli on the basis of his previous experiences.

Where environmental interaction has been restricted by limitations on physical mobility, by sensory deviations which limit or distort the environment, or by a combination of these factors, commonly employed "mental test" stimuli may often fail to elicit adequate responses regardless of the child's potential intelligence. It is commonly noted in situations where children with cerebral palsy are receiving clinical habilitation, that as the children begin to walk, to use their hands more efficiently, and to play with other children outside of the immediate clinical environment, their IQ scores, in general, tend to increase. In a study by Berko,[5] a group of severely motor-handicapped children showed IQ increases of as much as twenty-five points during an eighteen month period of intensive clinical and educational rehabilitative training.

The Brain-damage Syndrome as a Factor in Psychological Testing: The preceding sections of this chapter have given a broad generalized outline of the psychological characteristics of the brain-damaged child in terms of his various learning and general perceptual and linguistic problems. Some attention was also given to the role of experiential deficits in the social and intellectual development of such children, particularly those with severe motor disabilities. The inference which might be gained from the entire discussion is that meaningful, clinically-useful psychological testing data cannot be obtained from such children, or, more particularly, that estimates of present levels of intellectual functioning, and predictions of future mental development cannot be made. Such inferences are entirely unwarranted. Quite to the contrary, the role of the clinical psychologist in planning the habilitative program of the brain-damaged child can be one of utmost importance: First, the manifestations of the brain-damage syndrome are often demonstrated more clearly in the psychological testing situation than at any other time. Thus, it is largely the province of the clinical psychologist to make the preliminary analysis of the child's functional difficulties. Secondly, any habilitative program must be geared to the child's present level of intellectual development, and to some estimate of his potential for future development. Evaluations of this type are possible with most brain-damaged children. One of the keys to effective evaluation of brain-damaged children is the psychologist's knowledge of the brain-damage syndrome, and his ability to structure the testing situation in such a way that the child can function at his optimal level of performance. Therefore, what we should like to discuss at this point are some basic principles of interaction between the examining psychologist and the brain-damaged child which will facilitate optimal performance by the child being tested, and concomitantly, give the examiner the fullest possible amount of information about the child. We shall largely address ourselves to the problem of getting optimal performance in spite of the brain-damage syndrome. Therefore, some repetition of previously discussed concepts will be necessary.

Deviant Propositionality: The brain-damaged child is likely to be a child who has repeatedly been faced by frustration and failure. Thus practically every response that may be required of him can represent a threat to his self-esteem and personal security.

This is of extreme importance in the psychometric testing situation. It often occurs that the child's mere recognition of the fact that he is being "tested," or that his responses are being evaluated is enough to raise the propositionality of the situation to such a height that the child is unable to organize his responses or to do many things which he is able to do with relative ease and efficiency in situations which are less threatening to his personal security. For this reason it is necessary to avoid conveying to the child, insofar as possible, the impression that he is being evaluated or "tested." In most younger children, this is readily accomplished by imparting a "play atmosphere" to the testing situation. Generally, as the child is brought into the examining room, he should be greeted informally and warmly. A good "trick of the trade" here, is for the examiner to learn beforehand, of some favorite activity in which the child has recently, or is currently participating, and to greet the child with "Hi, Bobby. How's your new puppy today?" (Assuming, of course, that it is Bobby, and that he does have a new puppy.) The child may then be introduced to the testing procedure rather indirectly: a simple formboard, maze, or other low-level test should be on the table when the child enters the room. The examiner may say after greeting the child, "Look at this puzzle: bet you can show me how to work it."

Some children, especially many of those severely limited children who have repeatedly faced frustration and failure, may hesitate at attempting even the most simple form of puzzle. In such cases, the child should not be directly urged to perform, as this will further increase the propositionality. Rather, a usually successful approach is for the examiner to begin working the formboard or puzzle himself, and to appear to be enjoying it immensely. Usually, the child will join in and "help" the examiner. When the child begins, the examiner gradually ceases his own activity and permits the child to complete the task himself. After several performance items are completed in this manner, the shift is made to the actual testing material, and most children will continue to "play the games" until an adequate sampling of test performances has been obtained. The examiner should never directly evaluate the child's responses for him, although occasional offhand encouragement and expressions of approval are helpful in maintaining rapport and prolonging the child's performance.

Catastrophic Behavior: Catastrophic behavior refers to a pattern of nonadaptive behaviors produced by brain-injured children under conditions of emotional stress. It is of utmost importance that these behaviors be recognized during the process of psychological examination in that they are reactions which often prevent the child from performing at his highest level of efficiency, and thus may create an impression of lower mentality than is actually the case.

Various forms of catastrophic behavior are commonly noted in children with cerebral palsy and other brain injury syndromes. *Perseveration* is an often-observed catastrophic reaction. Under conditions of propositional stress, the child has a tendency to repeat previously-rewarded responses, rather than to make adequate responses to the succeeding portions of a series of communicative interactions. In the psychometric testing situation, perseveration is often the basis of "wrong" answers, when the child may repeat his previous "right" answer rather than risk error by making a new response. Generally, perseverative reactions can rather easily be broken by the examiner, simply by momentarily shifting the child's attention to some factor outside of the immediate testing situation. For example, when a child begins to perseverate on the Picture Vocabulary subtest of the Stanford-Binet, the examiner may interject a comment about the weather, thus giving the child a chance to "reorganize" before returning to the task.

It should be recognized that catastrophic reactions are reactions to failure, or to the imminent possibility of failure. In addition to perseveration, catastrophic reactions may take the form of a general disintegration of response organization: in response to a demand for any specific performance, the child may "simply freeze up and go blank"; he may make a completely nonadaptive response even though he is capable of giving the correct response; he may burst into tears, or he may show marked vasomotor lability.

Vasomotor lability is a catastrophic sign characterized by excessive perspiration, flushing, pallor, rapid breathing, etc., and is generally an indication that the child is, for the moment, being pushed beyond his capacity, and is under severe emotional stress. When this reaction is noted, examination procedures should be halted and the child should be permitted to do whatever he wishes until the signs are no longer noted.

It is quite obvious that propositional deviations and catastrophic behavior can, unless skillfully circumvented or avoided, detract most seriously from a brain-injured child's psychometric performance. Further sources of interference with the full expression of his abilities are emotional lability, hyperirritable attention and initiatory confusion and delay. These too, are reactions to psychological stress, but differ from those reactions previously mentioned in that they appear to have little or no direct relationship to specific situational factors, and are rather unpredictable in their occurrence and duration.

Hyperirritable attention is generally listed as a behavioral characteristic commonly noted in brain-injured children, and refers to the difficulty which many of these children display in selecting one stimulus complex out of a broader field of stimuli. This behavioral feature is not exclusively a catastrophic sign in brain injury inasmuch as it is often noted in situations where there is no apparent propositional pressure; however, it is often noted that hyperirritability of attention tends to increase as propositional pressures mount.

In children with brain injury, *attention disturbances* take several forms. *General hyperactivity* is a form of attention disturbance in which the child is in a state of general overactivity, either only for a brief period, or up to any length of time including, in some cases, most of his waking hours. This state of overactivity is generally characterized by excessive physical restlessness, inability to remain in one spot, or to attend to a single set of stimuli for more than a few seconds, and sometimes by displays of sham rage, screaming, kicking, crying, etc., especially when restrictions on physical activity are imposed. *Hyperirritable attention* as noted above is essentially a problem of poor stimulus isolation and selection. A child displaying hyperirritable attention need not, and often does not, display general hyperactivity. Yet he finds it difficult to attend to a given task. His "set" for any specific activity is very easily disrupted by extraneous field stimuli. In the psychometric testing situation, a child's attention to a formboard task may be diverted by the faint sound of an airplane passing high overhead, or by a shadow cast by a passing bird, or by any number of stimuli, out of the immediate field of activity, and of intensities so low that they would act as subthreshold background stimuli in the activity matrices of most children.

Attention disturbances have importance implications in the psychometric evaluation of children with brain injury. The essential point is that the examiner must conduct his procedure in such a manner as to guarantee that the child will attend to the tasks presented at his best possible level. The hyperactive child obviously cannot be satisfactorily examined in a state of marked hyperactivity. Yet, due to restrictions of staff time and facilities, clinical situations do arise in which it is necessary to make at least an estimate of the mental ability of an hyperactive child. In such situations, the clinician must do two things: He must arrange the environment in such a manner that it will be the least conducive to hyperactivity; and he must try to "key" his procedures to the child's general activity pattern. Cluttered, disorderly physical arrangements are conducive to hyperactivity in the brain injured child. Examining rooms should therefore be kept as simple and barren as possible. Wherever physical space permits, bookcases, typewriter, study desks, and other office furnishings should not be included in the examining room, as these objects will draw the child's attention from the tasks at hand. Wherever possible, the testing room should be soundproofed to eliminate extraneous auditory stimuli. Windows, if present, should be covered with opaque or translucent material to cut out unwanted visual stimuli. In testing very hyperactive children, it is also helpful at times to arrange the lighting in the room so that only the areas immediately surrounding the child, examiner, and examining table are illuminated. If the child remains hyperactive despite the greatest possible reduction of stimuli, it is then necessary to conduct the examination during the brief "calm periods" which many children of this type have between bursts of activity. Most of these children, under conditions of reduced stimuli, will remain quiet long enough to answer one question, or to partially complete a form-board. If permitted to wander about the room for a short while after completing a small work segment of this sort, they will generally return and do a little additional productive work before another burst of hyperactivity. By noting the quality of perform-ance during these "calm periods," a rough estimate of the child's mental ability may be obtained.

Most hyperactive children react negatively to direct pressure intended to restrict activity. Occasionally, however, one finds a hyperactive child whose activity overflow *can* be directly restricted. Such children are noted to react positively to bodily restraint, and they will perform well if they are held in the lap of the examiner or his assistant during the examination. One might hypothesize that such children gain a sense of security from the imposition of well-defined "activity boundaries" and are, therefore, able to react within sharply restricted physical limits more effectively than when they must select an activity area from a broader field of possibilities for interaction with the spatial environment.

In dealing with children having hyperirritable attention, but without marked physical hyperactivity, the same principles of stimulus-reduction apply: mainly, orderly and uncluttered physical arrangements and elimination of extraneous field stimuli.

Emotional lability is a behavioral characteristic often noted in children with brain injury, and is essentially a tendency to over-react to the emotional components of a situation. Children dis-playing this characteristic tend to laugh, cry, or become angry quite readily. Their emotional reactions are subject to rapid and frequent alteration and may at times be entirely inappropriate to a given situation. Observance of emotionally labile children in the psychological testing situation suggests that emotional lability has two basic forms. In some children, especially in those displaying general hyperactivity, there appears to be a rather constant emotional overflow. These children will laugh, cry, scream and manifest "temper tantrum behavior" with no apparent provocation. They are most difficult to deal with in the testing situation, and the emotional overflow must be treated as part of the general hyperactivity problem, as discussed in previous paragraphs. In other children, emotional lability is manifested as a direct reaction to situational stimuli. Such children laugh heartily, and at times uncontrollably at slight incongruities or mildly humorous situations. They may cry in response to any show of disapproval from the examiner, from recognitions of their own failures in a testing situation, as part of a startle response from a sudden sound or unexpected sight, or as a general fear response upon entering an unfamiliar situation. At times they may react with anger rather than fear to any new or frustrating situation.

In psychological examination of these children, emotional lability can generally be reduced or controlled by introducing the child to the testing procedures slowly and casually, by permitting him to "investigate" and play with the testing materials before they are used for test purposes, and by avoiding any implication of failure in the child's performance. It is also well for the examiner to avoid any sudden movements or noises. He should also introduce new test materials into the situation gradually and with some verbal reassurance that the next activity will be pleasant to the child and that he is certain to succeed with it. When emotionally labile reactions become severe enough to detract from the child's test performance, it is well to stop the activity at hand and either to sit quietly and do nothing for a moment, or to switch the activity back to a previous test item with which the child had had a considerable degree of success. It should again be noted that the emotionally labile child does not always react to a situation with an appropriate reaction. Thus, laughter, for example, may be an indication of distress rather than joy.

Perceptual Problems: We have raised the question of whether the perceptual difficulties noted in children with cerebral palsy are necessarily related to specific neurological lesions, or whether they may at times be associated with experiential and maturational deficits, and we have observed that some perceptual failures noted in children with cerebral palsy are similar to the perceptual performances of normal children at lower maturational levels. However, regardless of etiology, there seems to be general agreement that perceptual difficulties are a recognizable entity in the communication complexes of children with brain injuries. This is of considerable importance in the intellectual evaluation of children with cerebral palsy. Primarily, it is a factor which the psychological examiner must be prepared to recognize and to consider in his interpretation of test results. A child with cerebral palsy may, for example, fail most of the "drawing" items in a test such as the Stanford-Binet while passing all of the verbal items at corresponding levels. Such failures will, of course, depress the statistical test score, often to the point where the resulting IQ is not an accurate representation of the child's general mental ability. The examiner, in summarizing his findings, should always note factors such as these, and make some estimate of the child's level of ability in other areas.

The recognition of the existence of visual-perceptual problems in children with cerebral palsy has further importance to the proper selection of testing devices for the evaluation of the child's general level of intelligence. Within recent years, many workers, in attempting to circumvent psychometric testing difficulties arising from motor coordination and speech difficulties, have advocated the use of specially contrived "nonverbal and nonmotor" tests which are in the main composed of form-matching, form-differentiation, and matrix-completion items. While such tests are at times extremely useful, their use can result in highly erroneous evaluations when applied to children with unrecognized visual-perceptual disturbances. One recent study showed that some children with cerebral palsy earned considerably higher IQ scores on the Stanford-Binet than they did when tested with a well-known test of the aforementioned type.[8]

Defective Abstraction and Categorization: This refers to the tendency on the part of some children to perform abstracting and categorizing functions on the basis of factors not commonly or normally assigned the status of prime situational determinants. There are innumerable possible illustrations of this phenomenon. In psychometric testing situations, they are most commonly noted as failures in problems requiring the child to understand various grouping and matching concepts. The most common example is to be found in failures in various color-matching tests, in which a child may match colored objects on the basis of color saturation or intensity, rather than on the basis of more primary differences in hue. On a more complex level, a child may fail a picture-completion item by noting the absence of earlobe or eyelash details on the picture of a man, and failing to mention the absence of an arm or a leg. While these two examples appear to tap differing intellectual functions, they are similar in that the failures in both instances are based upon aberrant factor selection, in which secondary or incidental factors are weighted as prime determinants of situational context. In psychometric evaluation of children with brain injuries, such responses are unavoidable and must be assigned a negative score. However, they should always be carefully noted inasmuch as they give important clues to the subject's total mode of intellectual psychosocial functioning, and they may constitute a partial basis for some of his more complex emotional and social adjustment difficulties.

Finally, in noting the behavioral characteristics which may affect performance in a psychometric testing situation, *initiatory confusion and delay* must be considered. Many children with brain injuries have difficulties in response organization and initiation. Even when such children "know the answer," they may require an inordinately long time to organize an appropriate response. This appears to represent an integrative failure in which the various intellective and motor components of a response segment do not readily correlate themselves. In a testing situation, a child may sit silently for a very long time before initiating a response; or, he may make several tentative or abortive "starts," as though he were "feeling his way" into a good response pattern. The examiner must be cognizant of these delay patterns. In most children, when such delays occur, urging or "prompting" is generally not helpful, and in many cases will further confuse the child. Of course, if the delay is extremely long, e.g., sixty seconds or more, the examiner should reword or restructure the problem inasmuch as extreme delays may indicate that the child has forgotten what he was supposed to do.

Interpretation of Psychological Testing Data: The clinical psychologist, presented with the task of evaluating a brain-damaged child, should have some general philosophy, or set of informational objectives, which determines his general approach to the child, the testing instruments he will employ, and the interpretation he will assign to his observations and objective test results. Generally, psychological assessment of the brain-damaged child is requested either because the child is in a clinical rehabilitative situation and the clinicians and therapists are seeking information which will assist them in planning his training program, or because the child is *not* in a special training program, and is either not making physical and educational progress, and the parents, school authorities, or family physician are seeking some insight into the child's difficulties. Thus, the psychologist generally finds himself in either of two positions, that of having to make an original diagnosis of brain damage, or that of evaluating a child in whom brain damage is known to exist. Generally, in either case, the psychologist is expected to be of some help in planning the child's future, particularly with reference to educational or special training programs.

The largest section of this chapter has been devoted to a detailed description of the brain damage syndrome. Therefore, we do not feel that a lengthy discussion of procedures for the detection of brain damage in children is mandatory here. If the psychologist is aware of the generalized brain damage syndrome, his observations of the child's general behavior, plus his observations of test performances, particularly relative to his perceptual, perceptual-motor, and general linguistic and intellectual function, in terms of factors discussed at length in this chapter, will give an ample basis upon which a diagnosis of brain damage can be made. Such information can be buttressed by observational and case history data.

The diagnosis of cerebral palsy is, of course, a function of the physician, rather than the psychologist. However, the psychologist should be at least familiar enough with the gross motor manifestations of cerebral palsy to make a gross and tentative diagnosis of this problem. A detailed outline of the motor symptoms of cerebral palsy is outside the scope of this chapter. However, the psychologist should be aware that signs of neuromuscular disorder, such as muscular rigidity, tremors and involuntary movement, poor balance, gross speech defects in which the child actually seems to be having difficulty in moving his lips, tongue and jaw, are all part of the general picture in cerebral palsy, and hence indicate some form of central nervous system dysfunction.

Of course, not *all* individuals with cerebral palsy have the type of brain damage which is associated with disturbed linguistic and intellectual functioning. Our own clinical records suggest that roughly 20 to 25 per cent of the cerebral palsied have motor difficulties only and no defects in linguistic or intellectual functioning. But, as a general rule, the child with cerebral palsy can be expected to show the general behavioral syndrome of brain damage, as previously outlined in this chapter. In cases where there is no gross motor impairment, the medical history, particularly the birth history can be helpful in confirming the suspected brain damage. As discussed elsewhere in this book, prolonged and difficult labor, immediate postnatal anoxic conditions, and prolonged high fevers in infancy, are some of the more common etiological factors in childhood brain damage.

Therefore, in general, the detection of brain damage in children should pose no really difficult problem to the psychologist who is aware of the general symptomatology and of the etiological factors. In addition to symptomatological and etiological cues, certain features noted in intellectual tests give fairly reliable indications of brain damage. As Berko,[5] Doll[19] and many others have demonstrated, the "ragged psychometric profile," or "psychometric scatter" is, when used in conjunction with other indicators, a fairly reliable sign of brain damage.

The concept of "psychometric scatter" is based on a rather simple rationale. Psychometric tests, particularly tests of "intelligence" are statistically based upon performance norms of the "average" child of any given age. We shall not go into the vast statistical complexities of test construction here, but in a highly generalized way, mental age norms for various test items are established on the basis of "median cutting points" for any given performance. What this means (with some complex qualifications which need not concern us here) is that if we wanted to establish a mental age level for, let us say, simple object counting tasks, we would take very large numbers of randomly-selected children from each of several age groups, and see how many objects they could count. If we then found that roughly half of the five-year-olds (this is grossly oversimplified) could count five objects correctly, then "counting five objects" would become identified as the "normal" performance for the "average" five year old. With performance norms established in this manner for a variety of performance areas, such as size of vocabulary, ability to draw circles and squares, and any of a great number of other types of things which go into the construction of a general intelligence test, the statistical nature of the test becomes such that the normal child will function at about the same level in all aspects of the test. This means that within certain limits, a child with a five-year vocabulary level will also be at about a five year level in all of his other performances. Now, since the child with brain damage is, because of the nature of the brain damage syndrome, not likely to develop all his abilities at the same pace, it is likely that some of his abilities will be much more highly (or much more poorly) developed than others. For example, a child with apraxia may have a five year vocabulary level, but only a three year level in drawing ability. A child with abstracting problems may do excellently in concrete performance tasks with puzzles and formboards, but do very poorly in more abstract tasks, such as naming the major functional similarities between objects. This disparity of performance levels between various types of abilities in the same child, is what is commonly referred to as "psychometric scatter."

The concept of psychometric scatter can be an immensely useful one in the psychological evaluation of brain-damaged children. First, taken in conjunction with other diagnostic signs, it can be a fairly reliable indicator of brain injury. Secondly, with certain types of tests, particularly the Wechsler Intelligence Scale for Children, and to a lesser degree with the Stanford-Binet Scales, the scatter pattern can provide the major portion of the format for the entire evaluative process. In other words, by making comparisons between the levels of various aspects of performance, we can derive a great deal of important data about the actual dynamic and functional nature of the child's total learning problem. With the WISC, for example, problems such as poor abstract reasoning, various types of perceptual, or perceptual-motor difficulties, vocabulary deficits, memory span difficulties, etc., can readily be sorted out. The same is true of the Binet Scales, although the evaluation here is perhaps a bit more difficult because some of the functions tapped by the Binet items are not quite as readily identifiable as those of the WISC. Nevertheless, levels of abstract verbal comprehension, basic number concepts, abstract associative reasoning, social comprehension, numerical comprehension, auditory memory span, and similar factors can be isolated from both the 1937 and the later ("L-M") revision of the Stanford-Binet.

A third function of the psychometric scatter concept lies in its possible usefulness in refining the predictive aspects of raw IQ scores. Considerable discussion of various factors which may tend to seriously impair the predictive value of intelligence test scores, as applied to brain damaged children has been presented throughout this chapter. Naturally, the question arises: Is there any way of obtaining estimates of mental ability which have some real predictive value, or can psychometric measurement in the brain damaged be applied only in terms of assessment of present status? Some years ago, we[5] were highly encouraged by the possibility of using psychometric scatter as a predictor of the probable "maximal potential" of expected mental development for brain injured children, and some preliminary research in this area was performed and reported. Our rationale, and some of the preliminary findings, are summarized below.

> That intelligence test scores obtained by administering standard tests to brain-injured children often do not adequately predict the future course of mental development of such children, is attested to by comparison of original and retest IQ scores of brain-injured children participating in long-term programs of intensive general physical, educational and language habilitation. At the Institute of Logopedics, where habilitation is provided for large numbers of children with cerebral palsy and other brain injuries, records are kept of the Stanford-Binet IQ scores of such children upon admission to training and at various periods throughout the training program. In general, these records indicate that as the various problems of the brain-injured child are ameliorated, as walking and manipulation are improved, as communicative facility is increased and as emotional patterns are stabilized, IQ scores tend to increase.

Stanford-Binet IQ scores of fifty children with cerebral palsy (in training at the Institute of Logopedics) were studied over an average period of eighteen months. These children were not all in training during the same period, but represent twenty-five children of each sex, for whom Stanford-Binet test/retest scores, encompassing eighteen months of continuous training were available (although all of the children did not receive the same type of program). Each child participated in an habilitation program geared to meet his individual therapeutic and educational needs.

The children studied were twenty-five males and twenty-five females ranging in age from two years and eleven months, to sixteen years. The findings in this study are summarized in Table II.

TABLE II
STANFORD-BINET IQ SCORES FOR FIFTY CHILDREN WITH CEREBRAL PALSY, AT ONSET AND CLOSE OF AN EIGHTEEN-MONTH PERIOD OF HABILITATIVE TRAINING

	Test I	Test II
Mean CA	10-1	11-7
Mean MA	6-0	7-3
Mean IQ	59.5	62.5

As noted in Table II, the children studied showed an increase in Mean IQ of three points in an eighteen-month period. While this was not a statistically significant increase in IQ, for the whole group, intelligence quotient changes ranged from —5 to +25 points, with ten cases showing IQ gains of ten or more points. Of the five cases showing slight losses in IQ, one case with a five point loss was later subject to severe grand mal seizures. Another case with a five point loss had a respiratory disorder and showed extreme fatigability. Three cases showed two point losses which are well within the range of intratest variability. Obviously, for the ten cases showing ten point or greater increases in IQ, the original IQ score had little predicative value.

Some of the cases in this study showed little or no increase in IQ, while other cases gained as much as 25 points. Thus, the question arises, Of what practical value are the results of routine psychometric tests of children with cerebral palsy, if the IQ scores frequently do not realiably predict future mental growth in individual cases?

There is now evidence which is suggesting that analysis of Stanford-Binet "scatter distribution patterns" may provide a key for the prediction of the mental development of children with brain injuries. In a previous article it was demonstrated that comparison of equated groups of brain-injured and non-brain-injured children having the same mean IQ showed that the brain-injured groups' successful responses tended to "scatter" over a much wider range of the Stanford-Binet scale than did the responses of a non-brain-injured group of children of the same age, sex and IQ distribution. Various workers have observed and reported this phenomenon. The underlying rationale is that while, in general, the test performances of the non-brain-injured are limited only by their degree of mental ability, the brain-injured may fail certain test items because of specific factors in the "brain injury syndrome." Thus, a child with cerebral palsy (or other form of brain injury) may fail a fairly large number of test items which are below his general level of mental ability. The scoring procedures used in intelligence tests, such as the Stanford-Binet, are such that failures of the aforementioned variety will in many cases depress the total test score, thus giving an inaccurate impression of the child's general potential for mental development.

The concept of "psychometric scatter," refers to the vertical range of items passed on one test, between the basal mental age (the point at which the last of a consecutive series of items is successfully performed), and the highest year-level of the test in which any one item may be passed. For example, assuming that a brain-injured child, ten years of age, scores a Stanford-Binet basal MA of six years, and an additional year's credit composed of items passed scattered through the next three year-levels of the test (e.g., four months' credit in years VII, VIII and IX), he thus scores an MA of seven years and an IQ of 70. Considering, however, that he has passed some items in the eight and nine year levels of the test, can this IQ of 70 be interpreted as having the same meaning as an MA of seven years, and an IQ of 70 composed only of items successfully performed consecutively through the first seven years of the scale; or must the "range of scatter" be considered if the test score is to have predictive value?

On a purely empirical basis, it is felt that the range of scatter must be taken into consideration in the psychometric prediction of the mental development of children with brain injuries. Returning to the example cited in the previous paragraph, standard scoring procedure yielded a mental age of only seven years, even though the child gave adequate responses to items at the eight and nine year test levels. Hypothetically, the implication may be that the items failed by this child, below the statistical mental age level (in this case seven years), are items adversely affected by the conditions commonly existing in cerebral palsy: limited social experience, perceptual difficulties, visuomotor failures, and any of a great number of other factors associated with brain injuries. A further assumption, which can be made upon accepting the original assumption regarding the probable implications of the "scatter pattern," is that if the child were not subject to the specific limitations affecting his test performance, he probably would be able to pass most, or all, of the items between the basal MA and the highest level at which test items were passed, thus obtaining an IQ score somewhat higher than the actual statistical score. Applying this assumption to the case example discussed above, we might assume that this child potentially has a mental age of not seven, but nine years.

The latter assumption is the basis of an hypothetical construct tentatively called "Maximum Probable IQ." The "MPIQ" substitutes in the Stanford-Binet, the highest year level at which items are passed (beyond the year immediately succeeding the basal year) for the actual MA score value, as the numerator in the IQ formula. For convenience, the highest level is termed "Maximum Probable Mental Age," or "MPMA." Thus, while:

$$IQ = \frac{MA}{CA}; \ MPIQ = \frac{MPMA}{CA}$$

In the cited example of the child ten years of age, with an MA of seven years and scatter into Year IX, while the statistical IQ is 70, his MPMA is nine years and the MPIQ is 90. Obviously, the constructs MPMA and MPIQ cannot in their present form be statistically manipulated, inasmuch, as (for example) MPMA would in the cited case be nine years, regardless of the number of items passed at Year IX. These constructs, however, are not in their present level of development intended to represent finite statistical measures; but rather they are intended as tentative clinical tools for broad, general prediction of probable mental development in cases of cerebral palsy and other forms of childhood brain injury.

The value of the proposed constructs can lie only in the degree to which they can be used in the prediction of mental development. Specifically stated, the question is "Can children with cerebral palsy who will show increases in IQ during participation in an habilitation program be differentiated from those who will not show increases, on the basis of psychometric scatter?" Preliminary data are now suggesting that such differentiation is possible.

In a previous study, the "scatter score" was defined as the number of items failed between the last consecutive item passed and the upper limit of each child's total performance range. Earlier in this paper, a study was cited in which ten children in a group of fifty showed gains of ten or more IQ points in an eighteen month habilitation period. While the total group of fifty showed a mean gain of only three points in IQ, the ten children gaining ten or more points showed 14.5 points gain in mean IQ, with five cases showing very slight decreases. Thus, while the majority of the cases presented relatively unchanged IQ scores during an eighteen-month period, 20 per cent showed major increases in IQ. When the first-test "scatter scores" of the latter 20 per cent of the cases studied were compared to the scatter scores of the forty "nongaining" cases, it was found that the ten "gaining" cases missed 146 items between their respective basal scores and the upper limits of their performance ranges, compared to 218 items for the forty "nongainers." Thus, the group showing major IQ gains showed a "mean scatter score" of 14.6 as compared to 5.45 for the remainder of the cases. Within each group, there was little deviation from the mean number of items missed, with standard deviations of 2.97 for the "gaining" group, and 1.65 for the remainder. The greater homogeneity of the nongaining group, is of interest here, in that it suggests when predictions are based upon raw scores alone, each individual in this group presents a pattern which is rather more typical of his group than are the patterns presented by the group showing IQ gains. This further indicates the importance of considering psychometric scatter distributions in evaluating test results. Where there is a great deal of scatter, the raw IQ score is very probably of little value in the prediction of the future mental growth of individuals with brain injuries. The differences between the means were statistically significant at the 5 per cent level of confidence, suggesting that the two groups were highly differentiable in terms of psychometric scatter, with the group making major IQ gains showing significantly more scatter than the nongaining group.

As previously stated, the concepts of MPMA and MPIQ cannot be used as finite statistics, and a statistical evaluation of the accuracy of prediction of specific terminal IQ scores for individual cases is not possible at this time. Another weak point in the use of these concepts is that in their present form the time element cannot be accurately considered. The basic assumption is that items failed within the performance range of a child with a brain injury reflect the general communication difficulties imposed by the brain injury or lack of adequate social experience; and that as these handicaps are ameliorated through general language habilitation, the "psychometric gaps" will be closed, thus increasing the IQ score approximately to the point predictable by the extent of scattering on the initial test. Numerous cases are now being reexamined in which retest IQ scores are very close to the "Maximum Probable IQ" scores predicted by the method described in this paper. While it can be shown that, in many cases, gains in IQ are predictable, there is as yet no means of ascertaining the length of time that will elapse before the predicted scores will be approximated.

Through the use of the psychometric scatter concept, it is possible to get fairly reliable indications of present levels of functioning and of the probable course of future development. If the examiner is fully congnizant of all of the behavioral idiosyncrasies indigenous to children with brain injuries, and if he has adjusted his testing techniques to cope with these problems, the scores yielded by *standard* testing instruments are, in most instances, valid indices of the present level of mental development. Where the examiner feels that the score obtained may not accurately reflect the child's level of development, additional testing should be done with a test other than the one initially used. If the results of two or three different tests administered within a day or two of one another yield comparable scores, and if the examiner has the subjective impression that the child was performing at his optimal level, it is relatively certain that the child's true level of *present* mental functioning falls within a range represented by the obtained scores. Then, analysis of the psychometric scatter tendencies, as previously described, can provide important clues for the predictive interpretation of these scores.

A word of caution should be interjected here regarding the predictive value of scatter scores. One, or two or even three items passed beyond the basal MA level *do not* constitute predictively applicable scatter. One single item passed two to three years beyond the basal level generally represents a manifestation of a "restricted special ability," and has no predictive value. While data on this problem are not completed, they are suggesting that predictions based on scatter profiles are not valid unless at least 35 per cent of the test items lying between basal and maximal levels are passed.

During the ensuing years, several additional studies of the predictive value of psychometric scatter were performed, using the Stanford-Binet, and the WISC. These studies will not be reported in any detail here. In general, the results were not as encouraging as the early experiments seemed to herald. The differentiation between children who would show later gains in IQ, and those who would not, has held up quite well. Using several groups of children, ranging from twenty to fifty in number, we found that within any of several methods of scatter scaling and particularly with the method described for use with the Stanford-Binet in the previous paragraphs, differentiations between "gainers" and "nongainers" were quite reliable, with significances between scatter scores generally falling at a 5 per cent significance level, or slightly better. On the other hand, the "Maximum Probable IQ" concept has failed to be productive of any truly reliable predictive system.

In a follow-up study of fifty cases mentioned in the preceding section, no consistencies were shown between the extent of scatter shown on the first test, and the total gain in IQ over a three year period. In general, cases with the greatest amount of scatter seemed to show rapid gains in IQ during the early months of training, but, over a three year period, most of the cases followed-up *did not* achieve the "Maximum Probable IQ" which had originally been predicted. The general trend was for the lower level "psychometric gaps" to fill in rather quickly, thus giving a rather rapid initial gain in IQ. However, for some reason we do not understand and have never had time to investigate, the process of "filling in the gaps" was seldom accompanied by adequate extension of the top level of performance. In other words, taking for example our previously mentioned ten-year-old with the actual Binet MA of seven years and scatter into year IX: Over a three year period, all of the scatter "gaps" were filled; but, assuming that the MPIQ of 90 had been correct, his top level of performance should have extended to very near the twelve year level, whereas actually, on his thirteenth birthday, he had achieved a mental age of only eleven years, and a corresponding IQ of 84. This was rather typical of all the cases studied over a three year period: For those for whom the original scatter profiles predicted no gains in IQ, generally little or no gains were made. For those for whom the original profiles suggested the probability of IQ increase, there was generally some increase beyond the chance level, but seldom as great an increase as we would have predicted, largely due to the fact that the uppermost levels of performance rarely progressed at a rate which the MPIQ had predicted. We feel at this point that the generalized concept of psychometric scatter as a predictor of probable increases in IQ has considerable validity, but that the "Maximum Probable IQ" formula can serve only as a very rough approximation of the extent of gain to be expected, with most noted gains falling somewhat short of the prediction. We never had an opportunity to study a group beyond a three year period, nor an opportunity to see if IQ's continued to increase *after* the psychometric gaps were closed. Studies of this type should be done. Presently, however, the MPIQ seems to be only a relatively rough, and somewhat overly-optimistic estimate of the amount of gain to be expected, and should be applied with caution.

A generalized format for reporting the intellectual functioning of the brain-damaged child should report the following information:

1. A general, subjective description of the child's social interactions in the testing situation, including such items as the level of rapport that the examiner is able to maintain with the child: Does the child relate comfortably with the examiner, or is he shy, fearful, withdrawn, difficult to motivate, etc?

2. Description of the child's verbal functioning is basically the task of the speech clinician. However, some aspects of verbal behavior should be reported by the psychologist. Some assessment should be made of the child's vocabulary level, and general level of verbal comprehension. This information can be abstracted from the child's responses to selective portions of generalized intelligence tests, such as the Stanford-Binet, or the WISC. The psychologist may want to corroborate such estimates through the use of more specialized instruments, such as the Peabody Picture Vocabulary Test, or the Ammons Full Range Vocabulary Test.

3. Report of actual scores achieved on any standardized intellectual test: Actual MA and IQ should be reported, along with a detailed analysis of levels of functioning in the various areas tapped by the test (or tests) used. Where there is a great deal of scatter, this should be reported, and should be interpreted as suggesting that perhaps the achieved IQ score may be somewhat of an underestimate of the child's potential. The psychologist may want to use the MPIQ concept to make a rough estimate of the child's probable potential; but such estimates should always be accompanied with cautionary statements regarding their reliability.

4. On the basis of the psychologist's general observations of the child's behavior, and from his test responses, all evidence suggesting brain damage should be reported in detail. The general outline of the brain-damage syndrome given in this chapter should be used as a guide, and the psychologist should be fairly specific in describing the activities or reactions of the child which determine the signs to be reported. Some signs, such as hyperactivity, attention defects and emotional lability, can be easily noted in the examiner's preliminary observations of the child's behavior.

Other signs such as perseveration, abstracting difficulties and perceptual problems will be manifested in various aspects of the child's actual test performance. All of these various sources of observation should be tapped, the determining behavior, or test reaction, which identifies each sign of brain damage described, and the signs should all be listed, along with some comment regarding the relative intensity, persistence, or severity of each sign.

5. Finally, a "general summary," or "general impression" should be presented. The summary should restate the level of intellectual functioning, both numerically and in some practical, descriptive terms, such as "potentially within normal limits," "moderately retarded but educable," and "severely retarded but trainable." The psychologist should then attempt to relate all of the information he has acquired about the child to some practical factors in the child's life situation. In other words, is this a child whose problems are such that he could not be expected to progress in a normal school setting? Could he possibly get along in a "slow learners" special classroom in public school, or does he need the more highly specialized type of therapy and training offered by special schools and clinics for brain damaged children? In some instances, the psychologist may feel that the child is so profoundly mentally retarded that he would not respond to *any* form of training, and should be institutionalized. *Such a recommendation should never be made unless the child has already had several years of competent and intensive therapy from which he appears to have derived no benefit.* Where the child has not had adequate training, the psychologist should be frank in expressing whatever doubts he may have regarding the child's potential for improvement, but should always recommend a period of *intensive* specialized training, of eight months to a year in duration, followed by reevaluation, before any decision regarding institutionalization is made. Lastly, whenever possible, the summary should include some rather specialized or specific types of therapeutic recommendations based upon the child's test performance: Does he

need special practice in visual discrimination or in vocabulary-building; or, for example, does he need more preschool social group experience and visual-motor integrative experience?

The foregoing discussion of the "general summary" section of the psychological report clearly suggests that the psychologist evaluating brain-damaged children must be knowledgeable, not only in the special problems pertaining to brain damage, but also regarding the various types of therapies and training which are useful in dealing with these problems, and of the types of facilities, either within his community or his general area which might provide such services. For this reason, the psychologist employed by a clinic for brain-damaged children is probably in the best position to evaluate such cases. This is in no way intended as a disparagement of the abilities of psychologists working in other areas. Most psychologists now have considerable understanding of brain damage. The major advantage of the psychologist working in the special clinic is that he may be somewhat more familiar with the facilities of his own clinic. In many cases, however, school psychologists and psychologists in private practice have familiarized themselves with the facilities and training programs available in the community, and thus are extremely capable of giving appropriate advice regarding a child's training and placement needs.

In this discussion of testing, some readers may be distressed by our lack of discussion of appropriate tests and testing materials. This was an intentional omission. We feel that, insofar as possible, brain damaged children should be tested with standardized, well-validated clinical tests. The value of any of the better known tests, in our opinion, is more highly determined by the individual psychologist's familiarity with the test and its capabilities than by anything intrinsic to the test itself. In our own experience, we have found the Stanford-Binet and the Wechsler Intelligence Scale for Children best fitted to the testing orientation presented in this book. In testing children with severe speech and motor disabilities, the Leiter International Performance Scale has been extremely helpful, except in cases in which there were also severe disturbances in vision, or in visual perception. In some cases, the Bender-Gestalt test has been of value in ferreting out visual-perceptual, or perceptual-motor problems; but in many cases, these problems manifest themselves quite clearly in the S-B or the WISC and we rarely feel the need for specialized tests of perceptual ability. Similarly, the Goldstein-Scheerer tests are often useful in detecting abstracting and categorizing problems, but, with experience, such problems also come to the fore quite readily with the WISC, S-B, or Leiter. The choice of tests, therefore, appears to be largely a matter of individual preference, provided the psychologist is keenly familiar with the various manifestations of the brain damage syndrome, and has learned to relate these manifestations to the response patterns elicited by the tests he uses.

Evaluation of Extremely Handicapped Children: This is an extremely complex and difficult area, and one which should be treated in depth. Unfortunately, the length of this presentation has already gone far beyond our original intentions, and intensive treatment of this topic cannot be attempted at this time. At best, we can present here only a basic philosophy and some fundamental principles. Most of the material thus far presented in this section on testing has been presented with the tacit assumption that the child being evaluated has relatively adequate means of responding to examination procedures. Although this was not made explicit, we assumed, for instance, that the child had enough speech and motor ability to give test responses which were not contaminated by his physical disabilities. Now we must face the more difficult task of evaluating the child with very severe motor and speech problems.

One very simple solution to this problem is to make slight "adaptations" of testing procedures, or to use "conglomerative" results of items from several tests, or extrapolate partial results from one test. For example, the non-motor-handicapped brain-damaged child can, if the situation is properly structured, be held to a standard form of test administration. If he has little or no speech, nonverbal tests, such as the Leiter International Scale, or the "Performance" half of the WISC can be used to establish an approximate IQ, while tests such as the Ammons or Peabody can give considerable insight into his verbal comprehension. If a cerebral palsied child has a severe motor problem which invalidates the timing aspects of performance tests, he can be given the "Verbal" part of the WISC. If his speech is also badly affected, a nontimed performance test, such as the Leiter, can establish his IQ, and give a great deal of information about his general abstracting and categorizing functions: The Ammons or the Peabody can give a great deal of insight regarding verbal processes, and interpretation and reporting can still be done in the manner outlined in the previous section.

Major difficulties in psychological evaluation arise, however, when the psychologist is faced with a child who, for any number of reasons, cannot give adequate responses to any set of normal testing procedures. For example, let us consider the evaluation of the very severely disabled cerebral palsied child who is essentially speechless and who does not have enough muscular control to respond adequately to any formalized or standard testing procedure. When such a child is recommended for rehabilitative services, either on advice of a physician or through the aegis of a social agency, the clinical facility must have some knowledge of what the child understands in terms of his language development and general interpersonal comprehension before an adequate habilitative program can be planned.

In a situation such as the one presented above, the psychologist's task is to devise ways of "getting at" what the child knows, and how he thinks, and then to transpose his findings into a framework which is meaningful in terms of standard norms. In many cases, this need not be as great a problem as it might at first appear to be. Very often, it can be nicely solved by adaptations or minor alterations of standard testing procedures which need not affect the validity of the test. The first task of the examiner is to determine what modes of responses are available to the child. For example, can he *point* to objects with any degree of accuracy (providing the objects are placed far enough apart to avoid accidental contacts)? Does the child have any *reliable* way of signifying "Yes" or "No?" In brief, the psychologist must work out some reliable and systematic way of determining what the child is trying to indicate through whatever facilities are available to him. There are many pitfalls in making a determination of this type. For example, many children with cerebral palsy learn rather early in life that a broad smile evokes praise from parents or solicitous neighbors. In an examining situation, the examiner may show the child a picture of a cat, and ask "Is this a pig?" The child does *not* smile, and the examiner thinks, now, that a smile means "Yes," while no response means "No." This may be an initially correct assumption; but it may later become an *artifact* of the examiner's questions. For example, as long as the child *knows* the answers, there is no problem. The examiner, needing to establish some rapport with the child, will probably say "Right," or "Good" whenever the child smiles in response to a question in which "Yes" is appropriate; and will similarly give some sort of encouragement when the child makes no response to questions to which the appropriate response is "No." This works out very well as long as the child really knows the answers. But, trouble develops when the child begins to become unsure of himself. He may elect to keep smiling, to smile not at all, or to randomly smile or not smile. How does the examiner know when the child really knows the answer? If, for example, the questions are so arranged that "Yes" and "No" responses should fall into a pattern of consistent alternation, the child can be "right" half of the time if he just keeps smiling, and knows absolutely nothing beyond the first correct answer. He can still go through several dozen questions, and be "right" half of the time.

The above example, admittedly, is a *reductio ad absurdium* proposition; but it does illustrate the type of thing against which one must guard. When using the "Yes" or "No" approach with a child, the questions should be arranged so that no consistent pattern occurs. The child *still* will have a 50-50 chance of being right on any single question. But his chances of being right *consistently* are sharply reduced to the point where his chance of being right five times in a row by pure guesswork is only about 3 per cent, and his chance of being right four times in a row (or *wrong* four times in a row) is roughly 6 per cent. The same sort of principle applies in techniques where the child is required to *point* to objects. If a dog and cat are placed before a child, he has a 50-50 chance of pointing to the one asked for, even if he has absolutely no idea of what the objects are. Space does not allow a discussion of probability statistics here; but obviously where pointing or yes-no techniques are used, the tasks should be arranged in such a way as to minimize the probability of a large number of responses which are "correct" by pure chance.

Another type of pitfall to be guarded against is that of inadvertent "cueing" of the struggling child. This is difficult because it goes against the grain of the sensibilities of most individuals with an ordinary amount of compassion or empathy. For example, five colored blocks may be spread out before a child who is asked to point to the *blue* block. The child reaches, and twists and squirms and sweats and his hand finally brushes lightly against the blue block, at which point the relieved examiner immediately exclaims "Good for you!" But has the child *actually* given a correct response? Too often, the examiner *really* does not know. What should be done here, for checking, is rearrangement of the position of the blocks, to see if the child again strikes the blue block. One of the silliest examples of this type of situation we have ever witnessed was an examiner who was presumably testing number concepts: She would ask the child to hand her a given number of blocks, such as three, five or seven. The child would hand her one block at a time, and as soon as the asked-for number of blocks were in her hand, she would gleefully say "Right; good for you!" As an observer, it was obvious to us that the child did *not* have any concept beyond, possibly "three," and was simply handing her blocks until she withdrew her hand. For some reason, probably her great warmth and personal feeling for the struggling youngster, this seemed never to enter her mind.

In spite of all the aforementioned dangers, it is possible to find *some* means of setting up a situation in which, by nodding, pointing, reaching, blinking, etc., the grossly handicapped child can indicate what he knows. This requires ingenuity and patience, plus a great deal of rapport with the child and perhaps a little "scientific detachment" at the same time. Personal warmth and scientific objectivity are not mutually exclusive attributes: but it is admittedly at times rather difficult to keep both functioning at once.

After a reliable pattern of communication with the child has been established, adaptations of some standard testing procedures are often possible. For example, with the Leiter International Performance Scale, the child need not place the response blocks in the frame, himself. The general idea of the test, that of placing blocks within a frame in such a manner that they correspond to some aspect of the pictorial stimuli resting on top of the frame, can be explained and demonstrated to the child. Then a test card is placed in the holder, and the response blocks are spread out before the child. The examiner then points to one of the pictures and says: "Show me which block goes with this." The child can then, by some preestablished, reliable means of communication, indicate which block goes where and, except for the elimination of the normally required motor activity of having the child place a rather small block in a small aperture, the test can proceed and be scored in a standard manner. We favor this type of approach wherever possible, as opposed to the use of unstandardized testing materials. There has been, in our experience, rarely a situation in which materials for which there are well-established norms could not be adapted to the needs of the severely handicapped child without doing violence to the essence of the testing procedure; and we therefore feel that, even in most severely handicapped cases, testing should be done in terms of developmental norms established for the items being used.

The above does not imply that only complete, standard tests should be used in evaluation. Indeed, if helpful information is to be gained, we see no objection to using items from half a dozen different testing instruments. In fact, there are times when the greatest amount of information can be gleaned by using one or two items from each of several tests. This often occurs when the selection of testing items is highly restricted by the response capabilities of the child, and when the child shows a great deal of fatiguability, and cannot be expected to perform for any protracted length of time. In this type of situation, intellectual functioning is sometimes most readily assessed by a sampling technique approach. Here, norms from each test item, or partial test administered, should be used as an outline of normative data; and then test items drawn from any source which is appropriate to the child's behavioral capabilities can be employed, with the test results cast into scalar outline. It must be noted that evaluations of this type do not yield results which legitimately can be termed "mental age" or "IQ." The general report outline previously presented can be retained, but modified to accurately represent what was actually done. Rather than reporting any sort of overall "test score," the report should state that, for example, a six year level was achieved on the Peabody Picture Vocabulary Scale; that the seven year level was achieved in pointing out pictorial incongruities in the Stanford-Binet Form L; that Binet Year V number concepts criteria were passed; and that, regardless of what was tried, no success was had with any item drawn from any test above a seven-year-level (all test items attempted should be reported). In summarizing an examination of this type, one would state that the level of intellectual function appears to fall within a five to seven year MA range. If the child is, for example, ten years old, the psychologist might also say that the IQ appears to be somewhere between 50 and 70, implying that, while the child may be somewhat retarded, his potential seems to be somewhere within the "educable" range, and that he is intellectually capable of benefitting from habilitative training.

The approach described above is also one which is applicable to the very hyperactive, non-motor-handicapped, speechless child. The problem here is somewhat different, that of circumventing poor attention, lack of speech, and hyperactivity, rather than getting around gross motor disability; but the general philosophy of the approach to the problem is the same. The need is for the psychologist to find out as much as he possibly can about the child, by whatever means are available to him, and to cast the information obtained into some sort of meaningful framework. Sometimes the "means available" are rather unique, or even bizarre. Some very hyperactive children will absolutely refuse to perform at an ordinary table, and will scream, throw things, and run about wildly. The more the psychologist tries to force the child into the normal situation, the more disruptive and enraged he may become. Often, however, such children grab some toy, or test item, crawl into a corner or *under* the testing table, and begin playing rather quietly. If the examiner then quietly approaches the child in his chosen place (this is generally a place which has some physical aspect about it which makes the child feel secure), the child will often permit the examiner to join him, and some social interaction, built around the item with which the child is playing, may be established. Gradually, the examiner may bring in a simple formboard, or similar low level item which he is relatively certain the child can handle easily, and get him to play with it. As time passes, an assistant (where possible) can bring other testing items to the place where the child and the examiner are now "playing"; and gradually, in many cases, a good deal of information can be gotten relating to the child's level of mental functioning. Observations obtained in this manner are reported as discussed in the immediately preceding paragraph.

The approach described above demands a great deal of personal flexibility and quick, intuitive thinking on the part of the psychologist. It may be somewhat destructive to the idealized self-concept of the neat, well-groomed clinician behind the desk to suddenly find himself administering an examination on his knees, *under* the desk. On the other hand, the successful evaluation of a child, performed under these conditions, and against what may at first seem to be a totally disastrous situation, can be a source of pride and satisfaction. Your office is a wreck, your pants are creased and dirty, but you *got* the information you were seeking; and when you think about it, you know that you really accomplished something by using every facet of your skill and ingenuity and despite your rumpled hair, dirty hands and aching back, *you feel good!*

BRIEF COMMENTS REGARDING EMOTIONAL FACTORS IN BRAIN-DAMAGED CHILDREN

This closing section should in no way be regarded as an attempt to survey this vast and complex area. In fact, we are presenting this material with some reticence, fearing that an inadequate treatment of this topic may be of little or no value, whereas adequate treatment would require far more time than can possibly be allotted to this monograph. The following comments then, represent a perhaps unwise compromise between what *should* be said, and what can be said against the ever-mounting pressures of time. What is presented here is essentially a personal philosophy, based upon observations accrued over a fifteen year period of working with brain damaged children. We make no claims for scientific validity here, and quote no source materials. Our only justification for presenting this material at all, is the notion that fifteen years of close contact with brain-damaged children and their families may have taught us something about their emotional problems and needs.

A considerable portion of this chapter was alotted to a detailed analysis of the "brain-damage syndrome" as it applies to intellectual and linguistic functioning. If pressed to outline a "syndrome" of the *emotional* needs and characteristics of the brain-damaged child, we would reply that there is *none*. This statement is perhaps somewhat dramatic, and contrary to the entire tenor of the rest of this chapter, and therefore requires some clarification. We expressed, very early in this chapter, the concept that the brain-damaged child was not some unique creature unto himself: he was a *child* who happened to have some special problems which were in some ways related to the fact that he had brain damage. This, in brief, is our total philosophy regarding the emotional factors in brain-damaged children.

Every child has certain generalized emotional needs. As an infant he needs the love and tender ministrations of his mother. He needs to be fed, kept clean, loved and kept safe from harm. As he grows older, he needs environmental experience and stimulation if he is to learn anything about the world in which he lives. Later, he needs to begin to develop some self-indentity, some feeling of independence and some sense of mastery of his immediate environment. Still later, he needs to become less motivated by his immediate egocentric needs, and correspondingly more alert to the social environment, to his status as a member of the family and of peer groups. Finally, as he approaches adolescence and then goes into young adulthood, he needs to develop a general philosophy of life which, ideally, is a compromise between ego needs for success, esteem, general security and a general sense of responsibility towards the society in which he lives. Without arguing for any specific sort of "personality theory," we feel that this outline represents a more or less universal pattern of normal emotional development.

Now, any of a vast number of factors can arrest or distort the general line of development. Lack of interaction between mother and child can be disruptive whether the child has cerebral palsy, or whether he is a normal child whose mother is an alcoholic. Impoverished environmental and social experiences can constrict personality development because a child has sensory and motor deficits which restrict his ability to benefit from experience, or because he is a physically normal child who has grown up in a home where nobody bothers to talk to him, play with him, or take him anywhere. In other words, the personality development and emotional maturation of any child, handicapped or not is dependent upon the degree to which his experiences supply him with the resources for social and emotional maturation.

If there are any "special" emotional problems in brain damage, they arise from the fact that, in some instances, brain damage imposes restrictions upon normal social and environmental interactions. The degree to which this occurs depends upon a complexity of interacting relationships operative throughout the life of the child. Some of these factors are "real" in the sense that the child may have some physical limitations which cut him off from the world about him. Other factors are "imposed" by the reactions of the parents to the child, his reactions to their reactions, etc., *ad infinitum.*

The reactions of parents to a severely handicapped child, especially in the early years of his life, largely determine the type of emotional adjustment he will eventually achieve. (No, this is not going to be another of the very popular "blame the lousy parents" diatribe.) What we should like to present here is not a listing of all the things parents can do, and often *do* do, *wrong.* Rather, we should like to put forth here a set of suggestions about what parents can do *right* to give their handicapped child a firm basis for healthy emotional development. We feel that most of the errors parents make are motivated, not by guilt complexes, not by "rejection," but by an honest desire to do the very best for their child. When these good intentions go astray, it is generally because something in the complex of problems presented by the child, misleads the parents into reacting in some manner which "seems right" but which ultimately is not in the best interests of the child.

It is an entirely natural parental instinct to try to protect a child from physical harm. Where a child is handicapped this instinct is sometimes overaccentuated. No mother wants to allow her child to get himself into situations in which he is likely to be harmed. Whether the child is handicapped or not, there are two ways of approaching this problem. One is to keep him away from all situations which are dangerous to him. The better approach is to take the child out into the world and try to teach him what the dangers are and how to avoid them. The cerebral palsied child who walks on wobbly legs and falls often is not going to learn to adapt to his difficulties by being hovered over or confined to a play pen. As soon as the child is able to move about, whether by walking, or crawling, he should be given some sort of protective clothing, such as a helmet to protect his head and then be allowed to move about the house or yard at will. He will tumble and fall more often than the normal child, but the few additional scrapes and scratches are no more harmful to him than they are to any other child. All children get banged up a bit in the process of learning to get about, and restricting the child's activities in order to avoid injury is a self-defeating process. The less active experience he has, the less he will learn about his own abilities, and his bodily relationships to the world around him. Of course, ordinary prudence in these matters still makes sense. One does not let the normal child wander into a busy street before he is fully aware of the dangers of automobiles. By the same token, common sense demands that the handicapped child not be allowed to attempt things which will inevitably lead to disaster. The general rule, however, should be that the handicapped child should be exposed to, or allowed to partake of any type of experience that the normal child has, so long as he understands what is going on.

If experience is an important factor in personality development, discipline and learning to obey the rules are equally important. The handicapped child living within a family structure should be expected to learn to obey, cooperate and share in the same manner as any other child. Very often, it is a framework of discipline that gives the young child the idea that he is part of the family group, that he is cared about, that what he does is meaningful to others. This is true of the normal child. It is equally true of the handicapped child. Within the levels of his comprehension, the handicapped child should be punished for infractions of household rules and expected to share whatever household tasks are within his physical ability to share.

Children with varying degrees of mental ability are likely to develop different types of emotional difficulties as they grow older. For the severely retarded, exposure to varied experiences, discipline, and expressions of love and affection may be enough to give the child as much emotional and social maturation as they can be expected to achieve. The problems presented by the handicapped child with near normal to above normal intelligence are much more complex. As these children grow older, the realities of their handicaps begin to impinge upon their total life structure. One of the common denominators of childhood is that most children want to be like other children. When the relatively bright cerebral palsied child begins to realize that other children are walking, and he is not, when other children tease him because he "talks funny," when he is left out of the neighborhood games, this is where the real emotional pressures begin. This is where he begins to question his own worth as a person, and where he begins to ask "Why am I like this?"

The above is a difficult problem for the parent to face; and there are no easy, ready-made answers. Much of what the parents can do at this point depends on what already has been done. The child who has learned to cope with his physical difficulties is better prepared to cope with social pressures than one who has not. The child who has, through participation and discipline been integrated into his family structure, has a reserve of security to build and fall back upon, whereas the child who has essentially been an "outsider" in his own family totally lacks the resources to cope with the social pressures of the outside world. But none of these provide a solution. Sooner or later, the stark realities of twisted legs and garbled speech must be faced head on. The complexities of this problem are immense. One of the difficulties arises from the fact that peer group reactions to the handicapped child change. The moderately handicapped child, up to the age of three or four, is generally accepted by his peers. They may wonder a bit about why he walks oddly, or ignore his speech when they do not understand it; but open hostility is rare, and the child is generally accepted into play groups and permitted to participate in whatever manner he is able. However, somewhere about the beginning of the sixth year, attitudes change. Children become particularly aware of differences in others, and such differences become focal points of interest and curiosity, the basis of jibes and teasing and of mimicry. Thus, the handicapped child who was once an accepted member of his peer group may become a social outcast, suddenly sharply aware of his differences, and demanding an explanation.

Explanations are difficult to give, and difficult to accept. For this reason, it is best for the parent to help the child face the issue of his handicap earlier in his life. The child should be brought into contact with other handicapped children through media such as therapy sessions and preschool play groups for the handicapped. Here, the concept that he is different will occur to him more gradually, and not as a sudden shock at the age of six or seven. This will help; but it will not solve the problem. About the only effective help the parent can give at the age when the child begins to question the "why?" of his handicap is to emphasize the positive aspects of the child's life. He must be reassured that he is loved and that his family is proud of him. He may be told that those who tease and mimic him are the ones who are odd, because they lack manners and understanding. But, the ultimate question of "Why?" should be handled objectively. The child's anxiety and frustrations may temporarily be eased by being told that "this was God's way of testing you, and shows that he has special faith in you." But this is both a dangerous and unrealistic explanation. The idea of being a "special creature of God" may give solace for a while; but can easily be twisted into a new question: "Why did God do this to me? — What have I done to deserve this trouble?"

Factual, relatively hard-hearted explanations may seem cruel, and they are very difficult for a parent to give a child. But these are the only ones upon which a true foundation of personal insight and capacity for adjustment can be built. The child should be told that there are all kinds of people in the world — fat ones, thin ones, people with black skins, people with white skins, and that among all the types of people, there are people like him. Nobody knows exactly *why* there are so many different kinds of people in the world; but each person has to take whatever he is, and learn to use his abilities to do the very best he can for himself. The child, when he is able to comprehend, may be given inspirational examples of severely handicapped people who became famous in spite of tremendous physical odds — Helen Keller, Franklin Roosevelt, Charles Steinmetz to name a few. But perhaps closer to the child's own contact with reality would be more immediate examples: the blind insurance salesman down the street, or the pretty young mother who runs her home and family from a wheelchair.

The overall pattern of encouragement should never deny the handicap. It is there, and it is real. But the child should be reassured that something can be done about it. Maybe it can never be "cured," but, with hard work, determination, and professional training, the worst of its effects can be overcome, and that what the child achieves in terms of living a normal life is largely dependent upon what he is willing to do for himself. His parents love him, and will give him whatever help he needs. There are doctors and therapists who can help him to walk better and talk better, and teachers who can help him learn how to do things in the world; but what becomes of him is mostly up to him, to his willingness to work, to struggle, to accept transitory defeats, get up and try again, and again, and again, and then six times more if necessary. This is how *everybody* gets along in the world. It will perhaps be a bit harder for him, but he can do it if he really wants to.

Of course, the above is a synopsis of the types of attitudes which must be instilled over a period of years, not something you sit down and tell him once. The pattern of encouragement and support must be tempered with acceptance of the child's setbacks and failures. The child must know that you expect him to succeed. At the same time, he should not be given the impression that any failure or setback diminishes your love for him. The entire process of personal adjustment is one of learning to accept the reality of one's disability, and at the same time learning to drive oneself to the ultimate limits of his capacity. In other words, the well-adjusted individual, whether handicapped or not, is one who is willing to continually strive for some goal, or some level of achievement, but who is at the same time aware that life is not always good, success is not always easy, and, so long as you are willing to keep trying, temporary setbacks are not disasters.

Finally, in the process of teaching success orientation and frustration tolerance, the child must be taught that there is more to life than just "winning" or achieving goals. An attitude of self-worth is important, but an appreciation of the worth and of the needs of others is equally important. Respect for the needs and feelings of others must not be allowed to become overshadowed by the desire for achievement. The child must be taught that he has a responsibility to other people, and that their happiness and welfare are also important. Training in this area should begin at an early age in the home situation. Respect for the rights of others can be taught through sharing, through the occasional necessity for the child to allow the wants of others to take precedence over his own. Choice of television programs, selection of family activities, etc., should never be permitted to fall under the domination of the handicapped child. He should be given a chance to express his wants, and they should acquiesced to at times. But he must be taught that others have rights, and needs, and that these are equally as important as his. Without this type of training, all the success orientation, motivation and support create nothing but a willful, egocentric personality, an individual who will fail in the normal world, not because he has physical disabilities, or because of the prejudice of others, but because his egocentricity destroys his ability to get along with other people.

A SELECTED BIBLIOGRAPHY

1. ALLEN, ROBERT M., and JEFFERSON, THOMAS W.: *Psychological Evaluation of the Cerebral Palsied Person: Intellectual, Personality, and Vocational Application.* Springfield, Ill., Thomas, 1962.

2. ANDERSON, L. D.: The predictive value of infancy tests in relation to intelligence at five years. *Child Development,* 1939, pp. 203-212.

3. BAYLEY, NANCY: On the growth of intelligence. *American Psychologist, X:805-818,* 1955.

4. BERKO, M. J.: Mental evaluation of the aphasic child, X. *Amer. J. Occup. Ther., V,* 241-243, 1951.

5. BERKO, M. J.: Psychometric scatter: its application in the clinical prediction of future mental development in cases of childhood brain injury. *Cereb. Palsy Rev., XVI:2,* 16-18, 1955.

6. BERKO, M. J.: Some factors in the mental evaluation of cerebral palsied children. *Cereb. Palsy Rev., XI,* 6,11,15, 1953.

7. BERKO, M. J.: Some factors in the perceptual deviations of children with cerebral palsy. *Cereb. Palsy Rev., XV:2,* 3-4, 11, 1954.

8. BERKO, M. J.: The measurement of intelligence in children with cerebral palsy. *J. Pediat., XLVII,* 252-260, 1955.

9. BERKO, M. J., and BERKO, F. G.: Implications of language difficulties in the cerebral palsied adults. *Cereb. Palsy Rev., XIV:* 9, 11, 14, 1953.

10. BERLYNE, D.: Attention, perception, and behavior theory. *Psychol. Rev., LVIII,* 137-145, 1951.

11. BICE, H. V.: Psychological examination of the cerebral palsied, *J. Excep. Child., XIV,* 163-168, 1948.

12. BIRCH, H. G., Ed.: *Brain Damage in Children. The Biological and Social Aspects.* New York, Williams & Wilkins, 1964.

13. BORTNER, M., and BIRCH, H. G.: Perceptual and perceptual motor disassociations in brain-damaged patients. *J. Nerv. Ment. Dis., LXXII,* 49-53, 1960.

14. CLARK, R. M.: The child with unsuspected brain injury. *Talk, XXXVI,* 6-9, 1955.

15. CARDWELL, V. E.: *Cerebral Palsy—Advances in Understanding and Care.* New York, Association for Crippled Children, 1956.

16. CRUICKSHANK, W. M.: *A Teaching Method for Brain Damaged and Hyperactive Children.* Syracuse, N. Y., Syracuse University Press, 1961.

17. Cruickshank, W. M., Bice, H. V., and Wollen, N. E.: *Perception and Cerebral Palsy.* Syracuse, N. Y., Syracuse University Press, 1957.

18. Cruickshank, W. M., and Raus, G. M.: *Cerebral Palsy.* Syracuse N. Y., Syracuse University Press, 1955.

19. Doll, E. A.: Neurophrenia. *Amer. J. Psychiat., CVIII:*1, 50-53, 1951.

20. Doll, E. A., Phelps, W. M., and Melcher, R. T.:*Mental Deficiencies Due to Birth Injuries.* New York, MacMillan, 1932.

21. Dolphin, J. E., and Cruickshank, Wm.: Visual-motor perception in children with cerebral palsy. *Quart. J. Child Behav., III,* 198-209, 1951.

22. Ewert, P. H.: A study of the effect of inverted retinal stimulation upon spatially coordinated behavior. *Genetic Psychology Monographs, VII,* 177-363, 1930.

23. Ewert, P. H.: Factors in space localization during inverted vision: I. interference. *Psychol. Rev., XLIII,* 522-546, 1936.

24. Ewert, P. H.: Factors in space localization during inverted vision: II. an explanation of interference and adaptation. *Psychol. Rev., XLIV,* 105-116, 1937.

25. Field, J., and Magoun, H. W. (Eds.) : *Handbook of Physiology — Section 1: Neuropsysiology — Volume III.* Washington, D.C., American Physiological Society, 1960.

26. Gesell, Arnold, *et al.*: *The First Five Years.* New York, Harper & Row, 1940.

27. Gesell, A., and Amatruda, C. S.: *Developmental Diagnosis.* New York, Paul B Hoeber, Inc., 1951.

28. Gesell, A., and Ilg, F.: *The Child From Five to Ten.* New York, Harper & Row, 1949.

29. Gesell, A., Ilg, F., and Bullis, G.: *Vision: Its Development in the Infant and Child.* New York, Paul B. Hoeber, Inc., 1950.

30. Gibson, J.: What is form? *Psychol. Rev., LVIII,* 403-412, 1951.

31. Gibson, J. J., and Walk, R. D.: The visual cliff. *Scientific American, CCII:*4, 64-71, 1960.

32. Goldstein, K.: *Language and Language Disorders.* New York, Grune & Stratton, 1948.

33. Goldstein, K., and Scheerer, M.: Abstract and concrete behavior: an experimental study with special tests. *Psychological Monographs, LIII:*2, 1941. Whole No. 239.

34. Grinker, R. R., Bucy, P. C., and Sahs, A. L.: *Neurology, 5th Edition.* Springfield, Thomas, 1960.

35. HASTINGS, HOMER: The predictive value of individual items in preschool intelligence tests. Berkely, University of California, 1952. An unpublished doctoral thesis.
36. HAUSSERMANN, E.: *Developmental Potential of Preschool Children.* New York, Grune & Stratton, 1958.
37. HEAD, H.: *Aphasia and Kindred Disorders of Speech.* New York, MacMillan, 1926.
38. HEBB, D. O.: *The Organization of Behavior.* New York, Wiley, 1949.
39. HEIN, A., and HELD, R.: Minimal conditions essential for complete re-learning of hand-eye coordination with prismatic distortion of vision. *Paper read at* Eastern Psychological Association, Philadelphia, 1958.
40. HEIN, A., and HELD, R.: A neural model for labile sensorimotor coordinations. *Biological Prototypes and Synthetic Systems.* New York, Plenum Press, Inc., I: 71-74, 1962.
41. HELD, R.: Exposure-history as a factor in maintaining stability of perception and coordination. *J. Nerv. Ment. Dis., CXXXII:* 1, 26-32, 1961.
42. HELD, R., and BOSSOM, J.: Neonatal deprivation and adult rearrangement: complementary techniques for analysing plastic sensory motor coordinations. *J. Comp. Physiol. Psychol., LIV,* 33-37, 1961.
43. HELD, R., and HEIN, A.: Movement-produced stimulation in the development of visually guided behavior. *J. Comp. Physiol. Psychol., LVI:6,* 872-876, 1963.
44. HELD, R., and SCHLANK, M.: Adaptations to disarranged hand-eye coordination in the distance dimension. *Amer. J. Psychol., LXXII:*421, 1959.
45. HOLST, E. VON: Relations between the central nervous system and the peripheral organs. *Brit. J. Animal Behav., II:*89-94, 1954.
46. HONZIK, M. P.: The constancy of mental test performance during the pre-school years. *J. Genet. Psychol., LII:*285-302, 1938.
47. HONZIK, M. P., and MACFARLANE, J. W.: The stability of mental test performance between two and eighteen years, *J. Exp. Education, XVII:*309-329, 1948.
48. IRWIN, O. C., and HAMMIL, D. D.: An abstraction test for use with cerebral palsied children. *Cereb. Palsy Rev., XXV:*4, 3-9, 1964.
49. KOFFKA, K.: *Principles of Gestalt Psychology.* New York, Harcourt, Brace, & Co., 1935.

50. KOHLER, I.: Experience with prolonged optical distortion. *Acta Psychol., XI:*176-178, 1955.

51. LASHLEY, K. S.: *Brain Mechanisms and Intelligence.* Chicago, University of Chicago Press, 1929.

52. LASHLEY, K. S.: Factors limiting recovery after central nervous system lesions. *J. Nerv. Ment. Dis., LXXXVIII,* 733-755, 1938.

53. LASHLEY, K. S.: Functional determinants of cerebral localization. *Arch. Neurol. Psychiat., XXXVIII:*371-387, 1937.

54. LASHLEY, K. S.: The mechanism of vision: IV. The cerebral areas for pattern vision in the rat, *Pattern of Comparative Neurology,, LIII:*419-478, 1931.

55. LASHLEY, K. S., and RUSSELL, J. T.: The mechanism of vision: XI. A preliminary test of innate organization. *J. Genet. Psychol., XLV,* 136-144, 1934.

56. MAURER, K. M.: *Intellectual Status at Maturity as a Criterion For Selecting Items in Preschool Tests.* Minneapolis, University of Minnesota Press, 1946.

57. McCARTHY, J. J.: A test for the identification of defects in language usage among young cerebral palsied. *Cereb. Palsy Rev., XXI:*3-5, 1960.

58. MECHAM, M. J., BERKO, M. J., and BERKO, F. G.: *Speech Therapy in Cerebral Palsy.* Springfield, Thomas, 1960.

59. MICHAL-SMITH, H.: Problems encountered in the psychometric examination of the child with cerebral palsy, *Cereb. Palsy Rev., XVI:*3, 15-16, 1955.

60. MILLER, E., and ROSENFELD, G. B.: The Psychological evaluation of children with cerebral palsy and its implications in treatment. *J. Pediat., XLI:*613-621, 1952.

61. MURPHY, G., and HOCHBERG, J.: Perceptual development: some tentative hypotheses. *Psychol. Rev., LVIII:*332-347, 1951.

62. NIELSON, H. H.: *Visual-motor Functioning of Cerebral Palsied and Normal Children.* Copenhagen, Ejnar Munksgaards Forlag, 1962.

63. NELSON, J. M.: *Agnosia, Apraxia, Aphasia.* New York, Paul B. Hoeber, Inc., 1946.

64. NELSON, V. L., and RICHARDS, T. W.: Fels mental age values for Gesell schedules. *Child Development, XI:* 153-157, 1940.

65. PALMER, M. F.: Aphasia and occupational therapy. *Amer. J. Occup. Therapy, IV:*3, 1950.

66. PALMER, M. F.: Recent advances in the scientific study of language disorders in cerebral palsy. *Cereb. Palsy Rev., XV:*3-4, 1954.

67. PALMER, M. F.: Speech disorders in cerebral palsy. In ABBOTT, M. (Ed.), *Proceedings: Cerebral Palsy Institute.* New York, Association in Aid of Crippled Children, 1952, pp. 47-64.

68. PALMER, M. F., and BERKO, F. G.: The Education of the aphasic child. *Amer. J. Occup. Ther.*, *VI*:241-246, 1952.

69. RIESEN, A. H.: Arrested vision. *Scientific American, CLXXXIII*:1, 16-19, 1950.

70. RIESEN, A. H.: Stimulation as a requirement for growth and function of behavioral development. In Fiske, D. W., and S. R. Maddi (Eds.), *Functions of Varied Experience*, Homewood, Dorsey Press, 1961, pp. 57-80.

71. RIESEN, A. H.: Studying perceptual development using the technique of sensory deprivation. *J. Nerv. Ment. Disease, CXXXII*:21-25, 1961.

72. RIESEN, A. H.: The development of visual perception in man and chimpanzee. *Science, CVI*:107-108, 1946.

73. RIESEN, A. H., and AARONS, L.: Visual movement and intensity discrimination in cats after early deprivation of pattern vision. *J. Comp. Physiol. Psychol, LII*:142-149, 1952.

74. RUCH, T. C., and FULTON, J. F.: *Medical Physiology and Biophysics.* Philadelphia, W. B. Saunders, 1961.

75. SMITH, K. U.: *Delayed Sensory Feedback and Behavior.* Philadelphia. W. B. Saunders, 1962.

76. SMITH, K. U., and SMITH, W. M.: *Perception and Motion.* Philadelphia, W. B. Saunders, 1962.

77. SNYDER, F. W., and PRONKO, N. H.: *Vision with Spatial Inversion.* Wichita, University of Wichita Press, 1952.

78. STRATTON, G. H.: Some preliminary experiments in vision without inversion of the retinal image. *Psychol. Rev., III*:611-617, 1896.

79. STRATTON, G. H.: The spatial harmony of touch and sight. *Mind, VIII*:492-505, 1899.

80. STRATTON, G. H.: Vision without inversion of the retinal image. *Psychol. Rev., IV*:341-360, 463-481, 1897.

81. STRAUSS, A. A. and KEPHART, N. C.: *Psychopathology and Education of the Brain-injured Child: Progress in Theory and Clinic.* New York, Grune and Stratton, 1955.

82. STRAUSS, A. A., and LEHTINEN, L. E.: *Psychopathology and Education of the Brain-injured Child.* New York, Grune & Stratton, 1947.

83. STRAUSS, A. A., and WERNER, H.: Disorders in conceptual thinking in brain injured children. *J. Nerv. Ment. Dis., XCVI:*153-160, 1942.

84. TAYLOR, E. M.: *Psychological Appraisal of Children with Cerebral Defects.* Cambridge, Harvard University Press, 1961.

85. TEUBER, H. L.: Sensory deprivation, sensory suppression and agnosia: Notes for a neurological theory. *J. Nerv. Ment. Dis., CXXXII:*1, 32-40, 1961.

86. WALK, R. D., and GIBSON, E. J.: A comparative and analytical study of visual depth perception, *Psychological Monographs, LXXV:*15, 1961, Whole No. 519.

87. WAPNER, S., and WERNER, H.: Experiments on sensory-tonic field theory of perception: Effect of body status on the kinesthetic perception of verticality. *J. Exp. Psychol., XLIV:*126-131, 1951.

88. WATSON, J. B.: *Behavior.* New York, Holt & Co., 1914.

89. WERNER, H., and CARRISON, D.: Animistic thinking in brain injured, mentally retarded children. *J. Abnorm. Soc. Psychol., LXI:*43-62, 1944.

90. WERNER, H., and WAPNER, H. S.: Toward a general theory of perception. *Psychol. Rev., LIX:*324-338, 1952.

91. WERNER, H., WAPNER, S., and CHANDLER, K.: Experiments on sensory-tonic field theory of perception. *J. Exp. Psychol., XLII:*341-357, 1951.

92. WERNER, H., and WEIR, A.: The figure-ground syndrome in the brain injured child. *Int. Rec. Med., CLXIX:*362-367, 1956.

93. WOLF, WERNER: *The Personality of the Preschool Child.* New York, Grune & Stratton, 1946.

Chapter VIII

SPECIAL EDUCATION FOR THE CEREBRAL PALSIED

A GROUP LANGUAGE LEARNING EXPERIENCE

FRANCES G. BERKO

INTRODUCTION

LANGUAGE, THE TOOL by which man communicates with his fellowmen and thus establishes his identity as a reasoning animal in the social world, may be broken down into four processes: listening, speaking, reading and writing. Developmentally, these four components of the language arts are mutually dependent. They follow a more or less definite order of appearance as tools of communication in the life cycle of each individual. The child must "listen" before he speaks; he must be able to use language orally before he reads, and he must be able to recognize the written form of the word before he can "write." However, there are children who are unable to hear, speak, read or write and they too must gain some degree of ability with the language arts in order to succeed in living within the normal social world. The deaf, the blind, the severe case of poliomyelitis whose normal ability is limited, the cerebral palsied child, and others, fall within this category. And for them, special techniques and substitutes must be found so that they too can learn the language arts, but in a different way. The most obvious examples of this is the deaf child who "listens" with the use of a hearing aid, through speech reading, or a combination of both.

It has already been well amplified in this text that speech therapy for the cerebral palsied individual encompasses far more than the development of articulatory intelligibility. In the production of speech sound alone, the teaching of the mechanics of speech, the therapist has to work with the basic reflexology of breathing, chewing, sucking and swallowing, the patterns of melody, rhythm and accent, the nasality problems commonly

261

associated with cleft palate difficulties and other problems of rhinolalia, retraining of the facial musculature so that the muscle spasm will not detract from the speech intelligibility, vocal fold valving, rate of speech production and similar problems. In fact, the teaching of speech production to the cerebral palsied may involve every known therapeutic technique commonly used with other types of speech handicapped individuals. For example, Jenna drill which is widely used in teaching the deaf may be one of the techniques used with the cerebral palsied who has no hearing loss in order to normalize the rate of speech. Yet, in many cases of cerebral palsy, speech production or speech intelligibility is not the sole problem with which the therapist has to deal; it may not even be the major problem. Although there are no statistics available to reliably attest to what percentage of these cases also have other handicapping conditions of childhood aphasia, hearing loss, visual difficulties, agnosias and apraxias, there is a clinical impression that the majority of these individuals react as if they also have one or more of these other handicaps. What this means on the clinical level is that the child must be taught to attend to the "listening-speaking" cycle of communication and to derive meaning therefrom. Often this precedes the teaching of speech itself. At times, both can be worked on concomitantly. Whatever the case may be, production of intelligible speech is contingent upon the child's ability to show specific attentiveness to speech sounds and to derive meaning therefrom, as well as to achieve a speaking competence which enables him not only to voice precisely his needs, pains and feelings, but also to express his abstractions or his observations of the world around him. This, of course, implies an awareness of his environment which may not be developed at the onset of therapy.

These facts set before the therapist a monumental task, seemingly too great to overcome in several half hour sessions per week. Various solutions have been practiced throughout the country, ranging from the delay of onset of speech therapy until the child has sufficiently "matured" (i.e., developed the communicative process on his own) to the complete ignoring of all language problems in the cerebral palsied, except the articulatory defect. Some have erected minimum standards of intellectual capacity for eligibility in the speech therapy programs; others have questioned quite seriously the value of speech therapy among these children.

Peculiarly enough, the basic language needs of listening and speaking which are required for effective intelligibility parallel the language achievements of the normal child of five or six which is entering the academic learning situation for the first time. Such a child is rather sophisticated in the communication cycle, and therefore he is deemed ready both to use his linguistic abilities as a tool to further learning and to develop greater proficiency in the communication processes. It seems obvious, in the light of this, that the development of language concepts of the cerebral palsied is not the responsibility of only the speech therapist, it is shared by the special education teacher as well.

In recent years, private agencies working with those who have cerebral palsy have adopted a "new" program, i.e., the "preschool." In most cases, such programs are open to children who, for a variety of reasons, may not be ready or eligible for special education classes. The majority of such programs seem to be aimed at several diverse purposes such as providing a socializing experience for the child, a "waiting area" for therapy, and relieving the parent of constant supervision for part of the day. Regardless of the relative merits of these avowed purposes of preschool programming for the cerebral palsied, there seems to be another which may override all others in its value toward the development of the cerebral palsied child to the maximum of his potential. The preschool program affords the ideal controlled situation in which the child's language-learning may be developed to the degree required for academic achievement. Thus, the preschool teacher who is properly trained can reinforce and develop in the social situation those language activities which do not involve the actual teaching of mechanical speech production.

It is with these concepts in mind that there is a change in emphasis in this chapter over its counterpart in our first book, *Speech Therapy in Cerebral Palsy*. The intervening years have proved, at least empirically, that the crucial learning period for the neurologically impaired is during the preschool years. Simultaneous with the individual therapies must occur the small group experience in a controlled environment where the child can be taught to perceive his world in the manner of his peers. Because the preschool experience is so vital to the future education of the cerebral palsied child, this aspect of his education is given considerably more attention.

Further, this text was originally conceived as a treatise on speech therapy, and the inclusion of the chapter on the education of the cerebral palsied was confined to the teaching of the language arts — reading and writing. Experience has since proved that mathematics also is a form of communication which requires similar abstractions, concept formations and linguistic abilities to those frequently found deficient in the cerebral palsied. Added to the present chapter, therefore, are some of the concepts pertaining to the teaching of arithmetic.

Finally, what has been excluded is specific methodology or technique. Each teacher, as each therapist, must create his own technique — and usually with each child. Man's knowledge of education, let alone special education, has not reached a stage of mechanistic perfection where knowledge can be programmed into the child's brain and, with computer-like accuracy, the educated, informed adult is the result. If this cannot be achieved with the "normal" or "unimpaired" central nervous system, how then can it be expected that specific techniques for teaching given material at given levels be universally devised for those children who by very definition have some insult to their central nervous system. It also seems necessary to state the obvious — there are children with cerebral palsy and of mild, moderate or severe physical involvement who can learn in a normal manner. For them, much of what is said in this chapter is not pertinent, any more than it pertains to the education of any child. In short, what is attempted here is a description of problems which may arise in the education of the neurologically impaired child, some understanding of why they arise, and some suggestions that approach their "speciality" in the educational environment.

WHAT IS EDUCATION?

To the layman, elementary education — academic learning — is the sum of reading, writing and arithmetic. He, therefore, has difficulty sometimes in approaching the importance of much that his child is taught under the core of curriculum of modern education.[11,12,30,38,51,56,57,64] For the child with cerebral palsy, this parental attitude often is intensified because parents seem to feel that, since the child has to combat the artificial barriers of his handicap constantly in acquiring knowledge, struggling to acquire the "frills" of learning is an unnecessary waste of time and energy. It therefore seems vital to the present approach to learning that education — academic learning — as it is meant in this chapter, be defined.

For the average child, learning begins shortly after birth. As he adjusts to his crib, his formula, and the warm hands that tend to his physical needs, his storehouse of experience is begun. This is equally true of the cerebral palsied child. But as the normal child grows chronologically, his experience increases by geometric progression. He learns to walk, and thus he begins to wander from the narrow environment of home and absolute supervision. He learns to communicate, and so, via the two-way process of listening and speaking, he gradually learns to interpret the world about him. By the age of five or six, when he is ready to intensify and formalize his learning process, he has some rudimentary concept of what he is to be taught during the next eight to twelve years. He has been to the store; he has spoken in rather detailed, complex sentences; he has seen printed and written words — maybe he even has attempted to read and write; he has experienced some sort of daily social grouping among the neighborhood children; he has completely investigated his environment; usually, he has experienced the individual discipline of the home and the group discipline necessary to behavior in public. Based upon these experiences, his years of academic learning can begin.

With the child who has cerebral palsy, this readiness for academic learning is not present usually by the age of six. His physical limitations have prevented him from doing much of what other children have done by the age of five. At best, these formative years have been spent as an observer, rather than as a participant in life, and frequently the child is not given the opportunity even to observe the activities common to his age level. Thus, he approaches "school age" as an academic retardate in that he has an experiential deficit in those areas upon which the primary education is based. For example, most preprimers tell the story of a brother, a sister and their pets, a cat and a dog. The average child may never have had a pet of his own, but most certainly he has played with his neighbor's or a stray. The cerebral palsied child, on the other hand, may never have stroked a cat and heard him purr; he may never have seen a dog fetch or beg for food. Therefore, the "story" contains no real meaning for him. Reading thus becomes a "trick," just so many words strung together which he learns to perform to please his parents and teachers. As will be pointed out later in discussing the approach to the cerebral palsied child, mathematics, especially the teaching of money concepts, bears this same quality of unreality in the life of these children.

Academic learning may be defined as the practical application of the communicative processes as they apply to the present and future life of the child. Not only must the child have considerable experience in both the speaking and listening phases of communication to participate in academic learning, he also must have shared the activities which are common to most children at the beginning of their formal education. Gesell has structured these activities according to the age at which they are assimilated by the average child.[34,35] *For the cerebral palsied child, an evaluation of his experiential development should be made at the onset of his classroom experience, and any gaps in this process of normal experiential development should be corrected prior to, or concurrent with the standard curriculum.*

One aspect of the vitality of the developmental approach to education might be gleaned from an understanding of what the child is asked to master in any academic learning activity. For example, what is reading? McKee defines reading as the "carrying out" of three major acts: (1) Identifying and recognizing printed words quickly and accurately; (2) arriving at an adequate understanding of the meaning intended by the writer and (3) making use of the meaning.[56] There are, therefore, five mental functions, aside from language ability, which are inherent in the reading process. These may be called *perception, specific attentiveness, abstraction, experience and integration.*

Perception: In order that the child be able to identify and recognize words, he must first be able to distinguish between the "h," "n," and "m," the "c" and "o," the "b," "d" and "p," etc., he must likewise be able to see the difference between "was" and "saw," "let" and "get," and "come" and "came." An inability to differentiate between letters or words may imply some deficiency in visual acuity which is a medical problem corrected by prescription glasses. However, there is a functional distinction between seeing a form and perceiving it or recognizing its shape. It is both of these functions which the reader is required to perform.

Specific Attentiveness: There have been countless experiments in psychology to prove that not everything that falls on the retina of the normal eye is perceived by the individual. What is seen is selected from the environment for specific attention in accordance with the individual's purpose at the given moment. One of the most debated issues in the teaching of reading today is that modern techniques, as most widely practiced, assume that the child has this ability to a highly developed degree and that this ability, plus an assumed ability to abstract on the words he is taught, will enable him to read all words.[11,56,57,63] In the term *specific attentiveness* is implied the ability to know what to select out of the environment for attention and a consciousness of all the elements of what is seen.

Abstraction: It is trite to point out that language is symbolic. In writing, the author substitutes a code, a symbol, to convey the idea he wishes to express. For example, seeing the letters *a p p l e* and actually holding, smelling, seeing and tasting an apple are two entirely varied experiences. Yet reading the sentence, "Mary ate an apple," implies that the individual must abstract not one but four symbols in relation to each other. For instantaneous comprehension, he must make a complexity of abstractions and check these in order to certify that the meaning he derived is the one that the author intended.

Experience: In order to understand the symbols we call language, the child must know the reality which the symbols represent. For example, to be able to make the abstractions necessary for comprehension of "Mary ate the apple," the child must have the experience of having eaten, at some time, an apple and thus actually know how it feels, sounds, tastes, smells, etc. In recent years, much point has been made of modernizing the primers and the first three readers so that the child would be familiar not only with the words used, but also with the experiences which are described in these stories.

Integration: Integration is the process by which the child combines what he sees, his attention to it, his recognition of it as a symbol of reality, and his memory of that or a similar reality in order to achieve an understanding of what the author means and to utilize that meaning.

THE APPROACH TO THE CHILD
WITH CEREBRAL PALSY

Before discussing the specific problems involved in educating the child with cerebral palsy, a word must be said about the teacher's attitude toward the child and his academic development. It is becoming almost trite to point out that the child who has cerebral palsy is primarily a child like all other children and must be approached accordingly. All too often, persons concerned with the habilitation of these children become so involved with the correction of their problems — the ways in which they differ from the average child — that they lose sight of the fact that essentially there are far more similarities than differences between these and other children, and it is these *similarities* that provide the key to successful habilitation. For example, proficiency in speaking, walking, reading and writing is not the primary need of the cerebral palsied child; without pressure from his parents and other adults within his environment, it is probable that the child would soon lose all drive to develop these activities to the best of his ability. However, the need for love, security, feelings of success and the knowledge of belonging to his environment is as strong in the cerebral palsied child as it is in any child. To be happy, he must learn to live with not only his family and his friends, but with himself. He needs to know that despite all he cannot do, he is a person of worth upon whom others are dependent for their happiness. These are the things taught every child as he matures both in the family and in the classroom group. These are the things which the child with cerebral palsy must learn. That he learn this well is vital to the formation of a healthy ego structure.

Psychologists have long spoken of the need for security in the life of the individual. Security may be defined as the feeling of "belongingness as a contributing member of the group." The human being is a social organism; he must feel a part of whatever group or groups with which his environment brings him into contact; he cannot bear to feel that he is merely an observer of, or tolerated by, all such groups. He must bring something to the group, give of himself, and to feel a part thereof — in other words, he must belong. A herd of cattle or a pack of dogs is not a *group*, because each animal is merely attending to his own needs and desires in the presence of other animals; the animal does not surrender part of himself to the benefit of all the animals present. The first attempts at parents' meeting in which individuals would take endless time on their own minor problems with the children who had cerebral palsy did not result in group feeling or group action. Before becoming a parents' *group*, the individual members had to learn to surrender part of their needs for self-expression; they learned slowly to give everyone a chance to speak and give — to help the more inexperienced parent through their experiences — as well as to assimilate whatever knowledge would help them in their problems. This is a learning process peculiar to man. The child must be taught it, and unless he learns it, he cannot be truly happy in our world.

Security, then, has nothing to do with material wealth. Except as a factor in obtaining membership and acceptance in certain groups, it matters little how many toys a child has or whether his clothes come from the best store in town. To the child, however, what may matter is that he has the same toys, the same clothes and the same privileges and responsibilities as the other children in his group; in a child's world, sameness, both in material things and in intangibles is the passport to belonging in the group — and thus to security.

In the family group, the child must feel that he is giving something to the welfare of the family, as well as getting something from it. In the case of the severely handicapped child with cerebral palsy, this is often an illusion most difficult to create, but created it must be. Perhaps the child can help mother dust the living room or show her onto what shelf each item in the grocery sack goes. He certainly can be made a part of family discussions concerning some of the decisions that are to be made, especially those that concern him, provided, of course, that these discussions are within his comprehension. For example, most children would have an opinion on whether the family should take a Sunday drive, stay home and watch television, or visit Aunt Jane. Yet inclusion of the child with cerebral palsy in the group that is making such a simple decision is often neglected, even when he is capable of such decision-making. How can the child feel wanted by and a part of a group that does not need him to help decide such matters?

Another basis for the child's security in the family is enlightened discipline. Discipline, when just, expresses to the child that you care what he does — that he is so necessary to the family group that any undesirable behavior affects the entire group. The type of discipline used is strictly personal to the family group. The strictness with which it is administered matters little as long as it is fair and enlightened.

Enlightenment in discipline concerns three factors: (1) How both parents agree to the boundaries beyond which discipline must be administered; (2) how they agree to the type of discipline administered and (3) what goes on in the child's mind both committing the misdemeanor and in receiving the punishment. Having cerebral palsy is not the horrible phenomenon in the child's mind that parents or any nondisabled person may think it is. Being handicapped from birth, the child has no actual experience with what he is missing. Although he has the insight of knowing that he physically differs from those around him and that he cannot do the things they do, growing up with a handicap is almost as natural to him as growing up without a handicap was to his parents. If this concept is understood and accepted by parents of a child having cerebral palsy, they will discipline their children without hesitation. In reality, however, the most frequent failures of discipline have occurred because one parent wavers. Either he refuses to discipline the child at all, or he lessens or negates punishment as being too harsh. There is nothing that a child learns more quickly than playing one parent against the other.

The child, on the other hand, has a mind of his own. Not only must parents reach some accord between themselves, but they also must have some real understanding of what goes on in the child's mind. The little girl with cerebral palsy who created absolute chaos in her mother's kitchen because she thought it was only right to cook breakfast for Mother on Mother's Day has never forgotten that the punishment for going to the flour bin and the dish cabinet, both of which were expressly forbidden, was not too severe; her mother knew that she was merely giving her a Mother's Day gift. A child's mind reasons; due to his inexperience, his reasoning often is faulty. Only with understanding and guidance can he learn to see all the aspects of a given situation. Thus sometimes (especially in first offenses not involving destruction of life and property), reasoning out the cause-effect relationship of the given situation in its most specific, concrete terms is sufficient discipline.

By the same token, the child must know clearly for what he is disciplined. No doubt can be left in his mind as to the cause-effect relationship as a specific, concrete sequence of events. The example of little Jimmie, who, after hitting a playmate and receiving a similar slap from his mother, said, "Why you hit Jimmie?" is most pertinent. Language concepts are difficult for the brain-injured and the experientially limited; before discipline can be effective, there must be certainty that the child understood what you meant and he deliberately disobeyed. If these conditions are met, the discipline is enlightened.

If enlightened discipline has been practiced in the home, both the child and the classroom teacher find themselves well along the road to acceptance of the group learning situation. If however, there has been little consistency of discipline in the child's previous life experience, the teacher should pause to teach both the child and his parents acceptance of the rules of group living. Frequently, the child can learn this more readily and by more direct means than his parents, and it seems advisable that he is taught group conformity first. Then by illustrating how he had gained under the more consistent approach, the parents can learn indirectly that he is, after all, a child like all other children and must be reared by the same code of behavior.

At the same time, however, there should be someone on the "clinical team" with the responsibility for parent counseling and education. This counseling process should interpret the child's language-learning needs as described in this section and as they relate to the total family situation. Causes of primary tensions within the family are often easily uncovered by having the mother give a detailed description of the child's daily routine. As the problems of discipline and confusion unfold, the counselor interrupts only to suggest alternative methods of handling everyday situations. These should be described as simply and as concretely as is humanly possible. Too frequent is the counseling error of assuming that even the most intelligent, well educated parent can comprehend fully the peculiar jargon of the professional worker. It should also be pointed out that the parent, because of his emotional involvement in the problem, needs much encouragement and reinforcement. One counseling session is insufficient to manifest any domestic changes.

One of the most frequent misconceptions of individuals concerned with the child who has cerebral palsy is that this child, once he learns to walk, speak, or use his hands in some manner, wants to learn to do these activities as normally as it is possible for him to learn them upon years of practice. Those activities are to the child not goals but tools by which he achieves group "belongingness." Unless he, through years of frustration, has resigned himself to a life of "not belonging," he never gives up the hope of speaking, self-locomotion, or use of the hands. But once he has achieved these activities, regardless of how imperfect they may be, the need seems satisfied and improvement for improvement's sake — working to make their performance better with no other goal in view — bears little or no importance in the child's mind.

The same is true of academic learning among those who are

educable. Without extraneous motivation forces, learning the essentials of reading, writing, and some computation seem to satisfy. Striving for the understanding of the more difficult concepts of elementary education cannot be achieved with the goal of "learning something new." This factor in learning is true of all children.[64] Among children who have cerebral palsy, however, there is the additional fear of failure, and each new concept, each new activity, presents a threat to the child's security. It is, therefore, important that short-term motivational goals and activities be afforded the child, both in classroom and in therapy, so that he may progress without the understanding that new material is being approached. Such things as competition between classmates, familiarizing the child with the information before he realizes that he will be required to assimilate it, and varying the materials and techniques used in teaching often overcome this hazard.

Most children who have cerebral palsy are multiply handicapped. In addition to the motor deviances in locomotion, use of hands and speech production, there may be present such additional handicaps as mental retardation, perceptual deviances, sensory intake disturbances including perceptual losses in one or more of the five sensory avenues, hearing and visual acuity problems, epilepsy, emotional overlays and a variety of other factors. Since these occur in a proportionally large percentage of the cerebral palsied, considerable attention has been given here to their description. The specialist, whether he be practicing special education or therapy, must understand and appreciate the nature of these defects and the clinical methodologies which tend to mediate their barriers to language-learning. However, it often seems that in the effort to gain understanding, the day-to-day contact with the child is in danger of becoming too analytical, too segmented. There may be a tendency to think in terms of the particular group of handicapping conditions toward which the lesson plan or modality is aimed, rather than the child with whom we are working. Herein may lie the major cause of such well known clinical phenomena as unmanageable behavioral reactions, learning plateaus and regressions and overall lack of progress. It is an empirical conviction that these *negative responses* to the clinical situation, if prolonged, are *artifacts due to improper handling* of the child, rather than any learning limitation which the child may possess. In short, temper tantrums, catastrophia, balking at entering the therapy room or group environment, weeks or months of working on the same concept with no evidence of learning, and similar behavioral manifestations are signs to the clinician that something is radically wrong with the approach used toward the child, and it must be reviewed and corrected immediately.

While each child differs, and therefore the root of negative reactions varies from child to child or from situation to situation in the same child, there may be a general check list which the clinician can follow in reviewing and analyzing what has transpired:

1. Is the activity within the child's developmental level of performance?
2. Does the child comprehend what is required of him?
3. Is the learning situation itself in proper structure?
4. Has the child been prepared for change when change in structure or situation is necessary?
5. What is the relationship between the child and the teacher or therapist?
6. How does the special education teacher, the clinician who teaches cerebral palsied children in a group, allow for these individual differences?

Is the activity within the child's developmental level of performance? If the child, aged five, functions at the level of a three-and-a-half-year-old, can the performance asked for be successfully completed by the average three-and-a-half-year-old child? Too often, stress is laid on the next developmental step in the modality without consideration of the overall development of the child.

Does the child comprehend what is required of him? Mention has already been made of the fact that, in determining the levels or various areas of performance, the child's level of verbal comprehension must be included. It cannot be overemphasized that language is a two way process of comprehension and output, and that many cerebral palsied children give the appearance of understanding what is said to them, when, in reality, there is little or no comprehension. This seems particularly true when a command or a choice is involved.

Both comprehension of commands and choosing are learned activities for all children. For a variety of reasons, the cerebral palsied or the brain-injured child might not have learned them at the normal age. This in no way infers that he is incapable of learning to follow a command or make a choice. What it does import is that until he has learned these language activities he should not be expected to do them as a part of another performance area in which the certainty of success is not present.

In view of the description already given as to the complicated abstractions involved in comprehending "Mary ate the red apple," it seems obvious that the command "Turn off the light" requires even greater abstractions and integrations. In addition to all that has been said, there is the additional factor of translating language comprehension into a motor activity. Memory required in performing a series of motor functions, ignoring or overcoming the distractions in the environment while carrying through the command, and even just performing a task which was not self-initiated, pyramid the barriers of successful performance.

When the element of choice is introduced, language comprehension is further confused. The child may always choose the chocolate cookies at recess. However, if one day the teacher asks "Teddy, do you want a vanilla cookie or a chocolate cookie?" the child may not be able to cope with the double propositionality of the requirement to make the motor-speech-behavior response of choice and/or of complicated language comprehension, even though he is perfectly capable of doing each of these individually.

Here again, in order to shed light on what may be happening in the child's mind, analysis seems to render the operating factors too complicated for successful handling in the teaching situation, whether it be in individual therapy or group learning. Actually, the experienced *clinician* will verify that ideally these should never have to be "handled" because they are factors which are anticipated in planning the approach to the child, and intelligent awareness that they might occur should forestall their actual occurrence.

For example, teaching the child to choose between two desirable or undesirable activities — and he must be taught to make both types of choices —should be reserved for "snack time" or the recreational period. Until the child handles choice well in the social learning situation, he should not have to choose in any of the "definite learning" situations, i.e., the therapies or the developmental learning groups. As choice becomes routine in one situation, then it is introduced into another. Here the professional personnel working with the child must decide in which situation the element of choice may be introduced with the least threat to the child. For some children, the occupational therapy situation where the child is working on a one-to-one basis on activities that naturally require the elements of choosing may be the second situation for choice. Other children seem to carry over the choice from the recreational to the developmental activities of the group environment automatically, and in these instances, they should be reinforced in the classroom or group situation quite some time before the therapists begin introducing them into the therapy program.

Comprehension of commands is part of language comprehension development. As such, the same rules apply to teaching the child to follow commands as to overall language development. Not the least of these is the recognition that there is a deficit of language comprehension. Once the clinician really understands and accepts this fact, the rest is almost axiomatic. Slower than normal rate of speech, in which melody patterns remain relatively normal but the rhythm and accent patterns are exaggerated and markedly stabilized is recommended. The teacher's total speech pattern gives the acoustical affect of normal speech slowed down thus allowing for the child's slower rate of input comprehension. Time is allowed for the child to respond before the command is repeated. The time required may vary up to ninety seconds, depending on the child. If he does not respond within that time (sooner if some noise or other distraction has intervened), repeat what has been said — at a lower language level if possible. In other words, while the child must *always* be approached within his level of language comprehension, one of the infinite times may be occurring when, due to his extreme variability of performance, his comprehension is lowered.

Incidentally, one of the home situations which must be carefully checked at the *clinical* level is the child's waking and sleeping habits. If the morning is one mad dash to the clinic, with a continual outpouring of commands and movements before the child is neurologically oriented for them, confusion has occurred before the clinician sees the child. Many children with central nervous system damage are "slow risers." For greatest clinical effectiveness, it seems basic that the parents must be educated to wake the child in sufficient time to allow a slow, calm approach to the day's beginning. This is especially true of those children who, upon waking, need a few moments in bed, awake, to neurologically orient themselves to meeting the new day. One of the best clues to whether a given child has this need is to have the parent describe what the child eats for breakfast. The "slow riser" usually refuses the large breakfast, and most parents of such children will attest that this is the meal of greatest family strife.

Is the learning situation itself properly structured? All that has been described above is how the clinician structures the language comprehension required of the child who is functioning at a relatively low level in this area. In addition to this, it must be recognized that the clinical environment and the routine which is followed in the learning situation has much to do with the quality of the child's language comprehension and behavioral performance. These have already been described in detail. It seems sufficient here to recall that the security the child derives from the stability of the environment and the firmness of the clinician's approach is fundamental to learning.

If he felt insecure by their absence or unpredictability, he could not function. He must be taught to cope with the uncertainties of the normal environment gradually. They cannot be thrust upon him without warning, and with the expectation that he will perform to his best abilities.

Has the child been prepared for the change? In our society, it is foolish to expect anything to remain stable indefinitely — including the clinical situation. Change will occur, the unpredictable will happen, scheduling conflicts and confusions will arise, and the unforeseen is ever present. The brain-injured child — regardless of the severity of his rigidities — can usually be taught to accept these. The few seconds taken from the instructional session to explain to the child in his own terms what is about to happen that is different often saves the value of the entire session. In these explanations, there are some simple cautions: Both the elements of question and choice should be avoided. The explanation should be transmitted with a quiet enthusiasm as if what is about to happen is the most pleasurable experience the child can have. Time should be allowed for the child to comprehend the change before he is moved into the new activity.

In speaking of change, there is one precaution that seems to be obvious, yet is so frequently overlooked. In any young child, concepts of the future are at best vague and uncertain. It requires a rather high degree of social maturation to cope successfully with the anticipation of something happening next Tuesday, next week, next year or even tomorrow. With the cerebral palsied, the brain-injured and the retarded child who find life sufficiently insecure and normally uncertain, telling him of some happening in the distant future is oftentimes too great a threat to his security, and this in itself may cause decreased levels of performance and increases in bizarre behavioral reactions. In general, the child should be informed of change only when it is imminent. However, experience has shown that even a highly motivated goal-directed activity can be interrupted by another activity successfully if time is taken to prepare the child.

What is the relationship between the child and the teacher or therapist? As part of the training for each of the disciplines working with the cerebral palsied child, time is spent in the teaching of establishment of rapport. Years of observation of clinicians has left the impression that often the definition of rapport itself remains obscure. Precise verbal descriptions elude even the most experienced. At best it seems that attempts to define the word should be abandoned in favor of description of some of its elements, with the full recognition that the sum of the parts fall far short of the whole.

The specialist is an actor, playing a role of his own choosing. He probably chose this role when he was quite young and there may be some question in his mind whether he would make the same choice today. He finds himself in the specialized situation primarily for two reasons — to earn a livelihood and because this gives him personal satisfaction. In other words, his motives are primarily selfish, and the sooner he faces and accepts that fact the more effective he is with the children under his care. In the total life experience of the child, the specialist's role is peculiar. In the first place, he is not the child's parents; he has no pre-rogatives of parenthood, except those specifically delegated to him by the parent during the time the child is within the clinic or school. Except by indirection and suggestion, the specialist can-not alter the child's home environment or the emotional inter-actions of the family situation. If he attempts to do this, he endangers his effectiveness with the child.

The specialist is a human being, with likes, dislikes, problems and discouragements which are apart from his professional life. Regardless of the severity of his home problems or his particular mood, reporting for work means that he is "on stage" — insofar as humanly possible, those personal distractions must be inten-tionally wiped from his consciousness. This is a matter of train-ing; he must train himself to do this mainly by placing his full concentration on the child at hand. Nor is the teacher expected to like every child with whom he works. However, just as forming too great an attachment to a child — becoming too involved with the child's problems and progress — is highly undesirable, over-emphasis on personal repulsions is equally unprofessional. How-ever, it frequently seems that the disliked child is the one that makes the greatest gains. The experienced teacher will attempt to analyze what it is about the child which repulses him and then seek to correct these factors first.

The role of the specialist — the act which he must artificially learn until it becomes a natural, automatic response — is that of friend-teacher who reacts with quiet enthusiasm as if each activity is new, challenging and extremely pleasurable. The boundaries of the teaching situation remain well defined, and the child knows and expects that he will be disciplined for infringements — but he has learned to accept this as part of his friendship with the clinician. The experienced teacher will avow that timing and responding to the subliminal cues of the child's reactions are crucial to successful teaching. Yet to describe precisely what he means by this seems an impossibility. Not all children respond to the same type of personality or the same manner of approach. Therefore, the teacher trains himself to be that type of personality and use that approach to which the individual child best responds. The experienced specialist is a chameleon, changing his personality at will, submerging his own ego to the needs of the child. Some children respond best to horseplay; others, to sternness and absolute propriety. The varieties of personalities to which individual children may respond are infinite; there is no way of predicting in advance what brings out the given child. The teacher must watch the child for cues and be able to change his approach instantaneously, if necessary, once he observes some behavioral regression.

A screaming child in a teaching situation, whether it be individual therapy or group classroom, is evidence that the teacher is not infallible. These errors are to be expected. However, the true professional admits readily to error and attempts to avoid repetition. It is ridiculous for any trained adult to assume that because Mary cries every day when she enters the speech therapy room that Mary should be dropped from therapy or that Mary's emotional instability, rather than the clinician's lack of proficiency, is at the root of these outbursts.

Equally disturbing and revealing in its lack of insight is the frequently met attitude on the part of many specialists of absolute boredom. If the teacher is bored, what about the child? Repetition is boring; some cerebral palsied children need a great deal of repetition to learn. It has always seemed, however, that there are ameliorating factors that should be able to prevent the clinician's doing the same thing the same way day after day, week after week, with no progress: (1) The professionally trained person should consider each child a challenge — if nothing else, a challenge to his own ego and years of education and experience. If he has little or no interest in the child, he can artificially create a challenge to himself, bolster his own morale by teaching the "unteachable"; (2) When a given approach or technique to a concept doesn't produce learning within a reasonable time, forget it. There are so many approaches to any learning problem that no teacher should be at a loss for techniques. In fact, the child's need for repetition for learning does not mean that the same technique with the same equipment should be used day after day until the child is letter perfect. With some exceptions, mainly in the selection of materials, each concept should be approached in as many different ways on the child's level as it is possible to conceive. The caution that must be observed in doing this is that there must be certainty that the variety of approaches does not present the child with some conceptual confusions. For example, in the early teaching of color concepts, the same shade of red, blue and green should be used. To say that the leaves of the tree are green may be confusing to the brain-injured child who looks at the tree and sees five different shades — or to him, five different colors.

How does the special education teacher, the clinician who teaches cerebral palsied children in a group allow for these individual differences? For the teacher to work effectively with a group, certain basic environmental factors must be present.

1. The physical environment of the room must be neat, well ordered, with a minimum of distractions either in color, or evident equipment.
2. The number of children being worked with at given time must be manageable. This varies with the size of the room, the number of assistants, and the level of the group.
3. The fundamental developmental levels of each child's various performance areas must be known and accepted: this seems to be the most difficult adjustment the inexperienced teacher must make.
4. There must be understanding of the multiplicities of each child's handicap and how they affect learning.
5. A workable classroom routine and discipline is established

in which the child is permitted only as much freedom to learn as he is capable of handling.

6. The teacher must be in the classroom ready to begin the school day before the first child arrives.
7. The first few moments of each school day begin with the same routine.

If the classroom teacher maintains these seven environmental controls, she seems to have less difficulty in adjusting her program to meet the individual differences and learning needs.

LEARNING PROBLEMS OF THE CHILD WITH CEREBRAL PALSY

It seems obvious that the child with cerebral palsy is not simply a youngster with a motor defect affecting locomotion, manual dexterity, and speech intelligibility, and that equalizing or overcoming his physical deficiencies alone do not solve his educational problems.

Severe Motor-physical Disabilities: Severe physical defects do affect learning, sometimes in more subtle ways than can be gleaned by the obvious physical limitations. Lack of muscular control of the head may prevent adequate visual fixation; lack of sitting balance causes discomfort which impedes concentration for learning intake; and inability to use the hands blocks a learning channel by which most children learn. These handicaps are sufficient to block adequate learning, but they do not describe the entire problem faced by these children. For the child whose physical handicap is so severe that sitting, head balance and voluntary grasp have not been mastered, the educational problem is not confined to providing special mechanical aids or artificial assistance, i.e., specially altered wheel chairs and bookstands. Nor does the additional precaution of designing the educational program so that vision and hearing are substituted for manual dexterity suffice in meeting the special learning needs of such a child. This is true even when the cerebral palsied student is deemed to have normal native intelligence and minimal sensory defects. Even if all these conditions are met, such a child could not learn in the same manner as the normal child of equal intelligence. Immediately apparent are two factors which contribute to a learning difference, namely language and experience. The child with severe motor difficulties is usually the most sheltered, the most confined to his immediate home environment, and the least adventurous of all the cerebral palsied. What he experiences is brought to him; he can never seek it out for himself. More important than this, however, is the fact that such a child usually has a severe speech involvement, making speech both difficult and unintelligible. Thus, what he gains from the few experiences he has in his environment is rarely known. Coupled with this is the fact that he often is preoccupied with his own physical discomforts, and this preoccupation keeps him from deriving from his limited environment those lessons which it affords. Thus, it might be said that he lacks specific attentiveness to environmental detail.

However, these factors alone do not describe completely the learning difficulties accompanying severe motor impairments. Such a child lives in a physically unstable world. He can never predict with certainty what his hands and feet will do. With his lack of postural control, he can never be sure of how his immediate environment will look, and, in truth, the way it looks to him changes from moment to moment as his head balance and sitting position shift. Since, to feel secure in his environment, the child must seek for himself some gauge of stability, he learns by trial and error early in life to rely on what he sees, hears and feels at the given moment. He is unsure of his future set in the environment, his perception of the world around him and its relation to him. Since experiences which would appear similar to others may not seem similar to him, he builds no backlog of past experiences from which he can abstract. He understands only the concrete. He is literally minded because he has learned to rely only on the immediate experience for interpretation.

Such a child may do well for the first two academic grades where all information is taught in the concrete form. However, beginning with the third grade, when abstractions are required, when concepts foreign to his own experiences are presented, and when symbols, not concrete objects, are used to express these new concepts and abstractions, the child falters. He falters not only because he has difficulty in understanding the abstract, but also because it represents to him intellectual instability which when added to his physical instability, threatens his security.

The final consideration in the learning of the severely motor-impaired is one of usage. Material newly learned only becomes one's own when the individual uses it repeatedly for his own purposes. Countless repetitions by other persons will not instill new facts in an individual's fund of knowledge until he himself begins to use these facts. Much of our primary teaching techniques and even the materials selected to be taught on this level are based on this principle of learning. For example, money concepts are taught on the second and third grade levels. By this time, it is expected that the child (1) has his own fund of coins which he hoards, counts, plays with, handles and makes simple purchases with; (2) goes to the store on simple errands for mother, and (3) receives a token allowance. The child with a motor impairment so severe that he is unable to handle coins has no use for money. As a matter of fact, he may never even have been in a store and seen a purchase made by another, for mother, in all probability, has left him in the car, at home, or out in the sun when she has gone shopping. To such a child, even if he has superior intelligence, money concepts are most difficult, oftimes impossible to master unless some means are found to make this knowledge a part of his life experience.

Learning Problems Resulting from Convulsive Disorders: Although epilepsy, its causes, control and effect have been studied and reported throughout the centuries, there seems to be a dearth of information pertaining to the special learning needs of the child with convulsive disorders. In fact, there is the persistent implication that the child with convulsive disorders reacts as the adult with epilepsy, and that once the seizures are brought under medicinal control, there are no special educational problems.

Experience in teaching the child with convulsions gives the lie to these assumptions. The primary differentiation between grand mal and petit mal seizures must be completely understood by the classroom specialist. Medication is most successful in controlling grand mal; petit mal, the fleeting disassociation of the mind from the immediate environment is oftimes not noted by the professional worker or controlled by drugs. Thus, petit mal becomes a factor in group learning. The child may have several of these "lapses" during an hour, each time missing the learning experience afforded during these periods. While the petit mal episode is momentary, there seems to be an aura, a somewhat longer period both before and after the seizure itself, when sensory intake is diminished. In the small group situation, the onset of the aura, which may be marked by a fleeting twitch of a digit, a momentary flushing followed by pallor or a variety of other vasomotor or psychomotor manifestations occurring several minutes before seizure, can be used to advantage. However, in the larger group, such as a regular classroom, there is little possibility for even the most observing, informed teacher to "catch" these periods of "no learning." In fact, parents are usually unaware of these signs until their attention is called to them.

Another seeming gap in the literature is the recognition of the fact that there may be certain factors in the immediate environment which precipitate seizures. Among these noise, strong odors, glaring and improper lighting and lack of proper room ventilation seem the most common. Recognition of these precipitants have several implications in the management and education of the child. The cerebral palsied child with epilepsy may have some of the other language-learning deficits associated with brain injury, particularly those associated with sensory-perceptual deficits. Yet, those techniques which involved the use of odor or extended rise in environmental noise level should be avoided.

One of the social implications rests in the persistent reports by parents and teachers that certain children with known epilepsy develop unpredictable patterns of negative behavior suddenly and without warning. It is submitted that these behaviors, usually reported as extreme negativism, stubbornness, lack of willingness to share, and finally, temper tantrums, occur neither suddenly nor without warning. Whether they occur in the classroom or at home, there seems always to be certain common factors to the situation. The noise level of the environment has been increased for an extended period of time, i.e., a family gathering or an active indoor group learning activity; the ventilation of the room has deteriorated via the increase in number of people, tobacco smoke, increased temperature, etc., and there is a demand for specific performance from the child, usually near his maximum level in the given area. Usually, removal of the child from the environment at the first sign of negativism—preferably into a quiet, well-aired dimly lit environment — even for a few moments may avoid a major behavioral crisis, not to mention a seizure. Within the special classroom, quieting all the children, turning off the lights, and opening the windows for a few moments often serves not only the child with epilepsy, but may also prevent behavioral crises in the other neurologically impaired children within the group. Since an increase of environmental noise level is usually gradual, and therefore unnoticed by the adult intent upon the activity, the epileptic child may well serve as the barometer for the rest of the group. That is, the environment may have reached the point where it can have a negative effect on each neurologically impaired child, and the one with seizures is the first to show the effect. On the other hand, but for the same reasons, behavioral problems may already be occurring among the other children, and thus further raising the general noise and confusion within the environment.

In the presence of convulsive disorders, the novice specialist is frequent to point out the difference in the quality of the first witnessed seizure from what she has been led to expect in the literature. It is baffling sometimes to see the child in grand mal seizure without the retracted tongue, the violent jerking of an extremity, the body rigidity and some of the other classical signs. Yet there are many epileptic children in whom these do not occur. Interestingly enough is the seeming change in quality of seizure that seems to occur in some children during adolescence. Thus, the child whose seizures did not follow the textbook pattern of adults with epilepsy may begin experiencing the more classical type of grand mal seizure two or three years after puberty. At that time, the learning difficulties and the environmental effects described here seem to pertain no longer.

Finally, it should be noted that medicinal control of seizures may not be permanent without periodic change of medication. It is a clinical responsibility to encourage parents to see the neurologist or prescribing physician periodically, at least once a year. Such a check up may indicate minor alterations of prescriptions and thus prevent further seizures and brain damage. It is remarkable how many parents when left to their own devices, continue the medication for years without ever thinking of having the child neurologically reevaluated.

Learning Problems Resulting From Sensory-perceptual Deficits: Many cerebral palsied children seem to demonstrate aberrant patterns of perception, abstraction, categorization and concept formation when neither their intellectual level or the degree of physical disability accounts for these behaviors.[74] Earlier in this chapter, the effect of severe motor disability upon learning was discussed at some length. These same learning patterns are seen in the less severely involved cerebral palsied child of normal intelligence and without any immediately apparent reason from the case history.

Sensory Disabilities: It has long been known that there is a relatively high percentage of *sensory* deficit or abnormality in cerebral palsy, occurring at the periphery or end organ. This is particularly apparent in the field of hearing or vision. In children with cerebral palsy who have poor visual acuity, it is not uncommon for the opthamologist to refuse or delay prescription of glasses on the basis that acuity deviance is centrally based and glasses will not assist in its correction. More recently, it has become commonly thought that the high frequency hearing loss associated with some forms of athetosis is a problem of the perception of sound, rather than one of auditory acuity. What all this means is that the same neuropathology which causes the gross motor handicaps associated with cerebral palsy may also cause aberrations in sensory input — in the information received by the individual about the world around him. This misinformation or absence of information can occur in one or more of the sensory avenues: vision, hearing, kinesthesia, proprioception and olfaction. It may occur at the end organ, so that no information of a certain type is transmitted, or at the level of integration, association, and cognition, where some concept, idea or generalization is made upon the information; or it may occur at the point in the central nervous system where it is recognized as meaningful, or at the point where the information is transmitted into a motor concept for behavior, or at any combination of these. In addition, there seems to be different degrees and types of deviances within each classification and for each of the sensory modalities, so that the variety of aberrations is infinite.

To illustrate by oversimplification: If the athetoid whose audiogram shows a moderate hearing loss at 2500 cycles with a sharp drop at 4000, were using his complete auditory facilities without amplification, he would probably hear "om aw the or" for "Tom saw the store." Thus, from the day he is born, most of what is said to him is sheer "gibberish." What is more, since it only serves to confuse him, he will tend not to attend to sound unless it is personally threatening or rewarding. There are other children — some of whom do not display any marked acuity loss in audition or vision — who do not learn automatically to perceive meaning in what they see or hear. These children also will tend to cut the confusing information from their conscious attention. Since these deviances in attaching meaning to sensory intake may be partial and may fluctuate from moment to moment, there arises a threat to new learning which is similar to that already described for the severely motor-handicapped child.

There is the child whose sensory intake in one avenue is so superior that in his formative years this is developed to the exclusion of the others. For example, the child with a superior visual intake and memory pattern may gain so much praise because he is able to read and spell at the age of four, that facility at learning through audition is ignored at the proper developmental period. Later in life, when he fails to realize the intellectual potential which seemed in previous years so obvious, it may be too late to embark on sensory learning in areas which have become deficient through lack of use. As a general rule of thumb, when a young child seems developmentally superior by two or more years above his chronological age in one sensory avenue, careful check should be made of other sensory modalities. If there are real deficit areas (one or more years below the chronological age), these should be developed to the temporary exclusion of further learning via the superior sensory modality.

Perceptual Disabilities: Over the past twenty years there has been a reawakening to the fact that cerebral palsy is a neurological disability in which the sensory components play a major role, markedly more basic than the more obvious motor involvement. As this concept grew, increasing reference was made in the literature to the cerebral intake deviances occurring in the area of perception, to a point where there seems to be considerable semantic confusion as to what is perception and what is meant by perceptual deviances. It seems advisable, therefore, to risk both oversimplification and repetition by pausing here to define perception and perceptual defects.

As has been already pointed out, sensory defects refer to defects in the sensory end organs. These are differentiated from perceptual defects or defects of sensory integration at the higher levels of the central nervous system. Brain-damaged individuals who have perceptual defects do not process all the sensory information taken in by the end organs.[74,79,80] They also may have difficulty in selecting which information to process toward the completion of a given task. An end-organ or peripheral defect can be compensated for almost completely by amplification, such as eye glasses and hearing aids, while a central or perceptual defect can only be partially or minimally compensated for by these means. The fact that amplification is of any compensatory value in central defects often serves to further confuse the issue. Although there are those who attribute the value of amplification in central defects to the resultant increase in attention to stimuli, there is also the factor that the resultant increase in sensory input must produce as a matter of course some increase in output. In the most simple terms, sensory input via the sensory end organs is conveyed to the central nervous system which acts as a decoder-recorder, transposing sensory information into terms which the brain can use.

Although it has yet to be proved experimentally and conclusively, there exists a basic assumption that if the individual is brain damaged, he can possibly have perceptual defects. Once this assumption as to the possibility of its existence is made, there ensues a series of assumptions based on the individual's performance and behavior under given sets of circumstances by which the presence or absence of perceptual deviance is determined. Of all the sensory modalities, vision seems the most amenable to use as an illustration of how this process works.

In terms of visual perception, the most obvious cue is that the individual's visual-motor performance is worse than might be expected just from his physical handicap. For example, a five-year-old, brain damaged child cannot adapt the circle, which the normal three-year-old can do without effort. This lack of form adaptation may be due to a most severe motor involvement, severe mental retardation or central perceptual loss. In most cases, the interference with performance by the motor involvement can be minimized by making it unnecessary for the individual to make a decision on what procedure to use to solve the tasks. In the event that he is motorally incapable of performing the task, an alternative of which he is capable must be found before his perceptual performance can be judged. There is frequently an intermingling of poor motor performance and perceptual deviance to the extent that such differential diagnosis becomes obscure. In such cases, it often is possible to differentiate by giving a parallel task which does not involve perception in its solution, such as handing the child the form and pointing to the proper recess in which he is to place it. There are other instances where the motor incapacity may be based upon inexperience or inattentiveness in hand-eye coordination. In such cases, one sharp reminder to look at what is being done usually improves motor coordination for the task markedly.

Differentiating perceptual deviance from severe mental retardation is a far more complex task, since it is not yet possible to isolate the general G-functions of intelligence from perceptual defects. It is, therefore, fortunate that, in most cases, all modalities of perception are not equally affected, and in those few cases where they are equally affected, such differentiation, even if it could be made, would be academic because there is no way on a clinical level to approach the child's therapeutic training successfully. Berko has already shown how by a series of subtractive procedures in the test situation one or more areas of function, designated as perceptual defects are finally isolated. Once this is done, there must be the determination of what the specific problem is and how it affects the individual's general functioning.

In each sensory modality—auditory, olfactory, tactile, proprioceptive and kinesthetic—perceptual defects may be of three general types, *stimulus differentiation, stimulus integration* and *meaningful manipulation* of *perceptual experiences*. Defects of stimulus differentiation are the most severe, most primitive types of perceptual deviance, and they are usually cited as being either failure in form perception or failure in figure-ground differentiation. While the latter has been the subject of the bulk of the investigations in perceptual deviance in cerebral palsy, there are still many operational unknowns.[21,80] Generally, figure-ground disturbances are considered to be in the nature of figure-ground reversals, figure-ground blendings or partial or mixed combinations of the two. However, there are some indications that the nature of the stimuli presented may be a variable to which differing figure-ground aberrations are attributable.

In the stimulus integration failures, the individual does not integrate figures into perceptual wholes. These are tested in the visual area by his ability to identify or reproduce three-dimensional geometric forms. Can he add mentally to defective drawings to give them reality? Can he see the cube as such, or does he see it as three squares? Does he see the drawing of a can as a can, or as two circles connected by straight lines? Individuals who have stimulus integration failures have difficulty visualizing diagonal lines, perspective in two dimensional drawings and test patterns such as those on the Bender-Gestalt Test.

Whether the meaningful manipulation or generalization of perceptual experiences can be considered a function of perception is subject to some question. Certainly, in this gray area of central nervous system function which is sometimes called cognition, defective perceptions alter or impair function. The justification for its inclusion as a higher level perceptual function may be found in the fact that the individual has the ability to function in these areas better in some sensory modalities than in others. What are defects in meaningful manipulation of perceptual experiences?

For most people, a stimulus complex retains its basic identity despite changes in various of its components; for those with perceptual defects, this is not always true.

Even though it seems most obvious, it should be stated that not all persons with central nervous system damage have perceptual losses or defects. Among those with cerebral palsy, deviances in perception are most commonly found among the severe ataxics who have disturbances in feedback and modulation and among the kernicterus athetoids with disturbances of the subcortical sensory relays. Perceptual deviations seem comparatively rare in other types of cerebral palsy, including epileptics and other athetoids. In such individuals, there is a likelihood of certain *attention defects*. Early differentiation of these attention difficulties from perceptual deviance is paramount. If this distinction is not made by the time the child is four or five and thus the attention difficulties are reinforced, they resolve themselves into clinical equivalents of perceptual defects which are approached by the same techniques. However, if the diagnostic differentiation is made in early childhood, and these attention difficulties are treated as such and according to the developmental approach, the performance typical of perceptual deviances tends to disappear as the attention becomes normalized.

Of particular importance here is the recognition that human learning is most effectively accomplished through partial frustration. To be unrealistic in praise — to give undue praise of performance well below the child's intellectual function because of his physical limitations or his innate cuteness — is further handicapping the child with attention difficulties. It is essential to normal living at the child's near-maximum potential that a *frustration tolerance* be built. Here again, extreme caution in diagnosis must be urged. Such an approach is disastrous with the child with a perceptual defect; it is basic at the child's level of performance in cases of certain attention difficulties.

Problems of Attention: Attention difficulties themselves fall within two major categories. Hyperattention, or the difficulty in selecting a stimulus from a complex stimuli, may coexist or result from perceptual defects. On the other hand, the lack of specific attentiveness, which must be differentiated from perceptual deviances early in life, has been described as the inability of the individual to select from the given attentional set those stimuli which the average person would select. For example, while being read the story of *Cinderella,* a group of cerebral palsied children may vary in behavior. All will listen attentively for a few moments. Then one child is likely to interrupt with "Miss Jones walked down the hall just now," a sound which none of the others consciously heard or noticed. This is called hyperattention. However, another child also may interrupt with, "We had pumpkin pie for dinner last night," as if the fact that turning the pumpkin into a coach was the most important point in the story. This second response may be due to difficulties in specific attentiveness, or it may be indicative of boredom, stemming perhaps from a lack of comprehension or an inexperience with imaginative play.

The average child begins some sort of training in imaginative play around the twenty-four month level.[34] The cerebral palsied child and his parents are too concerned with the immediate realities of feeding, dressing, medical care, and other concrete daily activities to indulge in this early development of fantasy. Between the ages of two and five, the normal child is learning to select specifics from his environment, to notice and ask, "Why?" Even at this early age, the cerebral palsied child is too preoccupied with his own problems and too limited in his contact with his environment and with other children to notice even the obvious. He thus misses much of the learning which primary education assumes, and it is this learning which is called experience.

LEARNING PROBLEMS RESULTING FROM ABSENCE OF NORMAL DEVELOPMENTAL EXPERIENCE

What Is Experience? Experience is anything that happens to the individual, or which the individual does and through which he learns and matures. Learning and maturation are integral to experience as it is used here, but the positive value of such happenings, in the eyes of the adult, is of no consequence. For example, few of our students with cerebral palsy ever read comic books, paper-back love stories, true confession-type magazines, dime mysteries and similar literary trash. The reasons are obvious. Rarely are they given an allowance for themselves which they can spend with no questions asked. Still more rarely are they able to browse at the magazine stand alone and choose what interests them. On the other hand, adults who choose these reading materials select "what is good for them" without remembering that they, the adults, in all probability, went through a period of reading paper backs and comics — usually against their parents' wishes — and that they outgrew this phase with an appreciation of the personal enjoyment of reading and a sense of discrimination which cannot be learned vicariously from the personal experiences of another.

Thus, from the adult viewpoint and that of formal education, experiences may be negative or positive. They may be of obviously good or bad influence. Of course, what is of bad influence is a matter of individual opinion. Not many school teachers and few adults, judging by the daily newspapers, see any advantage to the trash literature flooding today's market; yet stories from Dickens, Shakespeare and Hugo, to name a few of the classic authors, are as lurid, demoralizing, bloodthirsty and unrealistic as the average paper back or comic, if one chooses to view them so. The point is that most children are exposed to good and bad influences, and they learn to cope with both in the course of their daily lives. To limit the individual to either all good experiences or all bad experiences is to prepare him only partially for living among people.

Therefore, it behooves the adult within the handicapped child's environment, including the classroom teacher, to know what the average child experiences and to see that the handicapped child goes through the same processes of maturation. This is far more easily said than done. To illustrate the difficulties that may be encountered in this process, the example of the classroom of students who never "collected" may well serve.

The average child usually begins a collection from a need for personal possession, perhaps stimulated by a primitive fascination with the color or shape of the object. Soon, however, the collection becomes a matter of social interaction and prestige among his playmates, and, by the age of eight or nine, the group of children with whom he plays, his society, has set up a complex economic and/or social system through these collections. "Five marbles are worth one aggie," "Ten coke caps are equal to one milk carton top," or "A Willie Mays for three Preacher Roes." The idea of accumulating this wealth is, therefore, in the first instance self-motivated and later, through social pressure of the group, motivated by the child's natural society. Obviously, the more complex the economics of this society become, the more the child learns from his world that will prepare him for our adult society.

The teacher who recognizes that her severely handicapped students are missing this phase of maturation cannot meet these deficits, however, by having each member of the class begin a collection of items at her command. The value of the normal child's experience in accumulating objects comes from his self-motivation and the structuring within the child's world. The child cannot gain the same maturation from something imposed upon him by the adult. Or as one student expressed it, "My mother always told me that I should begin collecting matchbook covers, china figurines, or something, but I never got around to it."

What Is No Experience? Thus, there are three major factors operating simultaneously which limit the child's knowledge of the world about him and his relation to it: these stem from the inner insecurities of the severe physical impairment, from the skewed information of the sensory-perceptual defects, and from the absence of normal developmental experiences of childhood. Not only does the lack of normal experience not account for all the aberrations in cognition and general behavior of the handicapped child, but it has become increasingly obvious that, even if the child described here is exposed to all the experience situations of the normal child, there may be little, or no automatic improvement in the learning-behavioral deviances. In fact, there is some probability that these may be aggravated.

Most adult knowledge is not based upon direct experience. Rather, it stems from vicarious experience or inferences drawn from direct experiences. Man is a peculiar beast in the fact that even though each individual differs from all others, all people, but most especially all infants and young children share certain common experiences in the maturation process, and, within the framework of their culture, they all draw the same concepts or generalizations from these experiences. It is on this one peculiarity of man that all systems of public education and cultural mores can rely.

Therefore, when the child experiences a sensory-perceptual deviance from birth or early childhood even in a single sensory modality, there is an inherent effect on his developmental maturation as an individual in the normal society which has never been spelled out. For example, the child has a visual perceptual loss which makes him unable to differentiate the circle from the square, even though this activity is well within his level of overall developmental function. Obviously, until he learns to make this differentiation and many similar ones of increasing difficulty, he will be unable to learn even the most rudimentary concepts of reading and writing. But there is a factor even more fundamental. How does this inability to perceive the physical differences between roundness and squareness, and thus his inability to conceptualize upon their different properties, affect his knowledge of his environment, his interpersonal relationships, his body image and his self concepts? To date, this aspect of the problem has not been investigated, but certainly, it must have some effect — one which is perhaps correctable if the basic perceptual deviance is recognized and corrected sufficiently early.

Skinnerian operational conditioning points to another factor in human learning — reinforcement.[67] The effect of sustained perceptual deviance on the individual learning is perhaps the greatest of the learning problems which are involved. In the cerebral palsied child, there is a continuous feedback of misinformation along the neural pathways. This misinformation may originate from deviant intake of stimuli from the external environment or from the internal stimuli which are inherent to sensory - motor disturbances. However, in the light of present clinical methodology, the principal value of the recognition of the operation of reinforcement from faulty feedback seems to be as further justification for beginning educational and therapeutic training procedures as early as possible.

The literature has established that children with brain injury have difficulty in abstract learning.[10,66,69,70,77] While all primary and most elementary education today is based upon learning through concrete experience, these children differ from other children in three aspects of this learning process: (1) Materials and explanations used must be more concrete than those used in the public schools, and the teacher must continue using them for longer periods of time; (2) there is a marked difficulty in making generalizations or abstractions from a series of similar concrete experiences even when these happen in a rather close time sequence, and (3) there is equal difficulty in citing specific or concrete applications of general concepts. The meaning of familiar proverbs, for example, are among the most difficult to teach a group of adolescent cerebral palsied students of the junior high school level. Yet think of the frequency with which they are used in the daily life of the average individual.

Another academic concept which these students have great difficulty in mastering is counting by ones past 100. Usually, the average third or fourth grader is taught to count to 200, or perhaps in the case of the slow learner to three hundred, and then number sequence is taught in terms of hundreds, thousands, ten thousands, etc. Rarely can this procedure be effective in the student who has cerebral palsy. He must experience the actual counting to at least one thousand, oftimes higher; he does not usually grasp the repetitive pattern unless this is carefully pointed out and explained, even after this direct experience.

There are certain empirical factors which are observed in children who show little or no perceptual difficulties and which may, at least, partially account for some of these learning difficulties. Despite adequate sensory perception the child shows no sensory recall. Herein, sensory recall is used to refer to the ability to recall what a specific pleasant or unpleasant sensation "felt like" and to experience the same reaction that the original direct stimulus caused. This may be done directly, i.e., by saying, "Let's pretend that you are holding a piece of ice," and no further recall is needed; or, more commonly, the individual imagines the complete situation in which he had the sensation previously. These students seem to be able to do neither. Nor do they seem able to recall from a sight, sound or smell, detailed visual imagery of a previous experience in which that sensation was experienced. In fact, the imagination of most of these children leaves much to be desired.

Every school age child has a bit of the Rube Goldberg in him; daydreaming and fantasy are part of the maturation process, and, when done in moderation, serve many purposes in adult living. The lack of the ability to project oneself in a logical sequence of fantasy cannot always be accounted for by organic factors alone; many of the students in our experience do not know how to project themselves in this manner and/or have personality difficulties which bar them from this pleasure. In any event, every child's imagination should be nurtured and creatively channelized; however, the severely handicapped child oftimes must be taught first how to project himself consciously from the world of reality. Incidentally, in learning this, he also may acquire a knowledge of what reality is and its value to him, a knowledge so badly needed at the period when he makes his vocational choice and seeks job training and placement.

What Is Interpretation of Experience and Why Is It Necessary? If experience is any happening or occurrence of which the child is a part and through which he learns or matures, interpretation of experience is the process of making certain that (1) the child understands what has happened; (2) he has made the desired abstraction from the specific occurrence, and (3) he realizes the real importance of the occurrence to his future, if such realization is necessary to his maturation. For example, many of the children reach the upper level with good ability in mechanical reading but little or no comprehension of what is read. Further, they are impatient at direct attempts to gain comprehension because they have "read" the story and should be reading the next story so that they can finish the book. Finishing the book, and not knowledge or enjoyment, are therefore, the sole goals of this type of student. A similar reading difficulty is common among normal children and is most often a sign of poor teaching; however, it does not occur usually in the public school situation if the child can read the material orally without missing a word. Yet it does occur with alarming regularity among the students in our upper level cerebral palsy classroom, especially among those who have severe speech problems and/or extreme egocentrisms.

An example of the latter group is George, a fifteen-year-old, whose motor limitations eliminate use of the hands in the classroom, who does not have understandable speech but who, as far as it is measurable, has considerably above average intelligence. George has always read a great deal. From what the teacher understands of his speech, he recognizes all the words and knows their meaning. But he cannot repeat the gist of any material read on his level, and, what is more, no one has ever asked him to do this before. Ben, on the other hand, has barely understandable but fluent speech; so many of his consonantal sounds were missing. It is such an effort for him to read aloud that he could not bother with following the meaning of what he reads.

Claude and Laura have essentially the same reading problem, but in varying degrees. Laura is well past twenty and of normal intelligence, she has good speech and use of her hands. She "reads" well, but, in her own words, "It means nothing to me." In fact, the only things that hold meaning for Laura are factors in which she herself is emotionally involved at the moment. She considers herself someone who has nothing in common with other people because she has cerebral palsy. She becomes so immersed in her own emotions at the time she is reading, or doing any other activity, that she misses the meaning of the activity. Although she has been in eighth grade elsewhere, much of the knowledge that should have been gained as early as the second grade is absent because of this personality block to learning. This problem, the preoccupation with how they differ from others, is very frequent and difficult to overcome in the classroom. It is detrimental to academic learning, to seeking of experiences and, in fact, to interpretation of experiences and to all the components of social integration within the community, the specific aim of special education.

Preoccupation with matters other than what exists in the external environment, particularly thinking only of one's problems and emotions, and retardation in language usage due to severe speech handicaps may skew interpretations of what one sees, hears, smells, tastes and feels; so do aberrations in perceiving the sensation upon which the apperception is made. Therefore, the classroom program should include (1) drill in perception of figures, numbers and letters, both singularly and in series; (2) drill in perceiving through the five senses, particularly compensating for aberrant apperceptions based upon defective perception in one sensory avenue by sharpening perceptions in other sensory avenues; (3) use of oral language to express child's ideas, emotions, etc. This implies an environment somewhat more informally structured than the usual classroom situation; (4) group discussion of the handicap as it affects the individual, with emphasis on the similarities between his problems and these of other non-handicapped persons, and (5) through the group discussion, development of concern in the personal problems of another and broadening from there into interest in familiar, communal and national problems and their solution. The wide range of age, disability and achievement levels in the classroom makes this phase of the experiential teaching more natural and concrete.

THE PRESCHOOL GROUP LEARNING EXPERIENCE —
ITS IMPORTANCE, ITS PURPOSE AND ITS CURRICULUM

Most evident by now is the basic necessity of establishing a developmentally normal approach to learning and living in the neurologically deviant child. Too often this cannot be done in the home environment alone. Parents and family are too close to the problem, too emotionally involved in its solution, and too engrossed in the factors of sheer survival of the family group. Nor can parent counselling alone, regardless of how intensive, be expected to satisfy completely this need. Although the importance of ongoing, intensive parent counseling throughout the cerebral palsied child's formative years cannot be overemphasized, the sooner the child experiences separation from the parental home for part of the day and goes into the more objective environment of the school or clinic, the greater seems the probability that his social learning development will occur in a reasonably normal sequence.

This hypothesis is in direct opposition with some of the current practices throughout the country. Under the guise that the responsibility for child rearing is vested in the home and there it should remain, there seems to be an upsurge of home programming, where the child is seen periodically and as infrequently as once or twice a year in the clinical environment, at which time instruction is given to the parent to carry through the daily therapies and child rearing. Admittedly, any clinic administrator appreciates both the tendency of some parents to shift full responsibility for the realization of the child's potential to the clinic and the economic advantage of serving the greater number at far less cost through home programming. However, in view of the clinical learning problems involved — those resulting from severe motor involvement, from sensory-perceptual defects, and from experiential deficits — there is a growing concern as to whether this approach is truly satisfying its two basic objectives of forcing the parents to meet their inherent responsibility to the child and of conserving community or public funds. Of greater import seems the question of whether this approach truly helps the child realize his potential.

It would seem that there must be a continual reexamination of what the objectives are in the training of these children and in fact, what the very nature of the problem is. As has already been pointed out, the importance of the sensory input phase of the neurologic impairment has gained impetus in clinical practice. However, this impetus has not as yet kept pace with the revolution that has occurred in man's knowledge of the human nervous system since the late 1950's. Thus many of the so-called neurological approaches to the rehabilitation of the child with brain damage are based on concepts of central nervous system function that have been disproved by scientific research.[28,39,62]

What seems of greater concern in the overview of the child's development is that the techniques used in some of these approaches seem to ignore the basic precepts of human learning and maturation. To isolate the child further from his environment, to prevent him from playing with other children, listening to music, going to the store, to distort the family function and the rightful roles of each family member in relation to each other and the handicapped child insults one hundred years of research in human relations. What is more, even though the outcome may well be an individual who walks, talks and uses his hands in a normal manner, what happens to the child's social and intellectual development is subject to question.

On the other hand, the appropriate time for the onset of formalized group experience depends on many factors — the nature of the child's present level of function and his estimated potential, the particular program involved, including the nature of the qualification of the staff, the size of the group, and the amount of funds available for such programming. For example, since the normal child begins to experience some social contacts outside the home by the age of two, it may well be that some children can benefit from a limited type of group experience at this early age. However, if the child is functioning on a six to nine month level, if the group is larger in number than four, or if the clinician in charge is not fully cognizant of the purposes and procedures of such a group, its value is dubious. Children can be taught how not to learn just as they can be taught how to learn. Recognition of this fact alone has created greater emphasis on the need for highly qualified and trained personnel on this level as well as all levels of working with the neurologically impaired child. Where once the concept that any patient, motherly and loving adult could provide the neurologically impaired child with the proper group environment in his pre-academic years, experience has proved that often more is lost than is gained by providing the child such a group experience where only socialization can be afforded.

Another factor in determining the nature of the preschool experience is the estimated potential of the children involved. Here again, the clinician must face quite openly the realities involved. Up through the mid-nineteen fifties there was the open assumption that cerebral palsy being a primarily motorally based defect was disassociated from mental retardation, that most of those who had cerebral palsy were of at least average intellectual potential, and that the failure of the clinical psychologist to report this potential after psychometric evaluation was the fault of the psychologist, the measuring instruments or both.[14] In fact, Dr. John Little was often held in open ridicule for the statement in his 1862 paper that many such children were mentally retarded.[50]

Hohman has estimated that 84 per cent of those with cerebral palsy are of below average intelligence. He further stated that 30 per cent have an IQ below 50, 29 percent have an IQ between

50 and 70, and 25 per cent between 70 and 90.[43] In his New Jersey study, Bice reported that the mean IQ was 72.[9] In the face of these and similar reports, it seems imperative to the education of the majority of the cerebral palsied that the approaches used with the mentally retarded child are recognized as equally applicable, with modification.

It also must be pointed out that, among the 16 per cent who have average or better intellectual potential, there has yet to be reported complete amplification of the occurrences of the severe motor impairments, the sensory perceptual deviances, the language-learning-behavioral deficits, and the other factors already enumerated as considerations in the special education of the cerebral palsied child. It might well be coincidence that, over the twenty year period from 1944 to 1964, a variety of studies in various sections of the nation consistently reported that from 8 per cent to 12 per cent of the cerebral palsied adults were successfully employed, and this in the face of the fact that in the intervening generation, one of the most expensive, well organized and concerted efforts toward habilitation and employment of a specific, deviant group was made in countless communities throughout the nation.[6,36,60] These reports become even more disconcerting when read in the light of the eighteenth and nineteenth century papers on these conditions in which there are reported successful vocational adjustments in a limited number of the cerebral palsied.[16,50]

The point here is to question some of the currently prevalent approaches to the cerebral palsied child, not to intimate any aspirations on the economic and humanitarian wisdom in the use of clinical approach. For all children with cerebral palsy, every effort should be made to realize their potential in the community; for most, this includes the preschool experience.

The Intellectually Average or Superior, Nonsensorially Nonperceptually Handicapped Child: Even for those few of average or better intellectual potential and who have little or no sensory-perceptual deficits, the clinical preschool seems basic to their future development, even though the rest of the formal education may well be obtained in the normal group situation. For such a child, however, the emphasis of preschool learning may differ from these to be described here. As for all children the importance of group behavior is primary; second only to it must come the development of better-than-normal work habits. By this is meant that the physically-deviant neurologically-impaired child can compete successfully with his nondisabled peers, only if he learns to complete the task before him successfully, regardless of the amount of effort such completion requires. Historically, this attitude of stick-to-it-iveness has been developed in the individual in the home. However, this trial and error parental approach has so frequently resulted in personality insufficiencies, unrealistic self-concepts, and wide varieties of adjustment problems that it now seems far more efficient to develop within the child these resources at the same time that adaptation to his physical limitations are being created.

Not the least among the resources that all the grossly deviant need is a highly developed ability to tolerate frustration. Frustration is an integral part of social living — everybody experiences it. However, regardless of the degree of intellectual superiority or the degree of physical involvement, the individual with cerebral palsy who is to compete with his normal peers in their world will meet qualitatively and quantitatively a greater-than-normal share of frustration. While there is a great sympathy with those who hold that the more normal the learning environment these children experience, the greater their potential for successful competition, it seems reasonable to assume that this competition with the normal peer would be achieved with less insult to the personality if the child could first be prepared to meet these increased frustrations and given some general attitudinal approaches for adapting to these natural pitfalls of social living. Anyone who has worked with the cerebral palsied adolescent or adult, either educationally or vocationally, will attest that where the individual is physically and intellectually capable of employment, the greatest barrier to successful placement is the handicaps of personality insufficiency, rather than the fact of cerebral palsy or the employer's alleged intolerance.[36] It is about time that this fact was clinically recognized and handled sufficiently early in the child's development.

Finally, since what is said about the preschool education here is equally applicable to all children, the curriculum content for the intellectually average or superior, nonsensorially nor perceptually impaired minority is virtually the same. The difference lies in that these children will probably learn at a much more rapid rate, and in a more normal manner. Therefore, while the caution persists that no aspect of learning should be assumed in any child, the preschool groupings should be of sufficient fluidity, and the clinical personnel of sufficient astuteness to permit these children to progress at their own rate. One of the most disheartening occurrences in the classroom is to see the child who has no learning problems develop poor learning habits similar in nature to those manifested by children with language learning deficits. In the vast majority of these instances, the preoccupation of the teacher with the child with learning deficits in her group has been found to be the root of this problem. In any given group the abilities of the children vary vastly, and the good teacher, regardless of her field of education, learns to adapt her techniques to meet the needs of each child within the group. With normal or nonhandicapped children, this is taken as a matter of course. In special education, since the degree of variation may be somewhat broader, the number of children in the group is markedly reduced. There is no excuse for the special education teacher who paces the group learning to the slowest learner in the group, just as there is no justification for that teacher who so paces the instruction so that the slower child becomes lost. If it serves any purpose commensurate with its cost, special education must provide each child both individual instruction and group experience.

Preschool Groupings: Within the framework of this chapter, the preschool experience is a group therapy where the basic concepts of child development are molded together with the methodologies of the individual therapies into a meaningful, sequential approach to learning and living. The result is more than the sum of socialization, daily activities and group therapy, although all of these are included.

It therefore seems an artifact to speak of preschool groupings, or any educational groupings for that matter, for children with cerebral palsy. It is not the condition that necessitates preschool education; it is the child. Since segregation in our society is tenable only for constructive purposes which ultimately lead to the greatest possible integration, clinical approaches to the cerebral palsied child must, in a democracy, be founded upon this attitude. The specialized preschool approach is not only clinically advocated for the cerebral palsied child, it is equally important to the development of any grossly deviant child. The blind or visually handicapped, the deaf or auditorially impaired, the grossly psysically handicapped, the noncerebral palsied brain injured, and the mentally retarded child, among others, share certain language-learning-behavioral deficits. Although the underlying causes of these deficits, as well as some aspects of habilitative techniques for each may vary, the large areas of similarities of learning needs at this level suggest that perhaps these children may well be taught together. For example, the pre-Braille tactile techniques with the blind bear great similarity to the kinesthetic-tactile approaches used with the brain injured and the sensory approaches used for the auditorially impaired.[40,49,52,65,66] It also seems that in not grouping children according to type of organic disability, each child is afforded a broader experience, a greater opportunity for understanding others, and perhaps even a motivational force which the disability-segregated group cannot offer.

For example, what motivation has Johnny to walk if no other child within the group can walk? Empirical observation and clinical practice among both segregated and mixed groups in special education have been most convincing toward the argument that the mixed group better prepares the child to adapt to his limitations in a manner that insures greater success in normal social living. Of course, this can occur only where the teacher understands and programs for each child's needs, and where, within the group situation, each child has those instruments or devices which allow him to participate more fully in the group. For example, such a group could not be considered adequate for the profoundly hard of hearing child until the advent of the individual auditory training units, which, through their use, permit the teacher the same flexibility in auditory training for the single child with hearing impairment in the mixed group, as is advocated for all acoustically handicapped children.

It is recognized here that what is essentially being proposed is a radical departure from the historical approach to special education. More specifically, it implies a complete revision of curriculums for teacher training in special education, for just as the qualified therapist must be capable of working in all areas of the speciality, so the qualified teacher must be equally skilled in teaching children of all language-learning disabilities. This implies in turn as complete an understanding of the nature of the various disabilities on the part of the teacher as is afforded the therapist during her professional training.

If the children are not grouped according to disability, what then is the criteria. In New York state, for example, chronological age seems to be a major factor in grouping children for educational purposes. Here again, experience seems to negate theory. Theoretically, it is sound to presume that the child of ten can share few interests with the child of five and will feel out of place in such a grouping. On a practical level, however, whether this is true depends in each case on factors other than the fact of age itself. And so while chronological age may play a part in classroom groupings, using it as the sole or primary basis on such groupings seems both unwise and inefficient.

How then are such groupings to be made? Actually no one seems to have found the universally ideal criteria. In general, the most successful groupings are generally on the basis of developmental level. In the preschool, this approach can be more adequately defined as the developmental level for each learning area. Another approach, which is dependent on the size of the population to be grouped, may consider the following criteria in their respective order: (1) Mental age; (2) Level of verbal comprehension; (3) Sensory-perceptual deficits; (4) IQ; (5) Behavioral characteristics, and (6) Age.

If in a given school population there were eighty children, ages three to eight, of a variety of diagnoses, and each classroom grouping was to have a maximum of eight children, these then would provide an order of criteria to consider for the preliminary groupings. Experience has shown, however, that throughout the school year, it must be administratively possible to alter these groupings as each child and his needs alter and become more evident.

In preparing such groupings, the clinical psychologist's report is essential. As has already been mentioned, the phase of rejection of these reports as inadequate measurements of the child's potential is clinically passé. Not only have most psychologists become sophisticated in their techniques of measurement of the potential of the motorally and linguistically impaired child. Recognition has also been achieved that the child's functional level at any given time must be brought into comparison with the norm if there is to be realism in programming. On the other hand, the number label given by just stating an Intelligence Quotient or a Mental Age level has relatively little, if any, value in clinical programming. Berko has already described in detail the psychometric evaluation process. (See Chapter VII.) What is here emphasized is the importance of the detailed report on test performance to the teacher. Not only should such reports include the performance strengths and weakness, it should also make some determination as to the reasons for the individual failures. The psychologist's report is often the first clue to the nature of the child's language-learning deficits, and as such, provides the teacher and all clinicians working with the child much valuable, time-saving information.

The Preschool Curriculum: It was the original intention here to detail the curriculum of the preschool groupings whose purposes have already been described. However, a recent publication, Connor and Talbot's *An Experimental Curriculum For Young Mentally Retarded Children,* does this explicitly and implicitly.[19] Its thoroughness in presenting a sequalae of lesson plans at this level leaves any further attempts to do the unnecessary. However, there are some points which bear further amplification or discussion.

Connor and Talbot present a chart of 202 activities items which serves as the "Curriculum Guide" and the "Guide's Rating Base."[19, Pp, 18-33] On a five point scale the teacher can chart progress at stated intervals in each activity. There is no question of the excellency of this approach, but it seems that it might be somewhat difficult to achieve this type of reporting on the average clinical level. As a poor substitute, it is therefore suggested that a rating system based on the Gesell behavioral areas which gives both the child's present developmental level in each area of behavior and a brief verbal description of the progress made since the previous report may be more practical. The purpose of progress reports is to obtain a concise, objective and factual picture of the child's development in the preschool program. While on a theoretical level there is much to be said for longitudinal, narrative types of reporting, the average teacher does not seem to have the technical training needed to make these reports meaningful; nor does the average supervisor or program coordinator have the time to digest pages of verbal descriptions of each child's behavior several times yearly. For true progress measurements, there must be a measuring stick so that changes in personnel do not endanger the sequential development of the child in the program. While the Connor-Talbot Rating Base ideally provides a reporting system which fulfills the requirements, its length and detail may preclude its continued use as needed. Thus an alternative has been suggested, using the following basic activities as a guide.

GUIDE TO THE PRESCHOOL PROGRESS REPORT

All behavioral areas listed herein are defined and itemized into their various activities in Gesell *et al., The First Five Years.*[34]

Self Care — buttoning and unbuttoning clothing, putting clothing in the closet, taking off and putting on clothing, attending to toilet needs — or if physically impossible, consideration for those who assist by waiting, avoiding accidents, etc.; self-feeding activities, putting toys away, any other attempts to help themselves regardless of severity of physical disabilities.

Understanding Language. Understand simple commands as shown by carrying them out, how many commands can you give at one time and have them performed? Story comprehension — can the child answer questions about a story read to him? How complex a sentence does he comprehend?

Oral Communication. How does he express his wants, needs

and ideas: gestures, sounds, words, phrases or complete sentences. Parts of speech used in oral communication: nouns, verbs, adjectives, etc. Types of sentences used: simple, compound, etc. How well do you understand what he says? What does he communicate about immediate needs, past experiences, etc? How appropos are his answers to questions, does he speak when he isn't supposed to, i.e. out of turn, without propositional value, etc?

Hand-Eye Coordination. Does he look at what he is doing? Can he catch a ball or bean bag? Does he attempt to do these things, if physically unable to complete such performance successfully?

Form Perception. Can he always differentiate between circle, square and triangle, in matching, form board performance, etc., — regardless of varying size? Same with other more complicated forms. Puzzle performance. Does he restack disc on cone in organized manner?

Color Perception. Color matching, color naming, differentiating between different shades of a color, classification of shades according to basic color.

Basic Adaptive Activities. How appropriately does the child use objects, such as does he build with blocks or chew them, including food, toys, crayons, glue, and anything else he may get his hands on?

Understanding the World about Him. What new normal experiences has the child had during this report period- How well does he comprehend this experience? What has he gained in understanding his environment? Can he communicate these experiences?

Group Conformity. How does the child behave in the group? Does he do what the others are doing? This is individual behavior in the group situation.

Group Play. How does the child play with others, i.e., does he and one or more other children build houses from blocks, play house together? Cooperative play. How complex and abstract is this play?

Number Play. Rote counting, number concepts, — gross time concepts. Concepts of big and little, more, many, long and short.

(Time: when is yesterday, tomorrow, before and after, in terms of whether they have happened or are going to happen.)

Regardless of what reporting form is used, most teachers find that they cannot report with any reliability unless they keep for their own information daily notes on each child's performance and progress. These need not be detailed or complete. The daily "running report" notes serve not only as the teacher's source of immediate information at quarterly progress reporting time, but in the interim to help her see both areas of successful learning and areas of learning in which program revision is indicated.

Coupled with these daily notations is the matter of daily lesson plan and class schedules. For each child the teacher must have both long range and immediate goals in each learning area. Since hers is a group learning situation it is more likely that the various children within the group will have similar learning needs, and by shifting the child to the appropriate small learning group in each area, it is possible to meet each child's individual needs in the group situation. However, for the teacher to do this successfully, her day must not only be planned but that plan should be posted somewhere in the classroom where she and her assistants can refer to it with ease. It seems most efficient to do these class schedules on a weekly basis, so that from week to week the teacher can re-evaluate and revise her program and techniques as she prepares the schedule for the next five class days.

In lesson planning there seems to be one caution which most novices require. While it is an absolute necessity that the teacher prepare and post her lesson plans and schedule, equally vital is the recognition that there is nothing sacred in either once they are written. On any given day or at any given period of the day, the lesson plan outlined might not serve the immediate needs of the children. Alternative plans and approaches must be available and planned in such an event. One suggestion is that listed at the bottom of the weekly class schedule be a series of alternative activities — just in case.

Finally, the Connor-Talbot Curriculum includes only in most general approaches some of the specific learning needs of brain-damaged children discussed in this chapter. In view of their group this is understandable. However, to supplement their curriculum in these learning areas, the following section includes certain specific approaches to specific problems in the academic learning of the brain damaged child. Some of these are applicable on the preschool and kindergarten level. They are then carried through the primary years or as long as they are needed.

GUIDE TO VISUAL PERCEPTUAL TRAINING

Introduction: A visual perceptual difficulty may be defined as any perception or conceptualization of visual stimuli (what the child "sees" in the object he is looking at) which varies from the norm. While for many children with this problem seeing may not be correctable by glasses, correction is possible through training. Since "seeing" things as others see them is prerequisite to academic learning, training aimed at overcoming the visual perceptual difficulties becomes part of the special education curriculum.

Throughout the years many techniques designed to correct these visual difficulties have been developed. These are adaptable to use in the group situation of the classroom and provide a useful and essential tool in the reading-writing readiness program. Since they are also techniques requiring attentiveness, "looking," hand-eye coordination, conceptualizing and abstracting on what is seen following command and group conformity, they are of equal value to the brain injured child who does not display visual perceptual difficulties.

Nor are these the only ways of approaching difficulties in visual intake. Techniques for training other avenues of sensory intake must also be included in the program. It should also be stated that the suggested techniques enumerated here by no means exhaust the possible approaches. As you work with line and form perception, you will develop your own devices in form perception to enrich those described here. *If the child succeeds at one level of difficulty and fails at the next, return to the level of successful performance and then devise a half-step area of work at a level midway between where performance succeeded and failed.* This is a fundamental principle of teaching. The activities described here are integral to reading, and if the child cannot perceive these forms and lines, reading in its most complete meaning is impossible.

Section 1 — The Circle, Square, and Triangle: The normal child at the age of twenty-four months can perceive those three forms and adapt them in the form board. Since the children enrolled in the classrooms have a Mental Age of two years or more, inability to perceive these forms are a manifestation of their language difficulties, and it is believed that they can be taught and must learn such form recognition before academic learning is expected. Perception of the white form on the black background seems developmentally more primitive than the perception of the black on the white background. The white on black samples are therefore oddly numbered, and their counterparts in black and white are numbered with the next even number, the following order: circle, square, triangle; square, circle, triangle; circle, triangle, square; square, triangle, circle; triangle, circle, square; and triangle, square, circle, etc. (See Figure 3.)

Some suggested techniques are as follows:

1. With Sample 1 in front of the child, teacher draws one of the forms on the board and the child identifies it by pointing to the similar form before him.
2. Matching————————square   circle
   triangle   square
   circle   triangle
3. Finding things in the environment with similar shape.
4. Same as one with samples 3, 5, 7, 9, 11.
5. Same as one with samples 2, 4, 6, 8, 10, 12.
6. Drawing the three forms—first with the single sample of the form before them and then to the oral command. The circle may be called a ball; the square, a box and the triangle, a tent or teepee, for the younger child. The apractic child will have considerable difficulty in carrying through this activity. He may first have to trace around a model of the form, color it and cut it out. If he is unable to do this, it is suggested that coloring a stencil and cutting it out, or coloring a cut-out of the form is suggested. At best

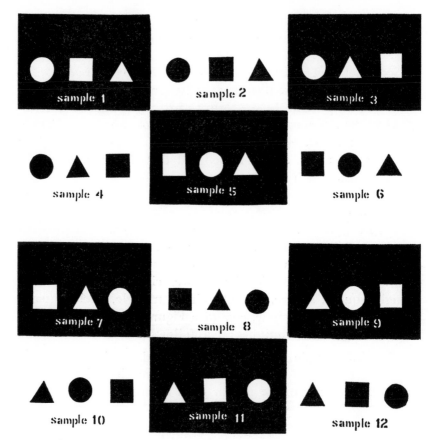

Figure 3.   Designs for visual-perceptual training: the basic forms.

for most children at this stage, good performance here involves showing the concept of no corner, four corners or three corners.

7. Blindfolded, the child identifies the form by feel. This is extremely helpful in working with the severely apractic child or the child with visual agnosia. It is suggested that work at this step be done with all children who have difficulty in drawing performance.

8. Using only the white on black samples (1, 3, 5, 7, 9, 11) present two samples at the same time and have the child tell you they are alike and how they are different. Many

of the children do not have the concept of the meaning of "different" — use the same and not the same, or alike and not alike. After they can perform the activity gradually intersperse the word different with "not the same" or "not alike." Or perhaps you would prefer to first teach the concept of "different" in another activity. The average child of three years has this concept. Do not expect the child to perform this or any other activity until he has at least reached the level of mental maturity where it might be expected in all children.

9. Same as 8 using the black on white samples (2, 4, 6, 8, 10 and 12).

10. Same as 8 using any samples in the folder—thus mixing black on white with white on black. For the child with abstracting difficulties, you are requiring conceptualization of two abstract concepts here, which is a difficult activity.

11. It should be remembered that perception of the solid form does not imply adequate perception of the linear form. Thus, the child must be checked on his perception of the circle, square and triangle, drawn with white ink on black construction paper and *visa versa*. The same procedures are used as described herein with the linear drawings if such failures are noted—beginning at the level of failure to perceive.

12. The child may have difficulty with the linear samples of the circle, square and triangle. If the child can successfully perform the first ten approaches using the solid shapes, the same approaches with similar samples in which the shapes are drawn in linear form should be tried. If the child has any difficulty with these linear samples, there is a figure-ground disturbance, and he needs more work with the solid shapes.

13. The average child has the concept of "big and little," in so far as a big circle and a little circle are both circles, at the age of two years. The brain injured child may have difficulties with this type of activity, even when his Mental Age is well beyond the two year level. Such drills as "picking out the two that are the same' 'or "crossing out

the one that doesn't belong" when presented with a large circle, large square and a small circle, may serve to correct several learning problems. In such drills at first, it is not unusual for the brain-injured child to select the small circle as not belonging. Thus he confuses the categorization of "big-little" with form categorization. It is well to preceed this drill with other form drills, so that a frame of reference be established for the child. Also he should be presented with all combinations of the three forms, before he is considered proficient in this aspect of visual perception.

14. After the child is able to draw the three forms to the single commands and all the other drills here described, these forms may be used to develop visual memory span. The average child at the age of five can reproduce the three shapes in the order presented after a ten second visual stimulation. The performance of the brain injured child may be far below this:

   a. Draw one of the forms on the blackboard, let the child look at it for ten seconds, erase it, and have him reproduce it on paper.

   b. If he cannot do this, repeat activity with another form, extending the time of visual stimulation until he succeeds. "Play this game" frequently, always reducing time of visual exposure until he can succeed with the ten second visual stimulation.

   c. Present two forms at the same time in the same manner. The child should reproduce the forms in the exact order presented. That is, if you draw a square then a triangle, the reproduction of the triangle first and then the square is not the desired performance Use the same approach as in "b" to achieve satisfactory performance. The child should finally be able to reproduce any two of the forms in the order presented without difficulty.

   d. Now introduce three forms in a similar manner. At first, draw them on the blackboard. Then use your samples for the ten second visual exposure.

e. For the very advanced student, this activity may later be extended to four, five and six forms. But this should not be attempted before the child has the Mental Age of eight or nine.

15. *For the most advanced students,* there is a final drill in symbolization, which is prerequisite to academic learning on the third grade and above. Give each form a symbol, i.e. circle—1, square—2, triangle—3, and repeat the activities described in item 14 — only this time the child reproduces the symbol for the form rather than the form itself. At the beginning the forms and their symbols may be left on the blackboard, but the goal is to have the child remember and reproduce the symbol for the forms.

16. It should be pointed out that the forms of circle, square and triangle are used as illustrations. While the child's perceptual retraining begins with these basic forms, by the time he reaches the mental age of four years, he is intellectually ready to work on the other seven forms of the Sequin form board. These are approached in the same manner and via the same steps as the circle, square and triangle. By this time the child should be ready for four or five shapes per page and your samples should be drawn from all ten forms, not just the seven new ones. That is, the circle, square and triangle should be included in the form differentiation when working on the other seven Sequin forms.

These activities are roughly graduated in difficulty. In some cases, especially with the student who has cerebral palsy, some of the activities cannot at this time be performed. It is suggested that those students be given their own sample set and if such activities have to be skipped, you "overdrill" a similar activity before proceeding to the more complex. It is also advisable to let the child try to perform the activity which you may think he cannot, by giving him a larger paper, a thicker crayon, etc.

It is suggested that these activities not be pursued for longer than fifteen or twenty minutes at a time. For some classroom groups, much shorter but more frequent sessions of visual perceptual exercises are recommended. However, these activities are desirable at least once a day. Those teachers who are on repetitive lesson plans of five and ten minutes duration, and identical sessions in the morning and in the afternoon, will probably include these activities as part of both the morning and afternoon sessions.

Once the child can perceive the linearly drawn circle, square, and triangle, he should be developmentally ready to learn how to perceive linearity without shape.

Section 2: Linear Differentiation — The Vertical, Horizontal, and Diagonal: The average child perceives the vertical line at about twelve months of age; the horizontal line at eighteen months, and the diagnonal at twenty-four to thirty months, when presented with a vertical or horizontal line, when the diagonal is presented alone at three and a half to four years of age.[35] Generally, the brain-injured child has minimal difficulties with the vertical and horizontal lines, but diagonal lines are most difficult for him to perceive, even when he has achieved the Mental Age of seven or over. Since much of the reading and writing activities involve perception of diagonals, linear perception is prerequisite to academic activities.

In accordance with the basic precepts of all special teaching that nothing is to be taken for granted, the approach to this area of perception is begun with the vertical line, matching, tracing, copying and drawing a vertical line in that order (Fig. 4).

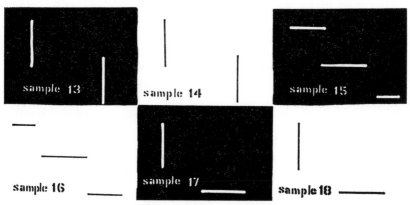

Figure 4.   Designs for visual-perceptual training: linearity.

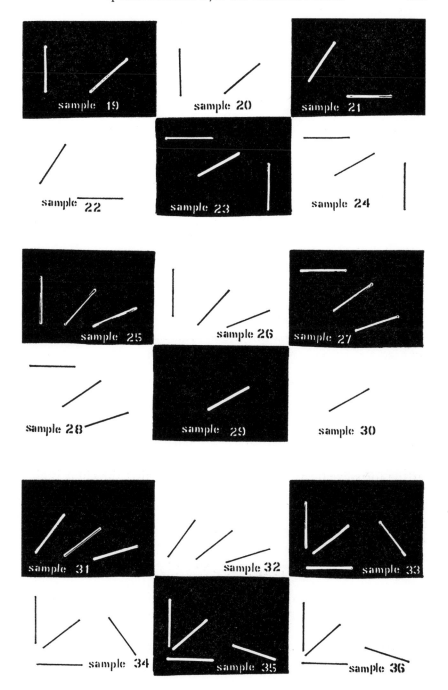

sample 19

sample 20

sample 21

sample 22

sample 23

sample 24

sample 25

sample 26

sample 27

sample 28

sample 29

sample 30

sample 31

sample 32

sample 33

sample 34

sample 35

sample 36

It will be noted that mastery of the vertical line presupposes recognition of all vertical lines regardless of the placement on the page. Here again, it has been presumed that white on black is easier to perceive than black on white. Thus, each sample is presented in two forms.

Samples 15 and 16 present the horizontal line in the same manner. Matching, tracing, and copying the horizontal—in isolation and in contrast to the vertical (Samples 17 and 18)—must be mastered before perception of the diagonal line is approached.

For those brain-injured children who have the physical capacity and do not suffer agnosia or apraxia of the arms, exercises in linear perception can be combined with work on body image and perception of body parts in space. Having the child place his arm and hand in the position of the sample presented allows the child with adequate kinesthesia to use this avenue of normal sensory intake in learning to adapt a deficient sensory avenue in a more normal manner. This is especially true when the child is learning to perceive the diagnonal.

For the average brain-injured child who is having difficulty in diagonal linear perception, it seems more logical to approach this learning area by contrast with the vertical and horizontal. Always remembering the four steps to learning in perception— matching, tracing, copying and drawing—(Samples 19 through 24) present some of the infinite variety with which the diagonal can be presented in contrast to the horizontal and the vertical. It should be noted that in these samples the diagonal is present at the forty-five degree angle. It is necessary that the child is able to differentiate the "pure" diagonal before he can be expected to recognize it in its variations.

Once the child can differentiate the pure diagonal from the vertical and horizontal regardless of the placement of each on the page, then he learns to differentiate the various degrees of slant from the horizontal, the vertical, and from other diagonals when two diagonals are presented with either a horizontal or vertical line (Samples 25 through 28).

Only after the student is able to recognize the diagonal lines in this manner, is he presented with an isolated diagonal for reproduction (Samples 29 through 32). Next he is taught to differentiate between diagonals without the presence of the vertical or horizontal as a reference point (Samples 33 and 34). Finally, the child is taught to recognize the reverse diagonal as a true diagonal when differentiated from the vertical and the horizontal (Samples 35 and 36).

Section 3: A Technique of Teaching Handwriting to the Brain-injured Child: Teaching of handwriting comes after work in form perception. The child must be able to distinguish between the circle, square and triangle. The difference between these figures should be presented in various orders. He must also be able to tell the difference between the horizontal, vertical and diagonal lines. Incidentally, the brain-injured child, especially one who has some visual perception difficulties, often has difficulty in distinguishing the various diagonal lines from the horizontal and vertical lines. These must be worked on first and the child must be able to draw these figures and lines before work on handwriting begins.

In reference to handwriting itself, much of the literature recommends the teaching of cursive writing. This was started by Straus and Lehtinen.[70] Their idea was that the brain-injured child has so much to learn and takes so long to learn it that they would shorten the process by skipping the teaching of manuscript writing. However, the most recent experience of other schools as well as our experience here shows that this procedure is not proper for several reasons. One is that cursive writing, as it has been taught for years in America, is not the best type of writing. It is often very difficult to decipher the handwriting of many nonbrain-injured people. Then too, both reading and writing are abstract activities, and, since most brain-injured children have difficulty in abstraction, to try to teach them two different sets of letters at the same time is most confusing to them. They can't see that "cat" and "cat" could be the same thing. All brain-injured children, whether they have cerebral palsy or not, are awkward in the movements of their voluntary muscles; even after they work for a long period of time to learn how to write cursively, they often cannot find their own mistakes in spelling and grammar.

Although the problems of the cerebral palsied child and the

brain-injured child are often different, this technique of teaching handwriting is equally applicable to both groups, even though the reasons for its value may differ with the individual child's problem.

The procedure for teaching manuscript writing is aimed at overcoming several of the writing failures common to the brain-injured child as well as teaching him to write legibly; particularly absent from the handwriting of children taught by this method are letter and number reversals.

Steps of Teaching Handwriting

1. The lines are five-eighths of an inch apart. Begin by teaching only the small letters.

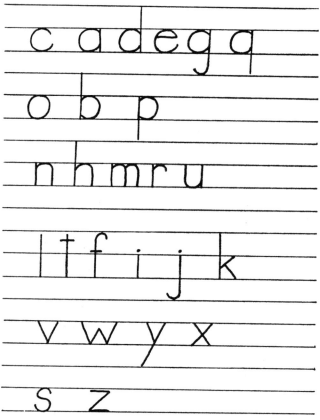

Figure 5.   Suggested letter forms for teaching writing.

2. Work on a *c* until you achieve two lines of round letters an equal distance apart. This may take weeks.

3. If the child persists in failing to approximate the vertical line properly to both ends of the *c* in its conversion to *a*, the child is not perceptually ready for further direct work on handwriting. This usually indicates inadequate or insufficient training in the developmentally earlier perceptual techniques. Additional activities at this point, however, might include formation of letter by fingers in the sand or finger paint, or with clay, or with pipe cleaners. In each activity, the letters should be formed exactly as described.

4. You alternate *c-a* until you get a perfect page and on that perfect page out of the *c* you teach them to make *d*, then you practice *d* by itself, then *a-d*, then *c-d*. On that perfect page of *c-d* you teach *e*.

5. The same procedure as above is used to teach *g*.

6. The same procedure as above is used to teach *q*.

7. Teach the *o* as the *c* that goes all the way around. Practice the *o* much as you did the *c*.

8. With the page of perfect o's you teach the *b*. In teaching the *b* the straight line is started from the top, thus completely distinguishing between writing the *b* and the *d*. This also applies to the *p*, as distinguished from *g* and *q*.

9. In teaching *p*, again the line goes up from below the *o* and touches the left side of the *o*.

10. Up to this point, handwriting has been approached as a perceptual activity, not an academic tool. Now academic meaning is being given to the activity, before the perceptual difficulties are not completely corrected.

One of the areas of perceptual activity which must be developed at this stage is the concept of the spatial relationship among the letters of the word and between the letters of different words. Since these are different activities, they are taught one at a time. While the child is learning spatial relationships of the letters within the word, words are written in vertical columns which are widely spaced so that there can be no confusion in which groups of letters belong together to form the individual words. After this conceptual relationship is rather firmly established in the child's mind, then you can begin to learn to copy simple sentences. Here emphasis is made on separation of letter groups called words, along the horizontal line in such a manner that sufficient space is left to keep each word an entity, yet the words remain in proper juxtaposition to convey both the meaning of the sentence and the concept of sentence formation by spatial grouping of words.

While the subject of copying the simple sentence is in mind, there is the point that some children who are ready for this activity may not be ready for the complexity of copying sentences from the chalk board. Others may not be able to do the activity when more than one three-to-five word sentence is presented to him at one time, even when such activity is given him by individual sample at his seat. If the adequately prepared child fails at copying the simple sentence, the teacher must ascertain the variable which is complicating the activity beyond his performance level. Once these are known their control is relatively easy to achieve.

Further, once meaning is attached to the handwriting activity, it may prove difficult to revert back to using it as a perceptual activity independent of the commonplace school activities. To avoid anxiety and precipitous use in the academic setting or at home, it may be well to begin to associate phonics with this activity. More will be said of the teaching of phonics later in this section.

11. During the classroom session the children are also learning their numbers. This system does not include the teaching of the writing of numbers because it has been found that, as the writing of the letters improve their perception, writing of the numbers also improves, provided one precaution is taken. Numbers in rote should be written in a vertical column such as $\begin{smallmatrix}1\\2\\3\end{smallmatrix}$ rather than in a hori-

zontal line. This keeps them as separate entities in the child's mind.

12. The next set of letters to teach are *n, h, m* and *u*. Watch the child who perseverates on the formation of the *n* and *m*. The best way to avoid this type of perseveration is, as you add each new letter, to add new words that he can write so that there is a time lapse between the teaching of the *n* and *m*.

13. The next step is using the straight lines to teach *i, t, f, l, j* and *k*. At this point, the only letter that might give difficulty should be the *k* because of the diagonal line. If the child has received training in other activities to perceive the diagonal, such difficulties should not occur. If they do, do not teach the *k* until diagonal perception has been mastered. The child now has enough letters without the *k* to practice writing innumerable words from his own vocabulary.

14. The next group is the *v* and *w,* which is two v's together, and the *y* and *x*.

15. The *s* and *z* you let the child figure out for himself from the model which you draw.

16. By the time the child reaches step fourteen he may be so advanced that you begin to teach him to connect some of the letters. The more the child does this, the more his letters begin to show his individual variations, and he may begin automatically to connect or have some of the letters in a word touch. It, therefore never is necessary to teach him to write cursively because he, with your encouragement, develops for himself the continental style of cursive writing.

17. On the fourth or fifth grade level, when it won't interfere with his own reading ability, you teach him to read cursive writing. You do not teach him to write capitals until he is writing sentences or words with capitals in them, then you teach them as they arise in his work. The reason for this is to prevent perservation.

Section 4: Other Visual Perceptual Activities — Design Perception: The third level of visual perceptual activity is concerned with designed perception. In psychometrics, such tests as the Kohs Blocks, the Bender Gestalt test, etc., represent this area of perception. Since it is a relatively higher level of perceptual activity, and therefore more children have difficulty in this area, there have been many published techniques designed to overcome such deficits. Outstanding among these is the Frostig curriculum on visual perception.[31,32] Every teacher of brain-injured children should be fully acquainted with this approach and have these materials in ready access.

However, there are children who need some intermediate approach. These are the children — whether physically normal or cerebral palsied — who have good form perception when the forms are isolated. But when the single form is combined with another concept — say color — then they are unable to copy the pattern — from the sample and/or from memory. The test for this is quite simple. Two red blocks and two white blocks are used to form a square with one side red and the other white. Give the child an equal number of similar blocks. (What is usually used are cubes with four sides painted four different solid colors, and the other two painted each with half the side one of the colors and the other half the other as if two adjacent triangles.) The design is shown to the child, with the instructions to look carefully because he will have to make one just like it. After fifteen seconds exposure, the design is covered and the child makes his replica. If he fails — (after an attempt of sixty to ninety seconds duration, the onset of further confusion is usually obvious) — the design is exposed and the child attempts to copy it. Three trials with as many designs should be allowed to permit some measurement of rapidity of learning.

If the child succeeds, a new design is introduced. This one utilizes two solid colors which form a diagonal with the two blocks of the same color at opposite ends of the pattern. If the child can reproduce this from memory and from copying, varieties of designs using both the solid colored and the dual colored sides are introduced. At whatever level of performance the child cannot readily complete the task is the level at which the training process must begin.

All the varieties of activities that can be used in this level of perceptual retraining cannot be enumerated here. However, in the selection of materials and patterns used, every precaution must be taken so that there is assurance that the child is receiving training in visual perception, and not in passing a very valuable psychometric instrument. It is preferable if the teacher or therapist has never seen either the Bender designs or the blocks. Similar blocks of different sizes and colors can be used if the clinician is unfamiliar with the Bender test patterns. Circles, squares, and triangles of various sizes and colors can also be used. However, the commericial block puzzle with all the various shapes in varying sizes and colors have only limited utility. This is because of two factors: (1) The number and variety of shapes and colors may be too confusing to the child; and (2) the number of similar blocks is too limited for use in this manner, even with one child.

Within this general category of perceptual approaches fall the use of other sensory avenues and the combination of two or more perceptual areas on the cognitive level. It must always be remembered that integration of any G-function into cognitive usefulness is the end goal. Adequate skill in perception is valueless if the child is not able to integrate this with other intellectual skills into a meaningful tool to further knowledge.

In general, the techniques used to develop adequate perceptions of form utilize the more normal sensory avenues. The child is taught to compensate for the defective sensory perception through cognition. If the child cannot differentiate the triangle from the square through vision alone, can he differentiate between them by touch, without vision? If he can, then have him combine touch and vision, while talking to him about the feel of the angles and the sides. If the child cannot differentiate the linear diagonal, then through such games as "Simple Simon" and "Follow the Leader," movement of body parts in those positions provide the beginning of the training process.

Actually, what can be done in these areas is limited only by the teacher's ingenuity. However, there must be cognition; at some point there must be awareness in the child that his arm is slanted instead of in a horizontal or vertical position in space. Of course, there must be recognition that any one technique does not approach an isolated problem of the perceptually deviant child. For example, the kinesthetic conceptual approach to the linear diagonal is also the approach to some problems of body image observed in some children. However, if the child seems unable to do the required motor activity to command, and without apparent physical inabilities, his body image problems may be due to other reasons, such as ideational apraxias and various agnosias including astereognosis. Once again, as always, teaching techniques cannot be based on the child's overt behavior. To know how the child learns best, there first must be the understanding of why he reacts as he does.

Similarly, the tonal differentiations, i.e., high and low notes, loud and soft noises, etc., which are stressed in early development of auditory perception are equally effective in overcoming some of the attention difficulties common to brain-damaged children, particularly the so-called "deaf athetoid." Most clinicians seem to affirm that, as a group, these children form the most perplexing clinical problems.

In the first place, audiometry, a hearing aid — even binaural hearing aids — while it assists, does not completely or automatically solve the hearing problem. In order for the child to gain verbal comprehension and fluency, in order for him to overcome the perceptual and attention problems, he must learn first to follow his hand to the object. This matter of hand-eye coordination in the deaf athetoid must be clearly understood. It must be a complete follow through. What is most usually seen, is that the child looks away before completion of the motor act. He has hand-eye coordination perhaps up to the moment of approximation of the hand to the object and then looks away. This is not good enough.

At a practical level, one of the major excuses expressed by good clinicians for failures in achieving the degree of hand-eye coordination described here is their own inability to follow the child's eye movement at the most crucial moment, since at that point the child is looking downward. This is entirely valid; however, nature provides its compensations. *When the athetoid child achieves this type of hand-eye coordination there seems to be a radical decrease of extraneous movement.* This is so marked and so immediate in the child's motor performance that the quality of the athetoidic movement can be used as a gauge for whether the child has achieved the proper hand-eye coordination. That is, if there is not this marked decrease of movement, then the child does not yet have the desired concept. Here again, is another clue to proper hand-eye performance; learning the activity is a process of conceptual development; the motoric performance is almost automatic once the child completely understands what is expected of him.

One technique is to have the child wear a ring or a fancy bandaid on his middle finger throughout his waking hours. Parents, therapists, teachers — everybody working with the child stresses this visual follow-through in all activities. Naturally, for this period, no other learning is expected; however, no other learning can really be achieved without this complete visual follow-through. If all concerned are really consistent in this, the habit pattern should be developed within a four-week period. If there is not this achievement, somebody is not being consistent.

In the "deaf athetoid," as in many other types of brain injured children, it is often difficult to distinguish between attention difficulties and perceptual difficulties beyond the age of four or five. Early differentiation is vital to more effective rehabilitation procedures. If the attention difficulty is permitted to persist beyond the age of five, it is resolved into the clinical equivalence of perceptual deviances and should be approached in the same manner.

Empirically, there seems to be a direct relationship between increased perceptual skills and major improvements in motor ability. This may relate to Carlson's theory of focus of attention.[15] In teaching typing to the athetoid, for example, marked decreases in involuntary movements were attained by a pretyping perceptual approach. In fact, the involuntary movements were so reduced that the children were able to learn to type meaningful material on an electric typewriter using the full keyboard and without the use of special plate guards.

The development of this technique is descriptive of the essence of this section, to wit, that the technique must be devised by the teacher for the individual child to teach him to succeed where he has failed.

The use of the electric typewriter in the educational setting as a tool of self-expression has long been advocated. However, years of experience of having an electric typewriter in an educational setting for severely impaired cerebral palsy students above the second grade level seem to teach that the further the manner of typing deviates from the norm, the less progress in language arts is experienced. For example, one unpublished survey of academic progress made under the same teacher during a five-year-period finds that children who typed with a stylus on their forehead made less academic progress than those who held a stylus in their teeth. Children and young adults who held styluses in the palms of their hands made markedly more progress than those who held the stylus in their teeth. The greatest academic progress in language arts was made by those children who typed with one or more of their fingers rather than with a stylus. Since these degrees of progress seem to hold true of children of equal intellectual ability and physical disability, it was concluded that the typewriter would be a more useful tool if more time was spent in teaching the child to use his fingers to type in some manner.[7]

In trying to carry through this hypothesis it was soon discovered that putting the athetoid child directly on the typewriter was too frustrating, even though the motivation for typing was extremely high. The involuntary motion caused so many keys to strike that it was impossible to achieve anything meaningful. Therefore, a chart was devised as a pretyping perceptual activity, a version of which is shown in Figure 6, which was made on a piece of heavy drawing paper or cardboard. This represents a series of circles the size of a penny and incidentally, the size of a typewriter key, in the same position as the keys on a typewriter. In the original chart, each circle was colored a different shade, and through focus of attention techniques, athetoids and spastics were taught to approximate the circle at dead center without tremor or involuntary motion. The instructions for achieving this were as follows: find the red circle on the second row with your eyes; keep your eyes on that circle and look at it so hard that you cannot see any of the other circles; now think about touching that circle with your typing finger-do not move your hand, just think about touching that circle; you see your eye moving and your finger sticking out and now it's getting closer and closer until it touches; there it is touching the circle. Usually by the time this or a similar pattern was repeated three or four times, the child's finger was on the proper circle without the child being aware that he had moved his arm. This drill was repeated several times a day for five or ten minute periods. Later, the chart was sent home for the child to practice on at night, once it was certain that the child had mastered the technique of focusing and had no anxiety about moving his hand.

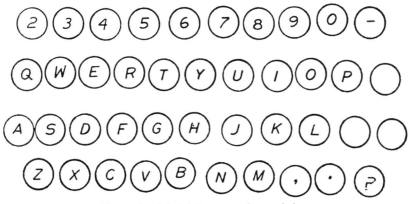

Figure 6. Model for pretyping training.

Later, all sorts of ramifications were devised: the chart was simplified sometimes down to one or two colored circles and the techniques of "pretyping" were introduced on the preschool and kindergarten level. It began to be used, with the brain-injured noncerebral palsied, the visually handicapped, the hard of hearing and all varieties of multiply handicapped children. The individual chart was complicated as rapidly as the child's progress would allow: colors were alternated with letters and eventually the typewriter was introduced at about the second grade level for all varieties of academic performance. One thing soon became apparent: for maximal learning, typing could not be an absolute substitute for handwriting. Wherever possible, regardless of severity of motor disability, agraphia, letter reversal and other writing problems, the student must have the experience of writing, because there is no known substitute for the learning that occurs when motor kinesthesia of the pencil on paper is coordinated with the intellectual function. It should also be remembered that the objective of using the typewriter in the classroom is not vocational. The goal is not to train a professional typist, rather this is another tool to motivate the child and give him a more pleasant and oftimes easier way of expressing himself in written language.

Section 5: The Educational Typing Curriculum: *Equipment.* For all students, regardless of disabilities, the use of an electric typewriter is recommended. First, it requires less physical exertion. Second, the results are easier for the child to read. Third, it gives greater satisfaction to him from the outset due to the evenness of the key pressure on the paper. The eventual goal of this program is to have at least one electric typewriter in each classroom, and more where the needs of individual students require the use of the typewriter by one student for a major part of the school day or where the student needs a special adaptation on the typewriter.

Objectives. 1. To motivate the student into greater written language facility.

2. To give him a less tiring means of self-expression in written language.

3. To assist in the development of a concept of meaningful reading. As the child types the egocentered material which he composes, he is better able to associate the typewritten word with the expression of ideas. Not only are such words and sentences more similar in appearance to the printed words and sentences in books than those which are written, but the visibility of his own ideas so written on paper is also the most concrete illustration of reading for meaning that can be afforded the student.

4. To integrate the multicomplexities of successful self-expression in written language.

a. Hand-eye coordination: Rather than the conventional touch-typing-system, the approach is predicated on the principle that the individual is permitted to look at the keys as much as he feels the need. Over a period of years, this need will automatically decrease, but for the cerebral palsied, the alexic, the agraphic, the amnesic, the apractic and the agnosic child, the fact that he is taught to look at the key, rather than to attempt to voluntarily hit the key is the core of the success thus far experienced with this technique. (It should be noted that the theoretic reason for this success in each type of student differs.)

b. Integration of motor and intellectual function: The activity of typing is far more complex for these students than even the activity of speaking. A child may be able to spell a word orally, yet unable to type the word correctly even after considerable experience in typing. The same is true in simple sentence construction.

c. Self-correction: For the reason in letter (b) among many, the teaching of self-correction and self-censorship of written language is essential. In the past, too many of these students have developed the concept that to err is nigh "criminal." Educational typing, when coordinated with correction of errors in typing and language, tends to mature the student's attitude in this respect and in all areas of academic functions.

5. To reinforce the meaningfulness of language. Brain injury, whether resulting in cerebral palsy or aphasia, has been described as a disorder in the human feedback mechanisms. By the same token, the child with moderate or severe hearing loss does not have a normal feedback mechanism. The spoken word once uttered cannot be recalled; there can be poor feedback censorship of oral language output in all persons. It is only in written language that correction of output can occur before the "receptor" enters the communicative cycle. For persons with deviant feedback systems, this phase of the program seems of special import. Experientially, there seems to be some "carry-over" into oral language.

6. To increase the visual memory span.

7. To develop and increase conceptual memory span. Even students who do not show amnesic signs will forget the five word sentence stated orally when they start the motor activity of typing the given sentence. The amnesic child, on the other hand, may type a sentence which is similar in meaning to the one given orally but different in language.

8. To broaden language concepts — Regardless of age or level of the student at the outset of the program, all sentences are extremely simple in construction, articles are frequently omitted, and the sentences invariably begin with the pronoun "I." For example, if the child is shown a picture of a cat and told to give a sentence using the word cat, he will say "I see a cat," but he will write "I see cat." To the child whose total development is above this level, the teacher must give the experiential background and the language ability to compose a sentence in which he is not a participant. Written language practice must also develop not only complete grammatic construction, but variations in sentence structure and concept. Since students seem better motivated toward developing linguistic skills on the typewriter, growth in written language skills probably is more rapid.

9. To reinforce the left to right movement of the eye across the page.

Who is eligible for educational typing? Most authorities on educational typing for the handicapped, the blind, deaf or orthopedically impaired do not recommend the introduction of typing in the classroom before the fourth grade. Some clinics working with the cerebral palsied child introduce typing at the kindergarten level. In our experience both extremes may be undesirable. What is more, there is nothing in the literature pertaining to teaching typing to the brain-injured child, except the suggestion that it might be a means of overcoming letter reversals.

Some sort of an educational typing program is recommended for every student who has achieved the academic level of mid-second grade. In short, all students who have some spelling abilities, a concept of a simple sentence, second grade reading ability, and some rudimentary concepts of adding and subtracting prove promising students for educational typing. The above requirements afford the foundation upon which this program is built.

There are, however, many linquistically-handicapped students whose physical impairment necessitates that, for maximum academic growth, the typing program may begin before the mid-second grade level. They generally fall into one of the following categories:

1. The cerebral palsied student who according to the clinical team working with him will not achieve a pencil grasp or sufficient pencil control to write a simple sentence.
2. The cerebral palsied child whose frustrations due to illegible and oversized handwriting are negating all motivations to learning and creating a behavioral problem in the classroom.
3. The blind child who has (a) mastered the rudiments of braille and (b) sufficient oral language fluency to express himself consistently in complete sentences.
4. The visually-impaired child, who, at the first grade level, cannot see the pencil markings on paper well enough to give him satisfaction in written language expression.
5. The severely cerebral palsied, profoundly deaf child may possibly benefit in developing eye focus, a sense of accomplishment, and even some concept of language function.

With the exception of the blind and certain of the motor-impaired students, no attention is paid to the fingering system. Most students are allowed to develop their own approach to the typewriter, unless they have been taught a particular typing system in occupational therapy. If they have, that approach must be carried through, provided consultation with the occupational therapist does not uncover a more efficient system. It has been found that with the emphasis on content, the one finger typing (one finger of each hand) with which most students first approach the typewriter is automatically transformed, through much typing experience, into the most efficient method of typing for the individual. Some students however, do need guidance in developing a technique for typing, such as:

a. The blind student obviously must be taught touch typing.

b. The hemiplegic will always type with one hand. As soon as such a student has confidence in the typewriter and what can be done with it, a one-handed touch system might be introduced. Caution here should be taken: *it is better that the student type with one finger, than destroy motivation by* teaching him any typing system. The fingering for one hand typing for the *right hemiplegic* is as follows:

qazxsw2   34erdfev   56tughjbnm   890iop½kl;',./
little finger   second finger   middle finger   index finger

left hemiplegic is:
qweasdzxc234   567rtyfghvbn   ui89jkm   l;'op½0-,./
index finger   middle finger   second finger   little finger

c. The cerebral palsied student who has no pencil grasp presents a special problem.

(1) If he can use his fingers or hands in any way to type, this is the preferable approach. Such students have learned to type by using a stylus grasped in their hands, or, unable to do this, by using one finger on one hand. *Heighten the motiviation and let the student figure out his own system.*

(2) In placing the typing stylus somewhere other than in the hand, there is one principle to remember: *the further from the hand the typing is performed, the slower and less satisfactory the progress.*

Thus, the student who types with the stylus in the mouth will make greater progress in written language facility than the one whose stylus is affixed to the forehead, but less progress than the one who holds the stylus in his grasp. Other things being equal, the student who types with one finger will progress with the greatest rapidity.

(3) Don't become discouraged by involuntary movements. Eye focus will minimize these, if it is properly taught. Along with the perceptual training which must at least partially precede the teaching of typing, a hand-eye coordination technique has been devised

for this purpose. This is described under perceptual training.

General Techniques:

1. All that has been said elsewhere about general teaching techniques for the brain-injured child applies here equally, as do the concepts of normal child development.
2. Never let the student "bang" on the typewriter. Either he types assigned meaningful material, or *he doesn't type at all.*
3. While eventually the student should and will carry out assignments on the typewriter without the teachers undivided attention, never "park" the beginning student at the typewriter while you go off to work with someone else. It is too frustrating an experience. Rather, for some time, he may need your undivided attention and guidance, while the others carry out assignments on their own.
4. Know your student. His production may slow down, rather than increase in rate and quality during the early typing experience.
5. For the cerebral palsied, do not seek an "easier" way too soon-obvious motor difficulties may decrease in a week or two with proper techniques of teaching.
6. Regardless of the student's academic level, begin with first grade material. The more he knows the material given to type, the easier it is for him to learn the technique, and the more rapidly he will progress, both in working alone and in working on materials of his present academic level.
7. Until the student does it by himself one day while you're busy elsewhere, or requests instructions on how to adjust the tabs and margins and you are sure that he comprehends them, do these activities in front of him but for him. Do not initiate teaching them to him.

First Lessons: Margin preset at ten and eighty; tabs at 20, 30, 40, 50, 60, 70; line indicator at triple spacing.

Deaf and Aphasoid. 1. Type name and date by teacher pointing finger at each letter and holding down cap and spacing where necessary.

2. Counting from one to as far as child is motivated to go and can easily go — instruct child to use tab key between numbers. Do not require child to remember sequence himself until about the fifth or sixth session.

3. Alphabet — done the same was as the counting using the tab key between letters. Do once in small letters and once in caps. The third time, have child do it without your pointing out each letter. Some children may not be able to do the whole alphabet by themselves at one time. Assist them in typing the first seven letters, then have them repeat the line by themselves. (For purposes of illustration have the assisted letters capped but on the child's own paper they should not be.)

A	B	C	D	E	F	G
a	b	c	d	e	f	g
H	I	J	K	L	M	N
h	i	j	k	l	m	n
O	P	Q	R	S	T	U
o	p	q	r	s	t	u
V	W	X	Y	Z		
v	w	x	y	z		

4. End the lesson at the end of the page. This gives the child a sense of accomplishment and at the same time calls a halt before he tires of the activity. If he shows signs of fatiguing or losing any enthusiasm, stop right there for the day.

5. From the onset, treat errors matter-of-factly: notice them, teach the child to backspace and cross out either with the "x" or the "/." Do not bother with erasing. It is too distracting.

Cerebral Palsied and Those Whose Hand-eye Coordination Is Poor. The procedure is the same except that the first lessons may not accomplish as much. One boy spent the first two weeks of lessons trying to type his first name without error — this was partially necessary because the teacher discovered that at first he wasn't quite sure how to spell it.

1. All students regardless of disability should be instructed to find the letter with their eyes and not to remove this focus until the key is struck. With the cerebral palsied, they must be further instructed *not* to *try* to hit the key — just to look at it, and think about how it would feel to hit it. When you are sure that the

child has this concept, and you have placed your finger pointing directly to the one key to help maintain the focus, the child will hit the key regardless of the involuntary motion.

2. If there is too much interference even with these instructions, consult the occupational therapist about the advisability of this child typing with a machine with a plate.

3. Sometimes, the total situation of typing on the typewriter is too great for the child to grasp at one time. Therefore, the concept of eye-focus-for-hand-coordination cannot be achieved at the machine. Practice for part of the period is done with the chart shown in Figure 6. The child is instructed to look at the letter you name until his finger touches it. "Touches" means goes directly on it without touching any other circle. These charts are also for home practice. Always make sure that the chart shows a keyboard identical to the one the child uses.

After the student is able to carry out the work of the first lesson on command without your undivided attention, typing activities are broadened.

Spelling: 1. Give the child the word. Have him spell it orally. Have him type it. Do this with four words, using the tab key in between words.

2. Have him type a line or the word (or words) he wasn't quite sure of.

3. Have him tell you a sentence with each word. Check his oral spelling of each word in the sentence. Show him how to type each word with the machine's motor off. Repeat total sentence, have him repeat it. Supervise his typing of it. Over the first two weeks or so, gradually release some of this supervision so that by the fourth or fifth week, he is just giving the sentence before he types it and then asking you to spell words he doesn't know.

cat	man	dog	have
have	have	have	have

I see dog
I see a dog.
The man came in the room.
I see a cat.
I have a dog.

4. It will be noted that the correction of the sentence was made immediately and directly under the original sentence. The ability to write four sentences before going back to correct the errors must be developed.

5. Gradually the complexity is built up to include copying of very short sentences from paper at the side, from the blackboard or from a book. More words are given at one time. More sentences are written before correction. Less assistance from the teacher is needed until finally the child can copy the daily experience or picture, although this may take months.

Arithmetic: All arithmetic processes can be performed on the typewriter. Under the alphabetic labels, an attempt was made to illustrate many of them. In each process the answer is put on paper in the normal manner through use of the back-spacer. In addition examples, however, to maintain the proper columnar alignment, the tab is set for the most frequently used number place and space bar or the back-spacer is utilized to place the other numbers in proper position.

Steps:	*A*	*B*	*C*	*D*
Simple adding	3	3	3	3
		4	4	4
				7
	A	*B*	*C*	*D*
Simple subtraction	5	5	5	5
		−2	−2	−2
				3
Column Addition	309	309	309	309
		6	6	6
		1987	1987	1987
			36	36
Column adding	309	309	309	309
	6	6	6	6
	1987	1987	1987	1987
	36	36	36	36
	8	38	338	2338
Subtraction	2987	2987	2987	2987
	−678	−678	−678	−678
	9	09	309	2309

Multiplication	3	3	3	3
		×	×5	×5
				15
	296	296	296	296
	×31	×31	×31	×31
		296	296	296
			888	888
				9176

Division:

```
9)  1962          9)  1962
                      18       2
                      16
                       9       1
                      72
                      72       8
                            Ans. 218
```

Division-Alternate Method:

```
                  9)  1962
            2         18
                      16
            1          9
                      72
            8         72
    Ans. 218
```

It will be noted that while the alternate method is more logical in that the number to be multiplied by the divisor is directly under the divisor, most students preferred the other approach. When they attempted the alternate method, the number of errors markedly increased, regardless of which method they were taught first. The reason for this is not understood.[7]

Fractions, decimals, and even square roots can be mastered as a typing exercise. Generally, however, above the level of long division, the student tends to devise his own system of doing examples on the typewriter. It should also be noted that when the student reaches the level of advanced arithmetic, it may be more profitable to have the typewriter manufacturer change the keys so that certain common fractions can be typed without effort.

Section 6: Development of Other Sensory Areas: Techniques for the development of visual perception have been dwelt upon in detail to illustrate what should be done in sensory areas where there is a perceptual defect. With equal emphasis on the developmental sequence, perceptual defects in audition, kinesthesia, proprioception, taste and olfactory can be lessened as a functional barrier to learning. Quite aside from teaching the child to make normal adaptations to sensory stimuli in spite of perceptual difficulties is the entire realm of sense training itself, even though, in the given child, the sense training techniques may serve to overcome the so-called perceptual defect.

Sense training is mental development. Its aim is to develop within the child as many tools as possible for him to use in the solution of daily problems. Within this definition of purpose is the consideration of what the "average child" at any age might be expected to do with special reference to his muscular coordination and his attention span. Within the framework of normal development, the child's aptitude, preferences and interests are observed. It is the teacher's eternal function to guide the child sensibly and naturally from the more interesting to the less interesting, and from the simple to the more difficult. The successes attained in sense training will depend largely on the adult's willingness to respect the child's individuality and to recognize his preferences and requirements which are more important than any arbitrary group of standards.

It is perhaps this basic precept that is most disconcerting to the objective evaluation of some of the sensory approaches now used. The goal of all therapy and special education is to return the child to the mainstream of normal development as quickly and as efficiently as possible. Segregation for the normal environment for this purpose seems tenable only as long as the developmental sequence is paralleled in the segregated situation, insofar as possible. However, when the segregated situation ignores the experiences of the normal child—when it seeks to overcome defects rather than develop children, a serious philosophic question arises. Of what value is the individual, who is sensorially and motorically perfect, to himself, his family and his community if experience to cope with life is totally absent from his training.

All of this is by way of suggesting a midground. Within the first two years of life, the emphasis on sensory development can be made to the exclusion, or near exclusion, of other developmental factors with minimal trauma to the individual's life function; for the achievements in a more normalized sensory intake gained in that period served the child in quickly overcoming whatever experiential deficits he has suffered because of this emphasis. However, beyond the second year of life, this compensation is not possible; the rapidity of the learning gained by the child relating the environment in a meaningful way multiplies in a geometric progression. What is more, most of learning can occur only when the child is ready, and never again. Therefore to place the child in an environment which does not afford this learning at the time when the child may be most receptive may well be the result of the exclusively sensory approach to neurologic problems. It is therefore suggested that, even though the sensory defect may not be "cured" by the more moderate approach, the child may be better equipped to realize his potential in society. To accomplish this, the crux lies in the recognition and definition of each sensory deficit as it affects learning. Once it is understood exactly what is barring further learning, it is relatively simple to devise the means of teaching the child to compensate for or adapt to them.

In addition to what has already been said in the area of vision, color concept development is stressed. The teaching progression is the same; Matching of like objects, matching of unlike objects of the same color, use of the color chart and finally the coloring of pictures with pencils, crayons, paints, and similar activities. Around the time that the use of the color chart is introduced, the color name should be learned. As many teachers seem to have difficulty in the teaching of color concepts, there seems to be one additional point to be made. Since the brain damaged child may have difficulty in abstracting and generalizing, care must be taken that in early color concept development the same shade of the color is used in all activities. Calling a dark green, a medium green, and a light green all by the same name may confuse the child, because he is not developmentally ready to see the similarities among the three shades.

Lassman described the techniques for the development of touch.[49] In general the child should be taught to identify by touch objects, forms, differences in weights, and surfaces and textures. Each of these are approached in three ways: (1) seen, then identified by touch; (2) touched, then identified by sight, and (3) identification by touch alone. Incidentally, this order is not necessarily developmental. There are children who can do the first and third of these activities with ease, but have considerable difficulty in selecting by sight the object felt from a group of objects on the table.

In similar manner, smell, taste and hearing can be developed to amazing acuity. In the case of olfactory training however, experience has proven that it should be completely avoided with children subject to petit and grand mal. Extension of the normal preschool and kindergarten techniques in audition, as so well described by Connor and Talbot, are suggested here. However, it is further suggested that no later than the lower kindergarten level, should the techniques of ear-training or phonetic development be introduced as a regular part of the curriculum. Some children, particularly the deaf athetoid and the severely retarded brain damaged, have to be taught that sound conveys meaning. While this is essentially a therapeutic procedure, there will be instances in which the preschool teacher is confronted with this problem. Basically, this is a learning procedure utilizing operant conditioning.

Finally, the development of auditory and visual memory is basic to learning. Such activities as remembering the order of objects placed on the table, discovering which if any objects are missing from the group, and verbally describing something in the immediate environment are enjoyable games which serve to teach the child to remember what he sees. By the same token, the ability to recite nursery rhymes, simple poems, the alphabet, a series of words or nonsense syllables teaches the child that what is heard is to be remembered. These are the fundamental tools for all learning.

Section 7: Problems Involved in Teaching the Cerebral Palsied Child to Read: *General Statement.* According to most modern texts on the teaching of reading and remedial reading, it should be impossible to teach the average child with cerebral palsy to read.[2,11,38,48,56] The causes of reading problems among normal children are usually listed as (1) Problems of vision (occular); (2) Difficulties in visual perception; (3) Emotional problems within the home; (4) Mental retardation; (5) Difficulties at symbolization—defects of abstraction, categorization and concept formation; (6) Defects of auditory perception; (7) Speech impairments; (8) Emotional and social immaturity; and (9) Short attention span.[46,56] All of these factors, except the emotional problems at home, have already been discussed as learning problems frequently found among cerebral palsied children. It is obvious, however, that most cerebral palsied children can learn to read, in accordance with their their mental age level. Part of the discrepcancy between the texts on reading and the empirical facts as seen in special education may well lie in the modern concepts of reading. Remedial reading problems among normal children are at an all time high in this country. Without becoming involved in one of the major controversies of modern education today, it is safe to point out that each of the listed causes of reading problems in normal children can be overcome, at least partially, as they appear in the cerebral palsied child provided that (1) the child has the intellectual capacity to read; (2) he is given sufficient time to learn without outside pressures, emphasizing the importance of the reading act itself, and (3) he is taught by special techniques suited to his disability.

Intellectual Capacity and Reading: Correlations between mental age and ability to learn to read show a fairly high degree of relationship.[46,p6] Most authorities placed the Mental Age for learning to read with comprehension between the mental ages of five and eight with an M.A. of six and one-half years as the most frequently cited age for normal children to begin the reading process.[11,46,56,57] While reading readiness programs can be and should be begun considerable time before this, the M.A. of six and one-half to seven years is considered minimum for the child to be able to (1) perceive the words used; (2) comprehend the ideas expressed; (3) react to these ideas, and (4) integrate them into his experience.[45]

For the mentally retarded child, Kirk gives the following guides to reading potential:

1. Children with chronological ages seven to nine and with mental ages of four to six:

    a. Have not begun to read.

    b. Should be showing interest in reading, in books, and in pictures, in the interpretation of pictures, labels, their own names and so forth.

2. Children of chronological ages nine to eleven and with mental ages of five and one-half years to seven years:

    a. Should be having an intensive reading readiness program with incidental reading of charts, signs, labels, etc., if readiness is not adequate.

    b. Should begin reading stories of their own experiences from the board and from charts if readiness is established.

    c. Should be interested in drawing pictures, interpreting pictures, and reading and writing stories about these pictures.

    d. Should be able to make booklets of their own stories that they have told and which they have read from charts.

    e. Should begin to read preprimers, and simple books.

3. Children of chronological ages eleven to thirteen and with mental ages of seven to eight and one-half years::

    a. Should be reading first-to-third-grade material with adequate understanding.

    b. Should be grouping words and phrases into thought units, but are slow in reading.

    c. Should be developing a method of word recognition and should be capable of recognizing new words from context clues, phonic analysis, and so forth.

    d. Should be interested in reading simple books for information and pleasure, and engaging in out-of-school reading such as newspapers, directions for games, and projects.

4. Children of chronological ages thirteen to sixteen with mental ages of eight and one-half to eleven years:

    a. Should be utilizing reading for many activities and using books from third- through fifth-grade level.

    b. Should be using dictionary, telephone directory, library, and reading newspapers and maps.

c. Should have increased vocabulary and fair comprehension with independent methods of word recognition.

d. Should be spontaneously reading for information and for pleasure.[48, pp 254-255]

Some cerebral palsied children who are capable of social adequacy may never learn to read for comprehension and enjoyment; similarly some dull normal individuals never learn to read with adequate comprehension, yet they are capable of leading average lives in the community. In these cases, care should be taken that the individual, especially the adolescent, can read danger signals, can read labels, street signs in his home community and enough of newspaper advertisements and bills to equip him to meet his social potential. By gearing the reading program around these materials, rather than prepared texts, adequate reading for social living in today's world can be achieved. However, this type of reading program should be used with great forethought and care, because the individual actually is not being taught to read but rather is being trained for social adequacy, principally through drill and memorization.

Another factor in the relationship between intelligence and reading ability arises from consideration of the mentally retarded adolescent, whether or not he has cerebral palsy, who has the capacity to learn to read. The principal problem here is usually the selection of materials of sufficient interest to a person of his maturity and still simple enough in wording and concept presentation so that he can gain comprehension. There are published materials which seem adequate in these cases, provided that the individual has reached the third grade level of reading. The Reading Skill Texts, Reader's Digest Skilltexts, the Weekly Reader, books in social science and science, books written for the U.S. Army during World War II to be used by illiterate inductees, abridgements of the classics, materials developed by Science Research Associates and Educational Development Laboratories, and similar literature are easily accessible. However, below the second grade level, it is far more desirable for the teacher to design

her own materials and place emphasis on reading readiness,
phonetic analysis and other techniques to be described than to
present the individual with reading material either too difficult
for him or so immature in interest level that he becomes bored.

Need for success. When reading materials are presented to
a mentally handicapped child before he is ready to learn, he
experiences continued failure in a reading situation. Such experience, resulting in frustration and avoidance reactions, is
not conducive to a desire for reading. It is consequently important that the confidence of the child be established and
maintained in a reading situation. This is best done by showing
the child success in a systematic program of instruction at his
level and rate of reading. Mentally handicapped children can
learn to read with pleasure providing the experience is not
frustrating to them. In most cases, they have been presented
with reading materials long before they were ready to read and
have developed a negativistic attitude toward reading.[48, pp 257,258]

Environmental Pressures and Reading: All too frequent in
the experience of teachers among the cerebral palsied is the appearance of the parent who insisted that his child be taught to
read because he is now seven years old. The tragedy of such situations lies not in the fact that the parent comes to the teacher, because with patience the teacher can make the parent understand
about reading readiness, social maturity and the other factors
involved in reading. It is what has occurred before the parent
comes to the teacher, the effort he has made at home to teach the
child to read and its resultant frustration, the emphasis he has
placed upon reading to the child which, instead of providing motivation for reading, has erected a barrier of undue pressure and
fear toward the reading situation, and finally the creation of anxiety in the child which may bar success.

Parallel to this situation is the emphasis placed upon "The
Reader." So many children come into the classroom with the idea
of "get the reader—how many pages did we read today—when will
we finish the reader—get a new reader," without any seeming
motivation toward knowing what happened in the story or any
seeming pleasure from the reading act itself. There are the
mechanical readers, the children who can "read" aloud without

stumbling on a single word and still not be able to tell what happened in the story. Correction of this type of reading disability is relatively simple if the teacher is given the opportunity to take the required time without extra-classroom pressure. As in all teaching of reading among the cerebral palsied in the primary grades, care must first be taken that the child knows, either from his own experience or vicariously, the experiences of the story he is about to read. In teaching reading comprehension to the mechanical reader, it is frequently necessary at the beginning to have him restate each sentence in his own words. This requires at least two readings of each story, one for sentence by sentence comprehension and the other for the meaning of the story as a whole. Prior to this, however, as in all reading situations, the child is to be made familiar with the story vocabulary so that he will succeed in mechanical reading.

A most common fallacy is that all cerebral palsied children should read and should enjoy reading. This occurs especially among the more severely handicapped. Thus you might find an adolescent of normal intelligence reading Shakespeare in the original despite the fact that reading tests show that she has barely a fourth grade reading comprehension level. What actually happens in these cases is that the individual reads words without any comprehension and thinks that is all there is to reading as done by her contemporaries who have read the same material. The difficulty arises when an attempt is made to introduce her to simpler material in the classroom situation, so that reading comprehension can be improved. She is sufficiently intelligent to realize what is being done and resents it.

The cerebral palsied with severe motor involvements are, in many cases, the most difficult of all remedial reading problems. On the one hand is the concept that, since reading is perhaps the only activity they can perform by themselves, they should read a great deal. On the other, since speech is often unintelligible and labored and there is little use of the hands, it is difficult and time-consuming to check thoroughly their reading comprehension. For example, in a special classroom of five to six students, it usually takes at least a concentrated hour to check the comprehension of a six-page story in such a pupil. Much of that time is spent in trying to decipher, mostly through trial and error, what he is trying to say. Experience teaches that such children of normal intelligence are rather sharp at picking up cues, and care must be taken during such checks to make certain that the pupil is expressing his ideas and not what he thinks the teacher thinks he ought to say. But what happens to the other students while this pupil is receiving the teacher's undivided attention!

For reading comprehension, the child must have experience. This cannot be too strongly emphasized. The child with severe motor involvements who has been anchored to the wheelchair and the home cannot be expected to have, upon entering the school situation, the experiences of the normal six-year old. The child who demonstrates some of the brain injured learning patterns may or may not have been exposed to some of the normal experiences, but those he has met have not been interpreted with him. Thus, with his skewed perceptions, categorizations, abstractions and concept formations, it is likely that he has not integrated them in the same manner as other children. What all this means in the education of the cerebral palsied child is that systematized reading readiness program should be begun as early as possible and should continue for a longer than normal period.

Section 8: Techniques of Teaching Reading: *Reading Readiness.* Reading readiness may be defined as those experiences in the young child's life which prepare him for the adventure of reading. Such experiences might be classified as (1) learning that sounds have meaning and that some sounds stand for words; (2) learning that there are all sorts of things in this world; (3) learning primitive give and take of the group situation; (4) wanting to read; (5) using language to express simple wants, fears, and experiences; (6) learning to listen; (7) learning to look carefully; (8) learning to remember, and (9) learning to interpret.[45]

The problem of reading readiness among all children has received much attention within recent years. With the modernization of most prepared reading texts and their accompanying Teachers' Manuals, there is little need to repeat readiness teaching methods here.[2,38,56,57] There are, however, some additional techniques which may be suggested for use among the cerebral palsied because of the additional burdens placed upon his learning to read with comprehension. First in emphasis are the techniques for overcoming perceptual difficulties as has been discussed. Of equal importance is making certain that he achieves the same experience as other children in the nine areas of experience for reading readiness already cited. A third consideration, that of importance of controlling the learning environment, stems from the behavioral manifestations of the brain-injured child at the beginning of formal learning.[10,20,21,29,66,69] Because some cerebral palsied children display hyperattentiveness and other brain-injured behavioral signs, it is necessary to minimize the stimuli within the immediate environment at the onset of education.[20,21] The effective teacher knows, however, that gradually the environment should become less structured and more normal. The child's educational experiences cannot be gained in a vacuum. Group participation and adjustment to the distractions of group or classroom activity are essential. Reading, writing, and all other academic learning are but tools to be used in the group or social situation, and the child learns to use them only when he is so taught.

Motivation for Reading. In addition to those factors already discussed, the problems of emotional maturity and stability bear a direct relationship to reading ability. This is seen most obviously in the older cerebral palsied student where the years of frustration have taken more than their toll on the personality. For example, the adolescent who sees her problems as peculiar to herself, and not in relation to the problems of other people of the same age, sex and social position, will have difficulty in reading comprehension because she cannot understand of what importance comprehension of what she is reading is to her. An overprotected, socially and emotionally immature young man of eighteen does not understand a social science book about Africa and says to his teacher, "Why should I read about Africa? I have cerebral palsy." These problems and techniques for their solution have been discussed elsewhere. Because they are verbalized by the adolescent student who is equipped to speak his mind, there is a probability that these same attitudes are developing in the younger child. It would be well to forestall their development rather than seek their correction at some later date.

Section 9: The Experience Story: *What is the Experience*

Story? While most teachers are familiar with the technique of "News" or "Show and Tell," both in the oral and written forms, they are also aware of the fact that writing the news daily on the chalkboard becomes repetitious and boring in most of the classroom groupings. Special children do not have enough variety of experience to report to sustain interest and enthusiasm for reading, if the daily story is confined to "News." By the same token, the daily weather report, which may or may not be incorporated in the News, is inclined to become too routine and confining in concept and vocabulary to motivate enjoyable reading comprehension. These techniques are only four of a wide variety of topics that are a part of the "experience story" approach to reading. Each story should vary in subject matter and content.

In every classroom the children daily share at least one experience together. Often it is some special event, such as the circus, a party, or a field trip. More frequently, it is some experience that is a part of the every-day curriculum and art project, a lesson in environmental awareness, a musical experience, an academic activities game that was especially enjoyed, or a learning in personal conduct which the teacher wants specifically to emphasize. Thus the experience story is based upon a wide variety of activities in which the teacher knows each child in her group has participated and therefore has a vested interest.

When Should the Child Begin to Meet the Experience Story? After the students have had an experience, it should be discussed at the child's level of comprehension. During these daily discussions, the teacher must take care to use simple sentences of not more than four or five words—at the pre-kindergarten level. Repeated use of the preprimer vocabulary is essential, since these are the words which give backbone to early reading experiences.

The group discussion of each experience is mandatory since most brain-damaged students have difficulty in abstracting from any happening those lessons and generalizations which the adult considers obvious. It is unnecessary to mention that "discussing" is a two-way process in which the child contributes as much, if not more, oral language to the activity as the teacher, insofar as he is able. One of the most common failings is to presume that a brain-damaged child knows something because he has been taught it innumerable times. Until he has been able to tell it or answer questions about it, it must be assumed that he has not mastered the concept. Gradually, the child learns to recount an event. As he does so, he also learns to express himself in short, but complete sentences, if his speech warrants this level of production. If he cannot produce a complete sentence orally, the teacher must be quite sure in her own mind that he has comprehension of the complete sentence when he hears one. This is most effectively done by making certain that you always speak to the child in a complete sentence.[40,49] All of the techniques Mrs. Lassman describes for the young deaf child in her book should be used with all brain-damaged children at this level except that the acoustic equipment may not always be necessary.

Introducing the Written Experience Story — The Lower Kindergarten Level. By the Kindergarten level the child should have the oral concept of the experience story. It is then that the child is introduced to the wrtiten version, after it has been recounted orally. The procedure is relatively simple.

1. Teacher writes story on the chalkboard. Subject of each sentence is the name of one or more of the students in the group and/or the teacher's name. Excluding the names, no sentence should contain more than five words. Each story should consist of not more than five sentences, preferably four. Each sentence should begin a new line.

2. Teacher reads the story to the children three or four times.

3. By that time there will be a few children perhaps who have memorized the story. They are the first to be called on to "read" it. It is here likely, that the teacher will do more of the actual reading than the child, but each child must be called upon to "read." At this point the kindergarten child is not learning to read, but he is acquiring the concept of what meaningful reading is.

4. After all have "read" the story, the child is called upon to point to given words in the story, (1) beginning with his own name, (2) then the names of the classroom teacher and other children, (3) nouns — starting with the nouns in the sentence

with his name, (4) verbs, (use mainly transitive or action words),
(5) adjectives, (6) adverbs, (7) pronouns, (8) conjunctions, and
(9) prepositions.[55]

The Beginnings of Meaningful Reading — Upper Kindergarten — Lower First Grade. By the upper end of the kindergarten
level, the child should have the concept of meaningful reading
and should actually have a small reading vocabulary. The teacher,
in the meantime, *should have been keeping a copy of each experience story thus far presented* and have made her own flash
cards of the more commonly occurring words. It is also at this
level that each sentence of the experience story is put on a separate strip of paper or flashboard. Not only is the child taught to
read his sentence out of context, but he also matches it to its
twin on the experience chart. He is able to identify its sequence
in the story, and he can identify it when it is given aloud in or
out of context. At this point, the wise teacher makes individual
experience charts available to each of her students. These are
made from heavy cardboard (like that found on sides of boxes
or cartons) and gummed paper usually used to seal packages.

Normalizing the Reading Experience. By the time the child
is midway through the lower half of first grade, the teacher
should be able to write the story on the chalk board without the
child's participation. This is a most advantageous gain, since it
not only brings the child closer to the "normal" reading situation, but also permits the teacher to prepare the story for classroom use before class time. Thus, the routine is more easily kept.
The student, especially the hyperactive child, is less likely to
present a behavioral problem out of boredom while the teacher
is writing on the chalk board.

In addition to the procedures already described for teaching
the experience story, the child is now ready for some changes
in the story content, as well as some additions to the procedures
used. The length of the sentence is increased to about six or
seven words, and the names of the children are used less frequently. At first, not all of the children's names are used in the same
story. The children learn to "take turns." This time Johnny's
name is used, next time Mary's. Some of the names are used as
the object, direct or indirect, of the sentence, so that there is a

variation from beginning each sentence with the name of one of the children in the group. Some stories may use only one or two names. The eventual goal, of course, is to write a story about a shared experience without using any of the group names:

> Timmy the turtle came to class today.
> He has four legs.
> A turtle has green skin.
> A turtle lives in water.
> He pulls his legs and head under his shell.
> That way he does not get hurt.*

The above also exemplifies another change. The sentences are longer than the five word maximum. While, at this level a maximum of six or seven words per sentence is desirable, there can occasionally be more if the meaning of the sentence is easily visible and understood to the child, as in the case of the live turtle in the room. While the matter of vocabulary and frequency of introduction of new words will be discussed later, these factors too must be considered in sentence length.

Then there is the matter of sentence complexity. This must be gradually broadened. The introduction of phrases and clauses begins at this level. The meaning of the small words — and, but, if, what, how, why — and how they effect what the sentence is saying has to be drilled. For example, in the following sentences, the child must be able to answer the companion sample questions correctly.

Sentences	*Questions*
No one but John is wearing a sweater.	Is John wearing a sweater?
Mary is going home, but Sam is not.	Is Sam going home?
John came to school with his pencil and pad but not his crayons.	What did John bring to school? Did John bring his crayons to school?
If it stops raining, we will go outside.	Will we go outside for sure? Why won't we go outside? When will we go outside?

The Child-made Primer — Something of Meaning, Something to Show. In addition to these changes in the story content,

---

*This is an actual experience story written in a kindergarten class for brain-injured children at the Institute of Logopedics during the Spring of 1962.

there are some new techniques which are now introduced. Perhaps the most important of these is the dittoing of the experience story so that each student may have his own copies, one for homework and one for school. It is advised that the story be printed on the lower half of the sheet, so that the child may illustrate each by drawing, finding, or choosing a picture to go with the story. When sufficient number of stories, five or more, have been mastered, then they can be stapled together between construction paper covers. Thus the child has his own reader. He is also better motivated to review previous experience stories, and this activity should go on continuously.

The increase in length and complexity of the sentences is accompanied by a concomitant increase in the length of the story on the upper first grade level. Now the goal is for a maximum of nine to twelve words per sentence, preferably ten, and perhaps ten or more lines per story. Each sentence does not necessarily begin a new line. Two or three sentence paragraphing should occasionally occur. While the techniques already described for teaching the experience story continue, the teacher will find value in introducing a wide variety of new approaches, like writing a sentence from the story on the chalkboard but one word is wrong, and letting the students find and correct the word. Or let the child create his own story on the individual experience chart with the flash cards, and "surprise the teacher." In fact, the variety of things that can be done is limited only by the teacher's imagination.

The "Do-it-yourself" Reading Workbook. However, at the upper first-grade level, whatever else is done, the introduction of oral and written questions about the story is essential. Basic language-learning techniques dictate that the sequence of introducing such questions is a three-step process: (1) Oral questions and oral responses; (2) written questions and oral responses, and finally (3) written questions and written responses. Within this framework, there is considerable variance in the type of question that was asked and the type of response the child is called upon to make: (1) Where the "yes or no" response is required first to a question and later to a statement; (2) where one or two other words are required in response — from a multiple choice either in response to a question or in the completion of a statement. While the written one or two word answers to a question, without being given a multiple choice, is really a second grade activity, the child at this level should be able to respond orally to such questions, whether they are asked in oral or written form. This type of questioning requires the comprehension of "who," "what," and "where." The "how" and "why" question comes later in academic development since they require the (3) complete sentence or the (4) multi-sentence response. However, before the child leaves the first grade, he should have some experience in orally answering this type of question. The written response in complete sentence form should not be required before the second grade, and the written response to the "how" or "why" question is not stressed before the third grade level.

Reading and Writing: Two Sides of the Same Coin? For the older child on the upper first-grade level, the experience story is often combined with written language practice. Namely, the child copies the story from the chalkboard. Where the child can do this, it is excellent practice for many reasons having to do with learning difficulties associated with brain injury. Frequently, such children also have difficulty in learning to read the word unless they have had the experience of writing it. However, the teacher must be aware that some children may not be able to cope with the complexities of copying from the chalkboard and/or with the propositionality of being presented with several sentences at the same time. Such children learn to do this by:

1. Writing one word from each line of the story when a copy of word is before him at his desk.
2. Finding the one word in the story on his chalkboard and writing it on his paper — without a desk copy of that word.
3. Copying one sentence from a desk copy of only that one sentence.
4. Copying one sentence from a chalkboard copy of only that one sentence.
5. Copying one sentence from a desk copy of the entire story.
6. Copying one sentence from a chalkboard copy of the entire story.

Before the transition to the reader is made, it seems advisable that the child experience working with stories which were used in other classes at the same level. Thus, he is enabled to read of the experiences of other children who are real and whom he may know. Yet, he himself was not part of the experience. This bridges the gap between the egocentric interest in the group experience story and the impersonality of the story in the reader.

Vocabulary for the Written Experience Story: Although the nature of the experience story precludes the use of an exclusive list of words at any given time, there are some "core" words, or words used commonly in many stories, by which the teacher may be guided. Generally, the vocabulary of the experience should be one grade-level ahead of that used in the reading series of the child's community, except as otherwise noted. However, at the beginning, it shall include words of particular meaning to the child; by the lower first grade, it should include family members, body parts, colors, furniture, eating utensils, common school equipment and simple weather concepts.

Since no two authorities seem to agree on the frequency at which new words should be introduced into the reading vocabulary of the normal child, it is useless to draw any hard and fast rules concerning our special children in these matters. A great deal depends on the nature of the group, the nature of the experience story, and the learning problems of the individual students. However, before any word is used in a written story, the child must know the meaning of the word as used in the story. The best guide which the teacher has to determine this is when the child is able to give orally a sentence of his own making in which the word is correctly used.

Many common words in our language have a multiplicity of meanings. The child must be taught all or most of the common meanings of the word separately and the given word should be used in its variety of meanings in the experience story. However, the child must be quite sophisticated in his ability to read before the same word is used as having two different meanings in the same story.

The addition of endings to known words in the reading vocabulary sometimes presents the perplexity of knowing when to call it to the child's attention and when not to, for fear of adding only confusion in the child's mind. In general, when the change of form of the word makes for a basic change in meaning, some simple explanation should be given. For example, the difference between "John runs home" and "John is running home" is too subtle in meaning for the student at this level to grasp. Thus, no explanation is needed or advised. However, the "s" added to nouns to mean more than one or the "ed" added to verbs to denote the past tense can be recognized at this level with sufficient drill. Since the presence of both of these effects a major change in sentence meaning, these differences must be pointed out to the child.

Frequency of Change of Experience Story. At the beginning at least, the average classroom group requires about two weeks to master an experience story. This means that the story topic must have sufficient import, universality and motivational impact to sustain the children's interest. As the students become more adept at reading, the frequency of new story introduction increases. The extent of that increase is dependent upon many factors, including the number of new words in the present story, and the ability of the teacher to create new language learning activities aimed at mastering reading vocabulary and comprehension of oral and written language. For an adequate program at the mid-first-grade level, not more than one or two new stories a week should be necessary. This assumes that the teacher is following all the procedures described here, as well as the teaching methods already available to her in her handbook and teacher's materials file.

The Experience Story and Program Continuity. In order to assure continuity in the child's educational program, copies of the experience story should be forwarded to the new teacher when the student is transferred to another classroom group. If all the students are transferred to another teacher, or if sufficient change in classroom grouping is made to alter the nature of the original group, the experience charts, flashcards, and other group teaching materials pertaining to the experience stories should follow the children for whom they were prepared into their new classroom group. Thus, the new teacher will be able to carry through the academic program with a minimum of interruption or regression. While she is not bound to continue use of the old experience story, she has both a good concept of what has comprised the students' previous program and materials upon which to start her own. At the same time, the child will feel more secure in his new classroom environment if familiar materials are evident, at least at first.

When is the Student Ready for the First Reader? There is no "pat" answer to this question that is equally applicable to all the students in all the groups. There is not a classroom grouping anywhere in the country in which all the students in the group are equally ready for the same activity at the same time.

The readiness of the individual student for meaningful reading from the first reader may be gauged by the following accomplishments:

1. He can read in a meaningful way experience stories which he has not been involved in writing and of experiences in which he has not participated.
2. He can successfully read and answer written questions on what he has read. The type of questions he should be able to answer has already been described.
3. He should have already been taught to respect books. He knows how to handle and care for them. He understands that the book he is about to receive holds a wonderful world of fun for him. He eagerly anticipates receiving its pleasure.

Section 10: Summary in Perspective: To say what has been presented thus far is a child-centered approach to the education of neurologically impaired children is insufficient. More descriptive would be some realization that the elements of learning herein set forth are integral to the academic success of every child. Most children develop these factors in the maturation process, and therefore it may be less damaging to their overall learning if they are ignored by their educational setting. The very basic manifestations of learning-language behaviors in neurological impairments are found in these areas. If the brain-damaged child is to learn what other children learn in their academic lives, he must be able to adapt to the very essence of the symptomology of his disorder.

Essentially, it is suggested that for these children special education may present little more than an historical relationship to the education of the normal child. It may be that special education is to education *per se* as physical therapy relates to physical education, occupational therapy to arts and crafts, or speech therapy to elocution and dramatics. Just as the therapeutic professionals have, within recent decades, completely broken the shackles which tied them to their historical field of origin, so might the training of the professional in special education be separated from the concept that it exclusively belongs to education.

Basically, what is proposed herein is the adaptation of methodologies and modalities used in the therapeutic care of the neurologically impaired child, adapted and modified to the group learning situation. This is a radical departure from present practices. However, it is generally recognized today that what is now being done is not getting the job of educating these children accomplished. Watering down the educational curriculum and using the same approaches to these children as for the normal child is frustrating to the child and his teacher. Neither is challenged to realize his respective potential; nor is either motivated to try. A lengthy visit to almost any classroom for the neurologically impaired in the country would reveal this most obviously. Perhaps the answer lies in this new concept that special education is an extension of some discipline other than teacher training, and that it more rightfully may be conceptualized as an extension of one of the therapies, either occupational or speech.

There is an additional import to this line of reasoning. If the neurologically impaired child cannot learn from his environment in the manner of other children, his learning must be guided by the trained person at an earlier age. While this fact has long been recognized in the literature, California is perhaps the only state which includes preschool for these children as part of the State educational system. Yet, getting the child as early as possible into an environment in which he can learn is crucial. If Holt's concept that, under present educational methodologies, most children in school are being taught "how not to learn," consider what a diluted version of the same methodologies does to the child who grossly deviates in his ability to conceptualize in the first place.[42]

Although this concept of special education as a vehicle for teaching the child how-not-to-learn is gaining voice in most professional circles, no one has set forth an alternative course. While such a possible alternative has been suggested here, it is recognized as being neither complete nor entirely satisfactory. One difficulty is that present concepts of *where* the neurologically impaired child fails academically and *why* are only now beginning to be understood. In seeking the solutions to some of the learning problems encountered by the brain-damaged child, it does not take long to discover that man's knowledge of how normal children learn is most incomplete. Thus, special education for the child with linguistic, learning and behavioral difficulties stands at the threshold of its own realization, poorly equipped to accomplish its preassigned goals because there presently exists no definition of what these goals are.

There is no better illustration of what has been said than the teaching of mathematics to the brain injured child. Only within recent years, and only with the interjection of the mathematician and the psychologist into the curricular devisement have the goals and techniques for teaching mathematical concepts to the normal and superior child begun to find definition. Only time will describe the effectiveness of such new mathematical curricula for most students, just as it will illuminate the areas where further revisions are needed. In the meantime, the special educationalist must attempt to teach concepts which are rooted in the problems caused by neurological impairment.

Section 11: Problems Involved in Teaching Mathematics to the Neurologically Impaired Child: *What is Arithmetic?* Arithmetic, or in its broader sense, mathematics, is a linguistic concept in which all variations on phenomena are abstracted from the environment, categorized and reduced to symbols which can be manipulated and integrated with other symbolized, environmental facts to enable the individual to better understand and control his environment. If recent years have taught one thing about teaching arithmetic, it has been that, in order that all children have some ability to utilize it as a tool, there must be true understanding of the nature of what is being taught.[51,71]

Arithmetic Is A Linguistic Concept. Numbers do not exist in a vacuum. Nor do they have meaning when divorced from the environment with which they are concerned. Two, for example, tells nothing until you know two what? Two fingers? Two houses? Two dollars? There is a difference in time between two minutes and two years, but this difference is in no way described by the number "two." Therefore, for arithmetic to have meaning for the child, the child must have some ability to comprehend oral language as a means of describing the world around him. As part of the development of this ability must come the analysis and categorization of things in the environment and various ways of relating one to the other, before he is ready to relate or categorize them in any quantitative schema. For example, the child must be able to differentiate his fingers from his mother's, or anyone else's, long before he is ready to learn that he has five on each hand. To teach a child to count to five, or ten, by rote before he has learned to identify objects in the environment and tell which go together, and why, is to defeat the very purpose of teaching the child any numbers in the first place.[17]

A number of years ago the linguistic nature of number concepts was reinforced by a visit to a first grade classroom for neurologically impaired children. On the wall there was an elaborate, colorful number chart with numbers from one to ten. Next to each number were the number words, and adjacent thereto was the correct number of pictures of different animals, i.e., *one* cow, *two* ducks, *three* horses and so forth. It was library hour when the visitors came, however, and little Johnny was looking at his favorite animal book. One of the visitors went up to John and, point to a picture of a horse said, "What's this John?" With a broad smile that could come only from sureness of response, John instantly replied, "It's a three."

The *abstracting* and *categorizing* problems of the brain-damaged child have been described in this text and elsewhere in the literature for years in detail. These are only two of the factors which cause integrative breakdown in the academic learning of the brain-injured child. Just as through memorization and other techniques the neurologically impaired child can be *taught* to be a mechanical reader, many teachers and parents of brain-damaged children seem almost driven toward making the child an automatic computer. Too many such children not only add and subtract all the number combinations to perfection, but they also do borrowing and carrying in their arithmetic examples; yet they consistently fail such questions as "Give me two blocks; how many legs does a dog have? If you have a penny and I gave you another, how many pennies would you have? Tom is five—Mary is six—who is older?" Seeing such children doing pages of arithmetic is reminiscent of the dog who sits on his haunches begging for a tidbit from the table. The child is seeking approval, not doing arithmetic. In fact, close observation of many such children reveals an autistic-like behavior, in which the child is virtually withdrawing from his environment by the number activity, instead of being made more aware of it.

Numbers are linguistic symbols which enable the individual to relate, integrate, and manipulate facts within his environment: The statement "Three boys and two girls are sitting around the table" provides the answer to an almost infinite number of quantitative questions, among which are the following:

> How many children are there *around* the table?
> At least how many chairs must be *at* the table?
> How many shoes are *under* the table?
> How many *pairs* of feet are under the table?
> How many *cows* are sitting at the table?
> How many people at the table are wearing *trousers*?
> How many people at the table have *longer* hair?

How many teachers of brain-damaged children would think to ask beyond the first or second of these questions?

Perhaps the most crucial innovation to mathematical teaching is the revision of perspective.[51] It used to be idiomatic that you can't add an apple with a pear, or a butterfly with a tree; today it is understood that you can, provided you ask the right questions, i.e. how many pieces of fruit, or how many living things? This means that to qualify for academic learning of arithmetic concepts, the child must first have begun to overcome what else-where in this text has been called *conceptual rigidities*.

To many this seems to be contradicting the age-old precepts that the neurologically impaired and the mentally retarded child must overlearn a concept, and that such overlearning is accomplished by many, frequent repetitions. Rather than a contradiction, it is a clarification of what is meant by repetition. The concept is to be taught repeatedly—with as many different materials and approaches as the teacher can devise: to use the same materials in the same way day after day insures boredom, which, in turn, blocks good teaching on the part of the teacher and all learning on the part of the child. Thus, while the child must first learn the concept through *one* approach and *one* set of materials, it cannot be assumed that he has mastered the concept until it is presented to him in as many different frameworks as possible.

While it is not the intent of this text to present a complete curriculum for teaching arithmetic to the neurologically impaired child, it does seem essential to review the hierarchy of conceptual development in arithmetic as a linguistic tool. Through the primary grades, such a hierarchy might be divided into four conceptual phases: classification, set, quantity and order.

Classification: Before the child is ready to meet numbers in any form, he must know by name the things within his environment and their relationship to each other — which go together. He must also have some linguistic concept that the determination of what goes together depends on what is being sought. For example, if you set before the child three objects, a yellow bird made of wood, a brown cow made of plastic and a brown table made of wood, the determination of which two belong together depends on whether the classification sought is animal, color, or from what the object is made. Yet, in response to direct questions, the child must be able to give the proper answer to each.

Not only does arithmetic readiness begin on the nursery or preschool level, but it should start long before the child is exposed to number words or any quantitative concept. It starts, perhaps, with the identification of body parts, articles of clothing, which pieces of furniture belong in each room of the doll house, and what foods are eaten at which meal. It is based in making routine not only the scheduled structure of the group learning situation, but also the entire day at home as well, so that the child begins to get some concept of order and sequence in daily living, long before he meets them in symbols. The establishment of a routine at home and in school in no way negates what has already been said about the need to teach the child to tolerate variations in the routine.

Beyond all this is the formal drill within the preschool curriculum on categorization and shifting of categories. Assuming that figure-ground perceptual disturbance is a distinct learning deficit, and not a secondary manifestation of some of the other learning difficulties encountered in the neurologically impaired, such work on categorization should begin with concrete, three-dimensional objects, rather than picture cards. Since the scope of objects which can be used within the environment can be greatly broadened through the use of picture cards, it is suggested that the shift be made as soon as possible. In selecting the pictures to be used, however, caution must be exercised to insure the child seeing in the picture what you want him to see. Colored pictures in white backgrounds, such as the Houghton-Mifflin Reading Readiness cards are excellent; various civic and social groups can be enlisted to make proper materials for this purpose. What should be avoided are cards which are too small, have printed words on the card, or are illustrated by linear drawings. In working on categorizing, the child must be able not only to verbalize which belong together, he should also be able to indicate *why* they belong together. He should master the reverse response — which one doesn't belong and *why?* This infers that he is taught the meaning of the word *belong* as going together. Further, he should have some experience in determining *what's missing, what's funny* and *what's different* (changed).

Set (Relativity): Once the child has mastered the concepts of things belonging together, and the other concepts described in the last section, to equal that of the average four to four and one half-year-old child, he is ready to begin to learn the next degree of arithmetic readiness. In general, this may be classified as understanding of adjectives and prepositions.[55] Such concepts as more and less, big and little, bigger and smaller, hard, harder, and hardest, in and out, over, under, and around, near and far, tall and short, fat and thin, and so on are introduced to the child. While most teachers include these in their curriculum, there are three common misconceptions: (1) That numbers or number words must either precede or be taught concommitantly with these concepts; (2) That the comparative and superlative forms of the adjective are comprehended by the child at a much later date, and (3) That if the child knows one concept, he automatically masters its antonym, i.e., if the child can tell who has more pennies, he knows who has less or fewer. Jean Berko's study of child language morphology certainly points out that linguistic development of normal children does not follow these educational concepts.[8]

Quantity: Now the child is ready to meet numbers, but only as having specific meaning to an object or group of objects. That is, the number stands for things: it is a specific symbolization which may be presented to the child only in relation to something else in the environment. Garton points out that, in teaching numbers as manipulative symbols (number concepts), the child is first taught one as opposed to more than one. Once he has overlearned this, the concepts of one, two and three and their varied relationships are taught.[33] Recent mathematical innovations have added that, along with the concepts of two and three, the child should begin to understand the conceptual function of the zero or nothing.[51] He is taught to manipulate objects in all arithmetic processes up to three, to recognize the numerical symbol, and to respond orally to numerical questions about these concepts without concrete objects before him. Moreover, the concepts of none, one, two and three are linguistically integrated with those previously learned concepts described under *Classification* and *Set.*

After the child has this mastered the concept of three, he is, *in the same manner,* introduced to and taught the concepts of one to five. Garton cautions against the assumption that all that needs to be done is add four and five to the previously learned concepts of one, two, and three.[33] Rather, the total process must be repeated from nothing through five, as described above, and then repeated again on the next level when teaching concepts of one through nine.

Order: What is here referred to is a linguistic extension of quantitative concepts in which quantity is used as an ordered series. Theoretically and ideally, *only* at this point should rote counting be introduced. However, regardless of the sophistication and high mindedness of the special educationalist, this theoretical ideal will seldom be achieved. Parents, in their anxiety to prove to themselves, their families and their neighbors that their handicapped child can learn, tend to stress rote counting earlier and with more emphasis than they do reading. Even if the child seems to be able to count by rote, such activity should be avoided with the group setting until the child has mastered the concepts already described. In teaching rote counting, at this point, there must be reinforcement of the concept that the numbers refer to bigger and smaller quantities, the smallest of which is zero, and not one. Since the child is now ready to write his numbers from one through nine, and since under the handwriting section of this text, it was suggested that brain-injured children be taught to write numbers in sequence on a vertical, rather than a horizontal plane, some confusion may arise at this point.

As will be recalled, the vertical writing of numbers was advocated because of the effects of defects in spatial perception on number confusion—without proper spacing between the numbers, one and two written in sequence on a horizontal plane can easily become confused with twelve and can lead to many complications in later arithmetic. However, at this juncture, you are presenting three objects, often in a horizontal plane, and having the child write the symbol on a vertical plane. Since numbers are symbolizations, the concept of which the child has already mastered, even if he cannot verbalize this explanation he should have no difficulty. When the written form of the arithmetic processes, adding and subtracting, are introduced, some confusion may arise since all learning is on the left to right horizontal plane in our culture. To avoid this, ordinal number, first, second, third, etc., are introduced and the child is taught, both in oral and written numbers, which numbers come before and after the numbers from one through eight. In reviewing his manipulation of the environmental facts through numbers, as described in the previous section, the word subtract is used along with "take away," so that the child is introduced into proper arithmetic terminology. At the same time, he is taught the plus and minus as symbols of the addition and subtraction processes.

The transference of written numbers from the vertical to the horizontal plane is inherent in teaching the written form of examples. For the child so severely involved physically that all written work must be done on the typewriter, this process has already been explained. However, for the child who is capable of using a pencil to produce written work of which he is sufficiently proud to take it home, handwritten work is preferable. At first, the teacher writes the instruction (i.e., *add*) and the examples with adequate spacing along the horizontal line, four to five examples per line maximum. The child fills in the proper sign, a plus, in its proper position and writes the answer. It is suggested that a line of subtraction examples follow the addition examples, so that any given day's work is not devoted to one process. Another technique is to present the child with a page of complete examples, and either read to him, or have him read number stories (problems) and designate which examples illustrate the problem's solution.

Those sophisticated in the teaching of modern mathematics will now realize that there is little new or original in what has been described here. The intent was to relate an approach which would enable the brain-damaged child to benefit from the recent, tremendous strides in mathematical teaching. If the child masters the concepts herein described, he is ready to learn via the new mathematics, at perhaps a slightly slower pacing. (Please note: *slower* means more time, experience and practice with each concept, not the dilution or elimination of concepts.) He is also ready to master perhaps a greater knowledge and understanding of the world around him, as exemplified by Dr. Sonesh's *Our Working World* curriculum, published by Science Research Associates.

AN OVERVIEW

There are many viewpoints from which the essence of this chapter could be restated. The various approaches described could be fitted into the Piaget stages of development:[30,61] Or any of the techniques described could be compared with the Montresorri system of child development and training:[58] Or the chapter content could be summarized in Skinnerian terminology.[68] All that any such effort would prove, however, would be that children are children the world over, regardless of how intact their central nervous system. It would serve no real purpose, except perhaps to reinforce the oft-restated concept that child development follows a sequence. To disregard that developmental sequence by ignoring primary stages may prevent the realization of the child's true potential.

Curiously absent from this discussion has been mention of any of the common topics associated with special education of the neurologically impaired, such as *how to motivate the child.* If the reader has not gleaned the reason for such absence from the text thus far, it well might be boldly stated. *Motivation for learning in a child cannot be created by the adult; it can only be destroyed.* What is called lack of motivation on the part of the students in special classes often seems like an almost intentional program of destroying the child's needs to know by the teacher's preoccupation with what is planned for the day's schedule. Motivation to learn is destroyed by boredom; and boredom stems either from insufficient challenge or too great a challenge. If the material presented and its manner of presentation is above the child's level of comprehension or performance, he will resign himself to not trying to learn, rather than coping with the resultant confusion. If the classroom environment persists in confusing the child, rather than teaching him, he will surrender forever his willingness and his anxiety, to learn. In a very narrow sense, this is perhaps the theoretical basis for the fact that children learn certain things at specific developmental stages, and can never truly learn them thereafter.

The essence of special education for the neurologically impaired children, therefore, is based not on theory, approach or curricula. It is founded on the teacher—how well she observes the child and understands *why* he is reacting as he is at any given time. It is rooted in the entire clinical and special education staff, particularly in the administration and how thoroughly they understand the fundamental principles of child learning. It is implanted by the individual needs of each child in the classroom group, and not in any text, syllabus or two-day workshop.

How program administration can affect learning of the children within the program has already been discussed in the chapter on Psychological Aspects. What only needs to be added here is an administrator's view. It is not beautiful buildings, attractive classrooms or elaborate equipment that makes for a good program. A facility or a classroom for brain damaged children can be outstanding, even when housed in the oldest building in town, in cramped quarters and with the most limited equipment. Children who progress make a program good, and children progress fastest when the staff is attuned to the needs of each child among them — when each clinician, including the special educationalist, is sufficiently sophisticated to observe constantly the child's reactions, understand the *whys* of each behavior, and individualize the curriculum while simultaneously affording the group experience.

A SELECTED BIBLIOGRAPHY

1. ALLEN, ROBERT M., and JEFFERSON, THOMAS W.: *Psychological Evaluation of the Cerebral Palsied Person: Intellectual, Personality, and Vocational Application.* Springfield, Charles Thomas, 1962.
2. ARTLEY, A. S.: *Your Child Learns To Read.* New York, Scott, Foresman, and Company, 1953.
3. AYRES, A. JEAN: Occupational therapy directed toward neuromuscular integration. In Willard, Helen F., and Spackman, Clare F.: *Occupational Therapy,* 3rd Ed. Philadelphia, J. P. Lippincott & Co., 1963, 358-467.
4. AYRES, A. JEAN: *Perceptual-motor Dysfunction in Children.* Cincinnati, Ohio Occupational Therapy Association Conference, 1964.
5. BEASLEY, JANE: *Slow To Talk.* New York, Bureau of Publications, Teachers' College, Columbia University, 1956.
6. BERKO, FRANCES, *et al.*: *An Adult Occupational Survey.* An un-

published paper sponsored by and submitted to United Cerebral Palsy Associations, West 44th St., New York, N. Y., 1956.

7. BERKO, FRANCES: *Objective Measurement of Academic Progress in a Classroom for the Brain Injured — A Five Year Study.* An unpublished paper done in conjunction with employment at the Institute of Logopedics, Wichita, Kansas, 1957-62.

8. BERKO, JEAN, and GOODGLASS, HAROLD: Aggrammatism and inflectional morphology in English. In *J. Speech Hearing Res., III:* 257-267, 1960.

9. BICE, HARRY V.: Psychological examination of the cerebral palsied. *J. Except. Child., XIV:*163-168, 1948.

10. BIRCH, HERBERT G. (Ed.) : *Brain Damage in Children: The Biological and Social Aspects.* New York, The Williams & Wilkins Company, 1964.

11. BOND, G. L., and WAGNER, E. B.: *Teaching The Child To Read.* New York, MacMillan, 1960.

12. BRUNER, JEROME: *The Process of Education.* Cambridge, Harvard University Press, 1961.

13. BURGEMEISTER, BESSIE, and BLUM, L. H.: Intellectual development of a group of cerebral palsied children. *The Nervous Child, VIII:*2, 177-180, 1948.

14. CARDWELL, VIOLA E.: *Cerebral Palsy — Advances in Understanding and Care.* New York, Association for Crippled Children, 1956.

15. CARLSON, EARL: The problem of cerebral palsy. In *Proceedings of The American Academy of Cerebral Palsy.* October 20-23, 1950.

16. CHEYNE, GEORGE: *The English Malady: or a Treatise of Nervous Diseases of all Kinds.* London, G. Strahan, 1735.

17. CHURCH, JOSEPH: *Language and the Discovery of Reality.* New York, Random House, 1961.

18. CONNANT, JAMES B.: *Education of American Teachers.* New York, McGraw-Hill, 1963.

19. CONNOR, FRANCES P., and TALBOT, MABEL E.: *An Experimental Curriculum for Young Mentally Retarded Children.* New York, Bureau of Publications, Teachers' College, Columbia University, 1964.

20. CRUICKSHANK, WM. M.: *A Teaching Method for Brain Damaged and Hyperactive Children.* Syracuse, Syracuse University Press, 1961.

21. CRUICKSHANK, WILLIAM, BICE, HARRY V., and WALLEN, NORMAN

E.: *Perception and Cerebral Palsy.* Syracuse, Syracuse University Press, 1957.

22. CRUICKSHANK, W. M., and RAUS, G. M.: *Cerebral Palsy.* Syracuse, Syracuse University Press, 1955.

23. DELACATO, CARL H.: *The Diagnosis and Treatment of Reading Disabilities.* Springfield, Charles C Thomas, 1964.

24. DENHOFF, ERIC, and ROBINAULT, ISOBEL: *Cerebral Palsy and Related Disorders — A Developmental Approach to Dysfunction.* New York, McGraw-Hill Book Co., 1960.

25. DOLL, E. A., PHELPS, W. M., and MELCHER, R. T.: *Mental Deficiencies Due To Brain Injury.* New York, Macmillan, 1934.

26. DUNSDON, M. I.: *The Educability of Cerebral Palsied Children.* London, Newmes Educational Publishing Co., 1953.

27. FEATHERSTONE, W. P.: *Teaching The Slow Learner,* New York, Bureau of Publications, Teachers' College, Columbia University, 1951.

28. FIELD, JOHN, and MAGOUN, H. W. (Eds.): *Handbook of Physiology — Section 1: Neurophysiology — Volume III.* Washington, D. C., American Physiological Society, 1960.

29. FENTON, JOSEPH: *A Curriculum Focus for the Child with Cerebral Palsy and Mental Retardation.* New York, United Cerebral Palsy of New York State, 1960.

30. FLAVELL, JOHN H.: *The Developmental Psychology of Jean Piaget.* Princeton, N. J., D. Van Nostrand and Company, 1963.

31. FROSTIG, MARIANNE: *The Frostig Program for the Development of Visual Perception: Teacher's Manual.* Chicago, Follett Publishing Company, 1963.

32. FROSTIG, MARIANNE: *Visual Perception Program.* Chicago, Follett Publishing Company, 1963.

33. GARSTON, MILDRED D.: *Teaching the Educable Mentally Retarded — Practical Methods.* Springfield, Charles C Thomas, 1962.

34. GESELL, ARNOLD, et al.:*The First Five Years.* New York, Harper & Row, 1940.

35. GESELL, A., and ILLG, FRANCES: *The Child From Five to Ten.* New York, Harper & Row, 1946.

36. GLICK, SELMA J.: Facing an unsolved problem: Employment of the cerebral palsied. *J. Rehab., XIX:*7-9, 1953.

37. GOLDSTEIN, KURT: *Language and Language Disorders.* New York, Grune and Stratton, 1948.

38. GRAY, W. S.: *On Their Own in Reading.* New York, Scott, Foresman, & Co., 1948.

39. GRINKER, R. R., BUCY, P. C., and SAHS, A. L.: *Neurology (5th Edition)*. Springfield, Charles C Thomas, 1960.
40. HARRIS, GRACE: *Language for the Preschool Deaf Child*. New York, Grune and Stratton, 1963.
41. HAUSSERMAN, ELSA: *Developmental Potential of Preschool Children*. New York, Grune and Stratton, 1958.
42. HOLT, JOHN: How Children Fail. *Ithaca Journal*, Ithaca, New York, December, 1964.
43. HOHMAN, LESLIE: The psychiatric problem. *Proceedings of Symposium on Recognition and Management of Cerebral Palsy.* November 29 & 30, 1964, New York, United Cerebral Palsy Association of New York State, 1964, 88-99.
44. Institute on Childhood Aphasia: *Childhood Aphasia,* San Francisco, California Society for Crippled Children, 1962.
45. JOHNSON, G. ORVILLE: *Educating the Slow Learner*. Englewood Cliffs, New Jersey, Prentice Hall, 1963.
46. KATTMEYER, W.: *Handbook of Remedial Reading*. St. Louis, Webster Publishing Co., 1947.
47. KEPHART, N. C.: *The Slow Learner in the Classroom*. New York, Charles E. Merrill, 1960.
48. KIRK, SAMUEL A.: *Educating the Retarded Child*. Boston, Houghton Mifflin Co., 1951.
49. LASSMAN, GRACE HARRIS: *Language for the Preschool Deaf Child.* New York, Grune and Stratton, 1950.
50. LITTLE, WM. JOHN: On the influence of abnormal parturition, difficult labor, premature birth, and, asphyxia neonatorum, on mental and physical condition of the child, especially in relation to deformities. *Lancet, II,* 1862.
51. LOVELL, K.: *The Growth of Basic Mathematical and Scientific Concepts in Children*. New York, Philosophical Library, 1962.
52. LOWENFELD, BERTHOLD: The child who is blind. *Exceptional Child., XIX:*96-102, 1952.
53. LURIA, ALEXANDER R.: *The Role of Speech in the Regulation of Normal and Abnormal Behavior*. New York, Liveright, 1961.
54. MALLOY, JULIA S.: *Mental Retardation*. New York, John Day Co., 1962.
55. McCARTHY, DOROTHY: Language development in children. In Carmichael, L. (Ed.), *Manual of Child Psychology*. New York, John Wiley, 1946.
56. McKEE, P.: *The Teaching of Reading in the Elementary Schools*. New York, Houghton Mifflin Co., 1948.

57. MONROE, MARION, and ROGERS, BERNICE: *Foundations for Reading.* Chicago, Scott, Foresman & Co., 1964.
58. MONTESORRI, MARIA: *The Montesorri Method.* New York, Schocken, 1964.
59. MYKLEBUST, HELMER R., and JOHNSON, DORIS: Dyslexia in children. *Exceptional Child., XXIX:1,* 14-25, September, 1962.
60. ODOROFF, M. E.: Vocational rehabilitation for the cerebral palsied. *The Nervous Child, VIII:2,* 1948, 214-221.
61. PIAGET, JEAN: *The Origins of Intelligence in Children.* New York, International University Press, 1952.
62. RUCH, T. C., and FULTON, J. F.: *Medical Physiology and Biophysics.* Philadelphia, W. B. Saunders, 1961.
63. SARASON, S. B.: *Psychological Problems in Mental Deficiency,* New York, Harper & Bros., 1959.
64. SAUCIER, W. A.: *Theory and Practice in the Elementary School.* New York, MacMillan, 1951.
65. SCHNEIDER, C. E.: Teaching the preschool brain injured child. *Cerebral Palsy Rev., XVI:2,* March-April, 1952, 11-15.
66. SIEGEL, ERNEST: *Helping Brain Injured Children.* New York Association for Brain Injured Children, 1963.
67. SKINNER, B. E.: *The Behavior of Organisms.* New York, Appleton-Century-Crofts, 1939.
68. SKINNER, B. F.: *Verbal Behavior.* Cambridge, Harvard University Press, 1948.
69. STRAUSS, A. A., and KEPHART, N. C.: *Psychopathology and Education of the Brain Injured Child: Progress in Theory and Clinic.* New York, Grune & Stratton, 1955.
70. STRAUSS, A. A., and LEHTINEN, L. E.: *Psychopathology and Education of the Brain Injured Child.* New York, Grune and Stratton, 1948.
71. TABA, HILDA: *Curriculum Development, Theory, and Practice.* New York, Harcourt, Brace, and World, 1962.
72. TAYLOR, EDITH MEYER: *Psychological Appraisal of Children with Cerebral Defects.* Cambridge, Harvard University Press, 1961.
73. WANN, K. D., DORN, MIRIAM SELCHEN, and LIDDLE, ELIZABETH ANN: *Fostering Intellectual Development in Young Children.* New York, Bureau of Publications, Teachers' College, Columbia University, 1962.
74. WAPNER, S., and WERNER, H.: Experiments on sensory-tonic field theory of perception: effect of body status on the kinesthetic

perception of verticality. *J. Exp. Psychol., XLIV,* 126-131, 1951.

75. WEBER, ELMER W.: *Educable and Trainable Mentally Retarded Children.* Springfield, Thomas, 1962.

76. WEPMAN, J. M.:*Recovery From Aphasia.* New York, Ronald Press, 1951.

77. WERNER, HEINZ: Abnormal and subnormal rigidity. *J. Abnorm. Soc. Psychol., XL,* 15-24, 1946.

78. WERNER, HEINZ, and CARRISON, D.: Animistic thinking in brain injured mentally retarded children. *J. Abnorm. Soc. Psychol., LXI,* 43-62, 1944.

79. WERNER, HEINZ, WAPNER, S., and CHANDLER, K.: Experiments on sensory-tonic field theory of perception. *J. Exper. Psychol., XLII,* 341-357, 1951.

80. WERNER, HEINZ, and WAPNER, S.: Toward a General Theory of Perception. *Psychol. Rev., LIX,* 324-338, 1952.

APPENDIX A

A NUCLEUS VOCABULARY FOR SPEECH THERAPY*

NOUNS

age
air
army

back
ball
body
boat
book
boy
business

car
case
chance
child
children
city
company
condition
country
course

daddy
day
dollar
dress

end
eye

family
fact
farm
farmer
feet
figure
fire
food
friend

game
girl
government

hand
head
home
hour
house

idea
interest

kind

lady
land
letter
life
light
line

---

*Taken from Mecham, M. J., and Jones, D.: A nucleus vocabulary for use in building oral language skills of the cerebral palsied child. *J. Except. Child.*, 22: 280-284, 1956.

man

matter

men

mile

mind

money

month

morning

mother

name

night

note

nothing

number

office

part

people

person

picture

place

plan

plant

power

present

president

public

question

reason

result

room

school

ship

side

sound

state

story

supply

system

thing

time

top

town

voice

war

water

way

week

woman

women

word

world

year

VERBS

am

are

ask

be

became

become

been

began

begin

being

believe

bring

brought

build

buy

call

came
can
care
carry
cause
change
come
consider
continue
could
cover
cry
cut

did
do
does
done
don't

eat

fall
fight
find
feel
follow
force
found
fly

get
give
given
go
goes
going
gone
got

had

happen
has
have
heard
hear
help
hold
hope

increase
is

keep
know

learn
leave
let
like
live
lost
look

made
make
may
mean
might
move
must

need

open
order

pass
pay
pick
point
play

produce	want
put	was
	went
read	were
receive	will
remember	wish
rest	work
run	would
said	*ADVERB*
saw	again
say	almost
see	alone
seem	always
seen	away
set	
shall	before
should	
show	close
sort	
speak	enough
stand	ever
start	
step	here
stop	how
suppose	
	just
take	
taken	late
talk	
tell	never
think	no
thought	not
told	now
took	
try	off
turn	often
	once
use	only
	out
walk	

perhaps

quite

rather

since
soon
still

then
there
today
together

up

very

well
when
where
while
why

yet

PREPOSITIONS
about
above
across
after
against
along
among
around
at

between
by

down
during

for
from

in
into

near

of
on
over

through
to
toward

under
upon

with
without

CONJUNCTIONS
also
and
as

because
but

either

however

if

or

so

than
though
thus

whether

PRONOUNS
anything

everything

he
her
him
his
himself

I
it
its

me
my

our

something
she

that
their
them
themselves
these
they
this
those
us

we
what
which
who

you
your

ADJECTIVES
a
ago
all
American
an
another
any

best
better
big
both

different

each
even
every

few
fine
first
five
four

good
great

half
hard
high
hundred

important

large
last
least
left
less
little
long

many
more
most
much

new
next

old
one
other
own

poor
possible

pretty

red
right

same
second
several
short
some
six
small
strong
such
sure

the
thousand
three
true
two

white
whole

young

AUTHOR INDEX

385

SUBJECT INDEX

A

Abstracting disturbances, 160 ff
  correction of, 167-172
Abstraction, 124-125, 160 ff, 267
Adaptation, 125
Affect disturbance, 156 ff
  emotional lability, 156
  reactive inappropriativeness, 156
Agrammatism, 174
Ammons Picture Vocabulary Test, 242
Amnesic reaction, 175-176
Anomia, 175-177
Anxiety, 26
Aphasia, 172-174
Apraxia, 188-191
Arithmetic, 363-369
Arm-hand involvement, 8
Articulation, evaluation, 56-57
  improvement, 138-141
  problems, 31-33
Association method, 132-133
Asymmetric tonic neck reflexes, 53
Attention defects, 125, 148-153
  hyperactivity, 150, 151
  control of, 151
  hyperirritable attention, 148, 149, 150,
    221, 222, 292
  drifting attention, 152, 292
  specific attention, 150, 292, 293
  vs. perceptual disturbances, 292
  effect of hand-eye coordination, 328,
    329
Auditory perception, 8, 115-120
Auditory training, 115-124

B

Bender-Gestalt test, 241, 291
Body image, 151-200
Brain damage syndrome, 146 ff
Breath control, 90-93
Breathing evaluation, 59-60
Breathing problems, 36-38

C

Case history, 49
Catastrophic behaviors, 155-159, 220
  reactions, 126-127, 157 ff, 162
  vasomotor lability, 157
Cerebral palsy
  learning problems, 282 ff
  speech, 21 (see also Speech charac-
    teristics)
Chewing, sucking and swallowing, 83-84
Choice, 275-276, 278
Classifications, 4-7
  ataxia, 6
  athetosis, 6
  hemiplegia, 5
  monoplegia, 5
  neurological, 5
  paraplegia, 5
  quadriplegia, 5
  rigidity, 6
  spasticity, 6
  tremor, 6
  triplegia, 5
Classroom approach to child with cerebral palsy, 268 ff
  competition, 273
  discipline, 270-272
  environment, 281-282
  motivation, 272-274
  role of teacher, 278-281
  routine, 282
Color-Form test, 161-163
Color sorting test, 169 ff
Concept formation, 28
Conceptual rigidities, 163-164, 206-208
Conditioning in learning, 296
Constancies, patterned, 190-193
Convulsions
  effect on learning, 284-287
Counting, rote, 363
Cranio-oropharyngeal reflexes, 31

D

Defective abstraction, 160 ff
Delayed speech, 24-29
Developmental approach to learning, 300 ff
Developmental problems, 7-17
  adaptive, 13
  adjustment, 14
  communication, 15
  educational, 8, 14
  environmental relationships, 13
  fear, 14
  feed back, 14, 16
  motor, 7, 15
  nonprogressive, 8
  progressive, 8
Developmental schedules, 133-135
Deviant
  abstraction, 160 ff, 225-226
  categorization, 160 ff, 225-226
  perception, 177 ff
  propositionality, 152-155, 218-220
  serial order, 176
Discipline, 270-272
Discrimination, 120-121
Disinhibition, 9, 125
Disordered feedback, 31
Dissociation, 9
Distractibility, 149
Drifting attention, 152, 292
Drooling, 84-86

E

Education, 261 ff
Educational problems, 261 ff
Ego space, 151
Emotional lability, 10, 97, 156, 223-224
Emotional factors, 9, 247-254
Employment, 14
Epilepsy, 8
Etiology, 4
Experience, 267, 293-298
  collection, 294-295
  definition, 293-294
  interpretation, 298 ff
  lack of, 295-298
  nucleus, 128-129
  structured, 129-130
Experiential contacts, 100-104

F

Family, 14
Focus of attention, 149, 329
Frustration tolerance, 144, 271-273, 292

G

G-factor of intelligence, 290, 327
General behavior, integration, 124
General rigidities, 205-206
Gestalt psychology, 177 ff
Goldstein-Scheerer-Weigle test, 161-162, 164
Growing up, 96-97

H

Hearing problems, 28, 41-42
Hearing testing, 60-63
Hyperirritable attention, 148, 149, 150, 221-222

I

Incline and plateau, 213-214
Infant test scores, 210-212
Initiatory delay and confusion, 208-209
Institute of Logopedics, 214-231
Integration, 268
Intellectual capacity and reading, 345-348
Intelligence, 11, 28, 134-135, 209 ff
Intelligence quotient, 209-210
  stability of, 210-214
Intelligence testing, 209 ff
  predictive aspects, 209, 210-215
  comparative implication, 210
  importance of, 302-303
Intelligibility, 31, 34, 58, 140-141
Interpretation of psychometric data, 226-237

L

Language integration, 127-133
Learning problems, 282 ff
  absence of normal experience, 293-298
  attention problems, 292-293
  convulsive disorders, 284-287
  severe motor disability, 282-284
  sensory and perceptual deficits, 287 ff
  sensory disabilities, 287-288
  perceptual disabilities, 288-292